Platinum, Gold, and Other Metal Chemotherapeutic Agents

Chemistry and Biochemistry

Platinum, Gold, and Other Metal Chemotherapeutic Agents

Chemistry and Biochemistry

Stephen J. Lippard, EDITOR

Massachusetts Institute of Technology

Based on a symposium

sponsored by the ACS Division

of Inorganic Chemistry

at the 183rd Meeting of the

American Chemical Society,

Las Vegas, Nevada,

March 28–April 2, 1982

ACS SYMPOSIUM SERIES **209**

AMERICAN CHEMICAL SOCIETY

WASHINGTON, D.C.   1983

Library of Congress Cataloging in Publication Data

Platinum, gold, and other metal chemotherapeutic agents.

(ACS symposium series, ISSN 0097–6156; 209)

"Based on a symposium sponsored by the Division of Inorganic Chemistry of the American Chemical Society at the ACS National Meeting, Las Vegas, Nevada, March–April 1982."

Includes bibliographies and index.

1. Metals—Therapeutic use—Congresses. 2. Chemistry, Pharmaceutical—Congresses. 3. Platinum compounds—Therapeutic use—Congresses. 4. Antineoplastic agents—Congresses. I. Lippard, Stephen J. II. American Chemical Society. Division of Inorganic Chemistry. III. American Chemical Society. National Meeting (1982: Las Vegas, Nev.) IV. Series.

RS431.M45P57 616.99′4061 82–24333
ISBN 0–8412–0758–5 ACSMC8 209 1–453
                 1983

ACS Symposium Series

M. Joan Comstock, *Series Editor*

FOREWORD

The ACS SYMPOSIUM SERIES was founded in 1974 to provide a medium for publishing symposia quickly in book form. The format of the Series parallels that of the continuing ADVANCES IN CHEMISTRY SERIES except that in order to save time the papers are not typeset but are reproduced as they are submitted by the authors in camera-ready form. Papers are reviewed under the supervision of the Editors with the assistance of the Series Advisory Board and are selected to maintain the integrity of the symposia; however, verbatim reproductions of previously published papers are not accepted. Both reviews and reports of research are acceptable since symposia may embrace both types of presentation.

CONTENTS

PREFACE

THE DISCOVERY OF THE REMARKABLE BIOLOGICAL ACTIVITIES of the anti-cancer platinum drug *cis*-diamminedichloroplatinum(II), *cis*-DDP, by Barnett Rosenberg and his collaborators comprises an impressive chapter in the history of bioinorganic chemistry. Efforts are currently being made by research groups throughout the world to understand the inorganic and biological chemistry responsible for the antitumor properties of *cis*-DDP, and this symposium was held to promote an exchange of information among many of the leading laboratories working on this problem. The aim of the symposium was to stress chemical rather than clinical aspects of the problem, which was consistent with the expectations of an audience of chemists rather than physicians. During the planning stages for the meeting, several colleagues reminded us that the use of inorganic compounds in chemotherapy was a broader subject than was embraced only by the antitumor platinum compounds. Consequently, the scope of the symposium was widened to include other metal chemotherapeutic agents, chiefly the gold-based antiarthritic drugs.

The inorganic and the biological techniques being used to study the mechanism of action of platinum antitumor drugs have become increasingly sophisticated. ^{195}Pt-NMR and other spectroscopic studies have revealed the complex composition of aqueous solutions of *cis*-DDP. DNA molecules of varying complexity, including superhelical DNA molecules, restriction fragments of known sequence, and Z-DNA, have been employed in *cis*-DDP binding studies. Also, nucleosomes and chromatin are being investigated; nuclease enzymes have been used to probe the platinum binding sites; the alkaline elution technique is being applied to study in vivo crosslinking; and antibodies raised against *cis*-DDP-modified DNA have been used to probe the in vivo binding of the drug. NMR spectroscopy has afforded a very powerful means of studying the stereochemistry of platinum–oligonucleotide complexes in solution. Attempts to find more powerful and less toxic metal-containing anticancer drugs have continued through synthetic and biological studies of platinum group and other transition elements.

Gold compounds have long been used for medicinal purposes, but a recent flurry of interest in these complexes by the bioinorganic community has arisen because of the development of the first effective, orally administered antiarthritic gold complex, RSAuPEt$_3$, where R is a thioglucose derivative. As with the platinum antitumor drugs, the most powerful new methods are beginning to be applied to studies of the mechanism of action of this and other chrysotherapeutic agents. Two of the new methods are multinuclear NMR and extended x-ray absorption fine structure (EXAFS) spectroscopy.

The present volume discusses these topics through reports from most of the laboratories represented at the Las Vegas meeting, including several interesting papers presented in the poster sessions. I am grateful to the authors for their prompt submission of manuscripts, assistance with refereeing, and overall cooperation in helping to make the meeting and this volume a success. I also thank Dr. Barnett Rosenberg and Dr. Luigi Marzilli for help in planning the symposium. Financial assistance from the Donors of the Petroleum Research Fund administered by the American Chemical Society; the Inorganic Division of the ACS; Engelhard Industries; INCO Research and Development Center; Johnson Matthey, Inc.; and Smith Kline and French Laboratories to support the symposium is gratefully acknowledged. Through their help it was possible to bring many foreign scientists to the meeting, the contributions of whom form an important part of this book.

STEPHEN J. LIPPARD
Columbia University

October 1, 1982

BIOCHEMISTRY OF PLATINUM ANTITUMOR DRUGS

DNA as a Target for Anticancer Coordination Compounds

J. J. ROBERTS and M. F. PERA, JR.[1]

Institute of Cancer Research, Pollards Wood Research Station, Nightingales Lane, Chalfont St. Giles, Bucks, HP8 4SP England

The notion that DNA is the likely target for anti-
tumour platinum complexes will be discussed on the
basis of their interaction with nucleic acids in
vitro and of their interactions with the DNA of both
cells in culture and cells in whole animals.
Biochemical studies suggest that interactions with
cellular DNA result in an inactivation of the DNA
template for DNA replication.   Support for these
views came from the demonstration that cells could
remove DNA bound platinum adducts by an excision
repair process that facilitated the recovery of
cells from toxic damage.

Since the first description of the biological properties of
platinum complexes there has been a considerable effort to
understand the molecular basis of their actions.   The clear
demonstration of the usefulness of cisplatin in treatment of
human tumours has added impetus to this work, because ultimately
an understanding of the mechanism of drug action should provide
a more rational basis for improvement in therapy.   Much evidence
is available now to support the view that platinum drugs exert
their cytotoxic effects through an interaction with DNA.   The
main purpose of this review will be to assess critically the
evidence supporting this hypothesis.   We will first briefly
summarise some of the biological properties of platinum compounds
other than antitumour activity that are probably a consequence
of their ability to react with DNA.   Then we will discuss the
interaction of platinum compounds with nucleic acids before
considering in detail the evidence that indicates DNA as a major
target for drug action.

[1] Current address: ICRF Laboratories, POB 123, Lincoln's Inn Fields, London WC2A 3PX England

Biological Effects of Platinum Antitumour Drugs Indicative of Interaction with DNA

Probably the first observation of an effect of a platinum coordination complex in a biological system and one which gave a clear indication of its biochemical mode of action was the observation that neutral platinum coordination complexes inhibited bacterial cell division and induced the bacteria to grow into long filaments (1). Filamentous growth in bacteria may be indicative of the ability of an agent to react with DNA leading to a selective inhibition of DNA synthesis, with no accompanying effect on other biosynthetic pathways such as RNA or protein synthesis. A variety of agents, such as UV- and X-irradiation and cytotoxic alkylating agents, can also elicit this response as a result of their common ability to damage DNA.

Further important evidence for direct attack on DNA came from the ability of platinum compounds to induce the growth of phage from lysogenic strains of E.coli bacteria (2). The release of the phage DNA to direct synthesis of new phage is normally a rare event. However, agents which can react with DNA can cause the phage DNA to be released and phage particles to be synthesized with consequent cell lysis. Reslova (2) was able to show that there exists an excellent correlation between the antitumour activity of platinum compounds and their ability to induce lysogenic E.coli to enter the lytic cycle.

The interactions of platinum compounds with viruses have further indicated the relatively greater importance of reactions with DNA as against those with protein in producing biological effects. Kutinova et al. (3) demonstrated the inactivation of the infectious activity of extracellular papovavirus SV40 by cis-DDP. The inactivation of B.subtilis transforming DNA by platinum compounds, likewise indicated the effect of these agents on the biological function of DNA (4).

The genotoxic nature of platinum compounds and the importance of the geometrical arrangement of ligands for biological effect, also emerges from studies on the mutagenic properties of these agents in a number of prokaryotic and eukaryotic systems (5-10). The cis derivatives were in all cases appreciably more mutagenic than the corresponding trans isomers. A comparison of cytotoxicity and mutagenicity, either per DNA interstrand crosslinked lesion (9) or per total number of lesions (10), for cis and trans-DDP showed that these two biological effects differ in their sensitivity to DNA binding. Thus, in a study of mutation at the HGPRT locus in Chinese hamster V79 cells, equitoxic doses of trans-DDP were much less mutagenic than cis-DDP, even though interstrand crosslinking for the two isomers was comparable (9). The study by Johnson et al. (10) in CHO cells revealed that the mutagenicity per molecule bound to DNA immediately after 16-24 h treatment was at least 750 times larger for cis-DDP than for the trans-isomer, while cytotoxicity per DNA lesion was a factor of 9 greater for cis than for trans-DDP.

Another property platinum antitumour drugs share with agents that interact with DNA is induction of cancer.   In vitro studies of morphological transformation, a property often correlated with tumour induction in vivo, showed cis-DDP was capable of transforming secondary Syrian hamster embryo cells (11).   The finding that trans-DDP transformed 10T½ mouse cells and 3T3 cells was of interest in light of the low mutagenicity of this compound (12).   In carcinogenesis studies in vivo, cis-DDP produced lung adenomas in A/Jax mice, skin papillomas in CD1 mice when adminis-tered in combination with croton oil, and sarcomas at the site of injection in F344 rats (13).   When administered at maximally tolerated doses, trans-DDP did not induce tumours in the lung adenoma or skin papilloma systems, as expected from its low mutagenicity (14).

Reaction of Platinum Drugs with DNA

Although other hypotheses have been proposed for the mechan-ism of action of platinum compounds (15-20), the bulk of the evidence at present favour the theory that DNA damage and synthe-sis of DNA on a damaged template is directly responsible for the cytotoxic activity of platinum drugs.   Before presenting the experimental evidence, it is useful first to outline the general argument.

Platinum antitumour drugs are bifunctional electrophilic species which react in a relatively non-selective fashion with nucleophilic sites in cellular macromolecules.   On a per mole-cule basis, DNA is the only target that is large enough to under-go one or more reactions per molecule at pharmacologically relevant doses.   Reaction with DNA results in disturbances in the rate of DNA synthesis, or the quality of nascent DNA synthe-sized, which leads to chromosome damage and cell death.   Cells possess to varying degrees the capacity to excise damage from template DNA, and moreover, cells vary in their capacity to synthesize DNA on a damaged template.   Thus cytotoxicity and cellular sensitivity to platinum drugs will be a function of the extent of reaction with DNA, the capacity to remove damage from the template, and the capacity to synthesize DNA on a template containing damage.

Thus evidence for this mechanism comes from studies of the interaction of the drugs with nucleic acids and nucleic acid components, from observations on the effects of the drugs on DNA synthesis, and from observations relating to repair of DNA lesions and cytotoxicity.   First we will consider the reactions of the drug with nucleic acids.

Reactions of neutral platinum complexes with nucleic acid components in vitro. Changes in the ultraviolet absorption spectrum of salmon sperm DNA after reaction with either cis or

trans-DDP provided conclusive evidence that both platinum compounds bind to the organic bases of DNA.   Spectrophotometric
studies further confirmed that the three bases, guanine, adenine
and cytosine would all react with both isomers, the rate of
reaction with guanine being faster than with the other two bases
(22,23,24).

By blocking the various possible binding sites in the purine
bases by either methylation or protonation, Mansy et al. (22)
defined the sites most likely to be involved in reaction with
either cis or trans-DDP.   They concluded that the cis isomer
forms a bidentate chelate with either the 6-NH_2 and N-7, or the
6-NH_2 and N-1 of adenine, and the 4-NH_2 and N-3 of cytosine.
The trans isomer, on the other hand, interacts monofunctionally
at the N-7 and N-1 of adenine and the N-3 of cytosine.   Both
isomers react monofunctionally with the N-7 of guanine and hypoxanthine.   X-ray diffraction studies of the complexes formed
between cis Pt$(NH_3)_2X_2$ and various bases have confirmed some of
the conclusions obtained from the early spectrophotometric
studies.   The product of the reaction between inosine and
Pt$(NH_3)_2I_2$ consist of two hypoxanthine rings bound to the
platinum ion via the N-7 position (25).   A similar structure
results from the interaction of PtCl$_2$ (en) with guanosine
(26,27);   again the N-7 position becomes occupied by the metal.

Other atoms which have been shown to have an affinity for
platinum include the deprotonated N(1) and N(3) positions of
guanine and thymine respectively as well as the deprotonated NH_2
group of cytosine (28).

There is no evidence yet from crystallographic studies that
the 0-6 position of guanine, the 6-NH_2 group of adenine or the
4-NH_2 group of cytosine can be occupied by platinum(II) ions.
A bidentate binding reaction between the N-7 and the 0-6 positions of guanine for the cis but not the trans platinum(II)
compounds was an attractive possibility to account for the difference between the biological effectiveness of the two isomers.
However, such bidentate binding to a single base has not yet been
identified unambiguously.

Cis-platinum compounds can induce the formation of interstrand crosslinks in isolated DNA (21,29-32) or in the DNA of
whole cells (33,34).   There is as yet no direct evidence to
indicate which of the many possible binding sites discussed above,
are involved in such a reaction.   A possibility, suggested from
examination of a DNA model, is that crosslinking could occur
between the 6-amino groups in adenines in opposing strands of
DNA in a dA-dT sequence (35).   These groups would be 3.5A apart
which approximates 3A;   the distance between the cis leaving
groups in cis-DDP.   There is some evidence to indicate that
cis-DDP can link two NH_2 groups in this way in a simple nucleotide (36,37).   Alternatively the amino groups of guanines or of
cytosines in opposing strands of DNA in a dC-dG DNA sequence are
theoretically amenable to crosslinking.   The preferential inter-

strand crosslinking of DNAs rich in guanine and cytosine was
noted from studies of the renaturability of crosslinked DNAs of
different G-C content (32), and from a study of the inhibition of
intercalation of 9-aminoacridine as a function of (G + C) content
of platinum-treated DNA or copolymers (38).

The frequency of interstrand crosslinks was originally estimated from a combination of measurements of the amount of platinum bound to Hela cell crosslinked DNA molecules of a presumed
size (29,30): it was shown to be a relatively rare event,
accounting for less than one per cent of the total number of
reactions with cellular DNA.   Recent quantitative studies of
crosslinking of Chinese hamster cell DNA, using a variety of
techniques, confirmed the rarity of crosslinks in whole cells at
the time of their maximum development (see below).

Despite the clear evidence for the formation of interstrand
DNA crosslinks both in isolated DNA and in the DNA of whole cells,
many recent observations indicate the likely formation of intrastrand crosslinking between adjacent bases in DNA by platinum
compounds.   Moreover the importance of this reaction as an
inactivating event in bacteriophage was noted, first, by Shooter
et al. (39) for T7 bacteriophage and, more recently, by
Filipski et al. (40) for phage λ.   For such a crosslinking
reaction to occur, local perturbation of the double helix is
required, and indeed, some observations of X-ray photoelectron
spectral changes (41,42,43) or CD spectral changes (42);
Tamburio et al. (43) support such a modification.   Marked enhancement of the CD spectrum of DNA was observed even at low levels
of reaction and this effect increases with increasing GC content
of several different DNAs (42).   The binding of platinum to the
N-7 position of guanine could weaken the G-C hydrogen bonding
which, it is suggested, makes the N-1 position of guanine
available for further reaction (44).   Covalent binding of both
cis and trans-DDP to closed circular PM2 DNA alters the degree of
supercoiling and shortens the DNA, as revealed by electron microscopy, presumably by disrupting and unwinding the complex (45,46).
Some recent elegant experiments by Cohen et al. (47) add further
strong support to the ability of cis but not trans-DDP to form
intrastrand crosslinks between adjacent guanines in a dGn dCn
(n = 4) sequence in circular pSM1 DNA at low levels of Pt/P
ratios.

Reaction with DNA of cells in culture.   Studies with
cultured cells have indicated the relevance of platinum-DNA
binding to cytotoxicity.   Pascoe and Roberts (29,30) studied
the interaction of several platinum compounds with macromolecules
at measured levels of cell kill.

To assess the possible importance of DNA, RNA and protein as
primary targets for platinum(II) compounds, these binding data
(expressed as moles/gm of macromolecule) were used to construct
curves of log survival against the amount of drug bound to each

type of macromolecule.   The resulting graphs were then
characterised in a manner similar to those relating log cell
survival to dose of drug given to the cells.   The shoulder
width of the binding curve was given the value B_q and the slope
of the straight line portion B_o.   For both cis and trans-DDP
the binding coefficients were higher for RNA than DNA.   However,
the true significance of these binding coefficients can only be
appreciated if account is taken of the molecular weights of the
molecules concerned.   If one assumes no selectivity in the
binding to any particular RNA or protein molecule, then it is
possible to calculate the number of platinum molecules bound to
each macromolecule at a given toxic dose.   The results of such
a calculation, performed at the concentration of cis-DDP which
reduced the surviving fraction of Hela cells from f to 0.37f
(this is theoretically the concentration at which one inactivating event occurs, on the average, in each cell) show the number
of molecules bound to DNA is strikingly more than that to either
RNA or protein, clearly indicating that DNA is the most suscep-
tible cellular target for cis-DDP.   The binding data further
indicate that at this concentration of cis-DDP approximately
only one molecule of protein out of 1500 molecules will have
received one platination reaction.   Unless there is considerable
specificity in the reaction of platinum drugs with a particular
protein enzyme molecule, then this level of reaction would be
too low to inactivate enzyme activity.   Moreover, the level of
reaction with rRNA, tRNA or mRNA would not be expected, again,
in the absence of any selectivity of reaction, to inactivate all
such molecules and lead to interference with protein synthesis.

Similar DNA binding and cell survival studies have been
carried out in Chinese hamster cells in culture with a number of
other platinum compounds that have shown encouraging activity
against a number of experimental animal tumours (48).   Differences of up to tenfold were found in the molar concentrations
of these agents that were required to produce equitoxic effects
on cells in culture following one hour's incubation.

The levels of reaction with DNA at equitoxic doses (B_o
values), on the other hand, were, for most compounds, of the
same order and differed by only a few fold (Table I).

Reaction with the DNA of cells in vivo. It is clearly
essential, for an understanding of the mechanism of the tumour-
inhibitory action of platinum compounds, to establish that the
sensitivity of tumour cells in vivo is related to the extent of
reaction of platinum with their DNA in a manner similar to that
for cells treated in vitro with these agents.   In a preliminary
study, mice bearing the transplanted ADJ/PC6 plasmacytoma were
treated with cis-DDP and two other active platinum congeners,
CHIP and cis-diammine(1:1-cyclobutanedicarboxylato)platinum(II)
at doses that had an equal inhibitory effect on the tumour
(ID_{90}) (49).   Despite the difference in the actual amounts of

Table I

Comparison of the toxicity of various platinum complexes towards Chinese hamster V79 379A cells in culture and plasmacytoma ADJ/PC6 tumour cells in vivo in relation to DNA binding (Roberts, 1981)

Compound	ADJ/PC6A Mouse plasmacytoma		Chinese hamster V79 379A cells	
	LD_{50} (mg/kg)	ID_{90} (mg/kg)	D_0 (μM/1 h)	B_0 (nmoles/gm)
cis-Pt(II)Cl$_2$(NH$_3$)$_2$	13	1.6	15	8.5
cis-Pt(IV)Cl$_2$(iso-C$_3$H$_7$NH$_2$)$_2$(OH)$_2$	54	4.2	48	2.5
cis-Pt(II)(1,1-CBDCA)(NH$_3$)$_2$	180	14.5	120	3.0
cis-Pt(II)(mal)(1,2-dac)	N.D.	N.D.	23	2.5
cis-Pt(II)(SO$_4$)H$_2$O(1,2-dac)	14	0.4	65	17.5
cis-Pt(II)Cl$_2$(C$_5$H$_9$NH$_2$)$_2$	480	2.4	120	N.D.

N.D.   Not determined

CBDCA   Cyclobutanedicarboxylic acid; dac, 1,2-diaminocyclohexane

the materials administered to the mice, the doses did not differ
by more than a factor of two when expressed in terms of their
molar concentrations.   Interestingly, the amounts of the platinum drugs bound to the tumour DNA at these equitoxic concentrations were all remarkably similar.

Pera et al. (50) studied the reaction of cisplatin and
hydroxymalonato diammine platinum(II) with DNA of B16 melanoma
and bone marrow in C57BL mice.   Inhibition of tumour growth,
and colony formation assays for melanoma cells as well as bone
marrow stem cells, were used to quantitate toxicity and to
indicate antitumour selectivity. $Pt[OHmal(NH_3)_2]$ produced
greater selective inhibition of tumour growth and more selective
tumour cell killing compared with cisplatin.   In the case of
cisplatin, binding of platinum to DNA at measured levels of
survival in vivo was similar to values previously observed in
cultured cells, a finding that again strengthens arguments
concerning the mechanism of action of the drugs based on in
vitro work.   The greater selective toxicity of $Pt[OHmal(NH_3)_2]$
towards the B16 melanoma was associated with an increased
binding of platinum to tumour DNA, relative to cisplatin.   The
enhanced DNA binding in the tumour seen with $Pt[OHmal(NH_3)_2]$
was not seen in the marrow (Figure 1 A.B., Table II).   Thus
the increased antitumour specificity of the newer congener
probably results from pharmacologic factors that enhance delivery
of active drug to tumour cells.

Role of crosslinking reactions.   The structural requirement
for difunctionality and the principal biochemical effects of the
platinum compounds, as discussed below, suggest a parallel
between the platinum drugs and the classical bi-functional alkylating agents such as the nitrogen mustards.   The latter compounds
have been thought for some time to produce an inhibition of DNA
synthesis by their ability to introduce crosslinks into the
DNA of mammalian cells.   It has, however, been a matter of
contention as to whether the principal lesion is a crosslink
between strands of the DNA helix or crosslinks between bases on
one strand of DNA, or possibly, even between DNA and protein.
Crosslinking was estimated by Roberts and Pascoe (33) from
the proportion of 'hybrid' DNA formed by linking opposing strands
of heavy (BudR labelled) and light (normal) DNA.

The relative toxicities of the cis and trans isomers of the
platinum(II) neutral complexes, can be defined by the slopes of
the survival curves (D_o) obtained by treating Hela cells in
culture.   Comparison of these two sets of values indicated that
the relative abilities of cis and trans-DDP compounds to crosslink DNA in vivo (but not in vitro) were related to their cytotoxic action (29,30).   These studies therefore suggest that
interstrand crosslinking with both the platinum(II) compounds,
but not necessarily platinum(IV) compounds, may be important in
inducing their cytotoxic effects and that the cis isomer is most
effective in inducing the reaction.

A

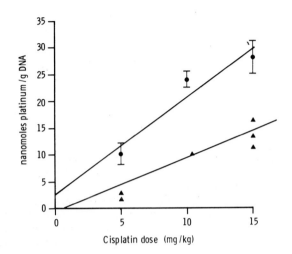

B

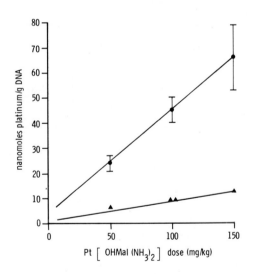

*Figure 1.   Binding of platinum to B16 melanoma DNA (●) or bone marrow DNA
(▲) following treatment of C57B16 mice with* cis-diamminedichloroplatinum(II)
(cis-DDP) *(A) and hydroxymalonatodiammineplatinum(II) (B).*

Table II

Amount of platinum bound to marrow and tumour DNA
of C57BL mice at doses of cisplatin or Pt[OHMal(NH$_3$)$_2$]
producing 37 per cent survival of bone marrow stem
cells (CFU-S) or B16 lung colony forming cells

	CFU-S		$\dfrac{B16}{LCFC}$	
	D_{37}	Amount Bound	D_{37}	Amount Bound
Cisplatin	5 mg/Kg	4nmol/g	11 mg/Kg	22nmol/g
Pt[OHMal(NH$_3$)$_2$]	40 mg/Kg	5nmol/g	20 mg/Kg	12.5nmol/g

A reinvestigation of crosslinking of DNA by platinum(II) compounds using a different method from that described above, namely alkaline elution (34) has confirmed the greater ability of cis-DDP as compared with trans-DDP to crosslink cellular DNA. These investigators made the further interesting observation that incubation of treated mouse leukemic L1210 cells in a drug-free medium resulted in an increase in the number of DNA crosslinks. Crosslinking effects developed, following treatment with concentrations as low as 1 µm for cis and 5 µm for trans-DDP which permitted over 80% survival of colony-forming ability. The maximum crosslinking effect by cis-DDP required about 12 h post treatment incubation before it was fully developed by 6 h after exposure to the drug. The crosslinking effects of both agents were reversed upon further incubation of the cells, presumably due to the operation of a DNA excision repair process.

A further study employing alkaline elution showed that the crosslinking effect produced by cis and trans-DDP could be separated into two components, one proteinase-sensitive and due to DNA-protein crosslinking, another proteinase-resistant and due to DNA interstrand crosslinking (51). DNA protein crosslinks were at maximum levels immediately after drug removal, while DNA-DNA interstrand crosslinks reached maximum levels 6-12 hours after drug removal. Toxicity of the two agents in L1210 leukemia cells, and V79 Chinese hamster cells, correlated well with DNA interstrand crosslinking, but not with DNA-protein crosslinking (9,51).

Because the biophysical basis of the elution technique is poorly understood, quantitation of interstrand crosslinking with this technique is based upon largely unproven assumptions. Therefore studies were undertaken to compare elution results with the alkaline caesium chloride technique described above, alkaline sucrose sedimentation, and estimation of renaturable DNA in cell lysates. Direct quantitation of crosslink frequency following cisplatin treatment was thus obtained over a wide dose range using methods based upon known biophysical properties of DNA. The results showed clearly that alkaline elution following proteinase digestion gave an accurate measure of interstrand crosslinking, and showed also that crosslinks were only a small fraction of the total drug-DNA reaction products (52,53).

It has been shown that cells can be protected from the toxic effects of cis-DDP by preventing the formation of DNA crosslinks by incubating cells in the presence of thiourea immediately after treatment (54), a finding which further supports a cytotoxic role for DNA interstrand crosslinks. Further investigation in mouse leukemia cells and human fibroblasts of varying sensitivity to cisplatin, have shown that cellular sensitivity often correlates with interstrand crosslink formation (55, 56, 57). However, studies of certain mouse leukemia L1210 lines resistant to cisplatin (55,58), as well as studies of Walker carcinoma cells (59) have indicated that there is not always a simple correlation between crosslink formation and cell kill.

It is entirely possible that intrastrand crosslinking might provide an even better correlation, but it is not possible to measure this lesion in mammalian cells at the present time.

Biochemical Effects of Drug-DNA Interaction

Inhibition of DNA synthesis. The significance of the interaction of platinum compounds with cellular DNA is apparent from studies of drug effects on macromolecular synthesis. Cis-DDP selectively and persistently inhibits the rate of DNA synthesis as compared with effects on RNA and protein synthesis in cells in culture (60-63) and cells in vivo (64,65).

The likely basis for this selective biochemical effect on DNA synthesis came from the observation that the inhibition of DNA synthesis was persistent and progressive with time after removal of the drug.   It is now clear, particularly by comparison with analogous effects produced by direct reacting agents such as mustard gas, that both effects are consistent with the view that the primary chemical lesion is in the DNA of the cell, which is then inhibited as a template for DNA replication. Thus modifications to the DNA template will block DNA replication but not affect transcription or translation.   Under conditions of low cell killing, the selective inhibition by platinum compounds of DNA synthesis but not of RNA or protein synthesis, leads to the formation of giant cells, a feature observed in cells treated with a variety of agents also known to block DNA replication selectively.

Studies of synchronized V79 Chinese hamster cells treated in G1 with cisplatin showed that depression of DNA synthesis in these cells was the result of a decrease in DNA synthetic rate, rather than a decreased rate of entry of cells into S (62). As a result, S phase was prolonged in these cells (Figure 2). Following G1 treatment with cisplatin, synchronized Hela cells also showed a decrease in the amount of thymidine incorporation into DNA during S phase, but the effect was not immediately manifested in these cells (63) (Figure 3).   Thus cells differ in the way in which their replication machinery responds to cisplatin-induced damage.   Such differences might account for variations in cellular sensitivity (see below) and further studies in this area are warranted.

Johnson et al. (66) used an in vitro T7 DNA replication system which copies exogenous T7 DNA by a mechanism that closely mimics in vivo DNA replication to demonstrate the relative inhibitory effect of either pyrimidine dimers or bound ^{195m}Pt-labelled cis or trans-DDP.   It could be shown that cis-DDP and pyrimidine dimers inhibited DNA replication to the same extent per lesion (63% inhibition per 3×10^{-4} lesions/nucleotide phosphate) and the trans-DDP was 5-fold less inhibitory.

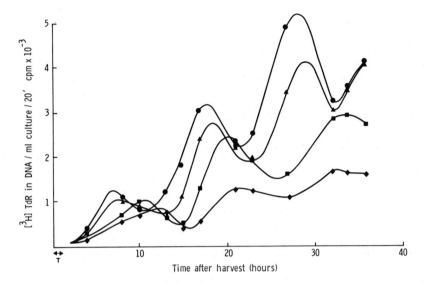

Figure 2.   Effects of cis-*DDP treatment in G1 phase on DNA synthesis in synchro-nized Chinese hamster V79 cells. Key to* cis-*DDP concentration:* ●*, 0;* ▲*, 1.0 μM;* ■*, 5.0 μM; and* ◆*, 10.0 μM. T indicates time of treatment.*

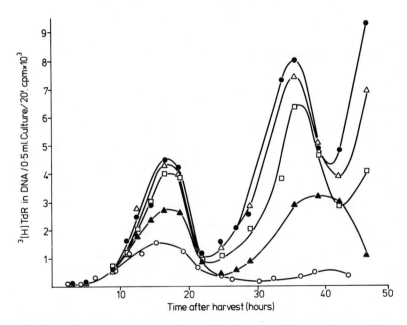

Figure 3.   Effects of cis-*DDP treatment in G1 phase on DNA synthesis in synchro-nized Hela cells. Key to* cis-*DDP concentration:* ●*, 0;* △*, 0.1 μM;* □*, 0.25 μM;* ▲*, 1.0 μM; and* ○*, 2.0 μM.*

The alternative possibility that DNA synthesis is inhibited because of the inactivation of enzymes involved in DNA replication seems contra-indicated, not only by the failure of cis-DDP to block protein synthesis, but also by its failure to inactivate DNA polymerase in vitro except with very high concentrations (67).

Relation between capacity to replicate on a damaged template and cytotoxicity. Further evidence relating drug induced alterations in DNA synthesis to cytotoxicity in bacteria and mammalian cells comes from studies of how cells cope with DNA template damage. Studies of excision repair of platinum induced damage, discussed below, indicate that the majority of DNA-platinum products, involving one strand of a double helix, are chemically stable and are only slowly removed from DNA by an enzymatic process. Thus it could be supposed that persistent lesions in DNA are circumvented during DNA replication by a process which is analogous to that which facilitates the survival of excision defective bacteria after UV-irradiation.

It now seems certain that mammalian cells also possess varying capacities to replicate their DNA on a template containing unexcised damage. It is also apparent, however, that the mechanism of any such repair process differs from that which is thought to occur in bacteria. However, irrespective of the mechanism involved in synthesising past radiation or chemically-induced lesions in DNA, it has been found that in some cells the process is amenable to inhibition by the trimethylxanthine, caffeine. Thus it has been shown that the rate of elongation of newly synthesised DNA in UV-irradiated or chemically-treated cells, was dramatically impaired in the presence of caffeine. As a consequence of this inhibition, many cell lines, competent in this replicative by-pass, are rendered extremely sensitive to the lethal effects of these agents by post treatment incubation in the presence of non-toxic concentrations of caffeine (68).

There is now ample evidence to indicate that UV- or X-irradiation or chemically-induced cell death is a function of the amount of chromosome damage which can be observed at the first or second mitosis after treatment. Post treatment incubation in the presence of caffeine enhances dramatically the chromosome damaging effects of UV-irradiation and chemicals in both plant and animal cells. The various cellular effects of cis-DDP and their modifications by caffeine, suggest that lesions are introduced onto DNA by platinum compounds which are also circumvented by a caffeine sensitive process (69). Post treatment incubation of cells in medium containing 0.75 mM caffeine dramatically potentiated the toxicity of cisplatin and increased the number of cells containing chromosome damage. Caffeine not only increased the number of cis-DDP treated cells containing chromosomal aberrations but it also enhanced the severity of the damage observed. The delayed appearance of chromosome abnormalities after cis-DDP treatment also suggests that DNA replication

is necessary for their formation, and in this respect cis-DDP
resembles UV-irradiation and alkylating agents rather than
X-irradiation (69).

The proposal has therefore been made that inadequate replication of DNA on a damaged template is responsible for both cell
death and chromosome damage and that post treatment incubation
of cells in medium containing caffeine, enhances these two effects
of DNA damage by inhibiting a process which would permit replication to proceed past lesions. Support for this notion has come
from studies on both the rate of DNA synthesis and the size of
DNA synthesised in both asynchronous and synchronised populations
of cis-DDP treated cells in the presence and absence of caffeine
(61,62). It was found that post treatment incubation in medium
containing a non-toxic concentration of caffeine, reversed the
cis-DDP induced inhibition of DNA synthesis in asynchronous populations of cells (61). The size of newly synthesised DNA in
cis-DDP treated cells may be contrasted with the size of such
DNA in cells treated similarly with cis-DDP and labelled with
(^{3}H)TdR in the presence of non-toxic concentrations of caffeine.
Under these conditions the size of nascent DNA was markedly
reduced as compared with that in untreated control or cis-DDP
only treated cells. The size of the DNA synthesised during 4
hours in the presence of caffeine in cis-DDP treated cells was
dependent on the initial dose of DDP.   It thus appears that
caffeine interferes with the mechanism by which the cell replic-
ates its DNA past lesions on the DNA template. Some support for
this notion was obtained from a comparison of the distance
between platinum-induced lesions on the template strand of DNA
and the size of the newly synthesised DNA in cells treated with
various doses of cis-DDP and post incubated in the presence of
caffeine. The distance between platinum atoms on one strand of
DNA was calculated from atomic absorption measurements of the
platinum bound to DNA isolated from cis-DDP treated cells and
this was found to correspond closely to the size of the newly-
synthesised DNA. It was concluded, therefore, that in Chinese
hamster cells all unexcised platination reactions are normally
circumvented during DNA replication by a caffeine-sensitive
process.

Relationship Between Excision Repair of Platinum-induced DNA Damage and Cytotoxicity

Fraval and Roberts (70) demonstrated removal of platinum
adducts from DNA of exponentially growing Chinese hamster V79
cells. The half-life of total drug-DNA reaction products was
approximately 28 hours. As such products are stable chemically
under physiological conditions, removal of the DNA adducts could
be attributed to repair.

Recent investigations using alkaline elution (51) or a combination of alkaline elution, alkaline sucrose sedimentation and

DNA renaturation, (53) have clearly demonstrated repair of DNA-protein and DNA-DNA interstrand crosslinks in cultured mammalian cells following cisplatin treatment.   Interstrand crosslinking in Chinese hamster V79 cells was demonstrated by a decrease in the rate of filter elution of DNA from X-irradiated, treated cells, a shift in alkaline sucrose gradients of DNA molecules towards the high molecular weight end of the gradient, or an increase in the rapidly renaturing fraction of DNA in cell lysates.   All of these drug-induced phenomena reached a maximum from 6-12 hours after drug treatment, then declined.   The half-life of DNA interstrand crosslinks usually appeared to be between 12-24 hours.   Some DNA degradation occurred, but it was insufficient to account for crosslink reversal.   Because crosslinks induced by platinum are stable in isolated DNA under physiological conditions, this reversal may also be attributed to repair, though the mechanism remains unknown.

Although correlations have been established in some cases between the extent of drug-DNA interaction and cytotoxicity, the relationship between excision repair of DNA damage and toxicity is not always clear.

The rare skin condition, Xeroderma pigmentosum (XP), is characterised by extreme sensitivity to sunlight and a predisposition to skin cancer.   Cells taken from persons suffering from this condition are more sensitive to UV-irradiation than normal cells and are deficient in excision repair of UV-induced damage. These same cells are also sensitive to other DNA damaging agents such as hydrocarbon epoxides, 4-nitroquinoline-1-oxide and 7-bromomethylbenz(a)-anthracene and sensitivity is again associated with decreased levels of various manifestations of DNA excision repair.   (For review see (68).   It has now been found (71) that these repair deficient XP cells are also more sensitive than normal foetus lung cells to cis-DDP, when the lethal effects of the drug are expressed as a function of reaction with DNA rather than as a function of dose of reagent.   It could therefore be reasoned that this increased sensitivity of XP cells is similarly due to their decreased ability to excise cis-DDP induced DNA damage.

Cells from patients with the genetic disease Fanconi's anaemia, show unusual sensitivity to the cytotoxic and clastogenic effects of difunctional alkylating agents.   These cells are also unusually sensitive to cisplatin (72).   Such sensitivity is not the result of decreased binding of platinum to DNA but it remains to be determined if repair of various lesions in these cells is abnormal.

If DNA synthesis on a damaged template is responsible for toxicity, cells that are allowed to repair DNA prior to S-phase and cell division should show less toxicity than cells entering the proliferative cycle immediately following treatment.   In an initial study, Fravel and Roberts (70) treated stationary Chinese hamster V79 cells with cisplatin and measured toxicity and plat-

inum-DNA interaction after various holding periods in the nondividing state.   The cells slowly excised platinum, and plating
efficiency increased.   There was a similar relationship between
the amount of platinum bound to DNA and cell survival whether one
compared the two immediately following treatment with several
drug doses, or after varying periods of recovery.

However, the cells used in these initial studies, Chinese
hamster V79 cells, do not tolerate the nondividing state well,
and it was later found that they do not recover from cisplatin
toxicity under some conditions.   Therefore, the experiment was
repeated using human fibroblasts (73) under conditions where
minimal DNA synthesis occurred.   These cells were healthy in the
nondividing condition.   The fibroblasts recovered from cisplatin
toxicity if held in the nondividing state, and they excised
platinum lesions from DNA by a first order process with a half-
life of 2.5 days (Figure 4).   DNA-DNA interstrand crosslinks,
measured by alkaline elution and by estimation of renaturable DNA
in cell lysates, were found to be repaired with a half-life of
about 36 hours (Figure 5).   DNA protein crosslinks were removed
at a similar rate and there was no evidence for any accompanying
degradation.   Thus the reversal of crosslinking was attributed
to repair rather than introduction of DNA strand breaks.   The
relationship between cell survival and the amounts of platinum
remaining bound to DNA at the time cells were plated out for
estimation of cell survival, was similar to that observed in cells
treated with several drug doses and plated immediately.
The results strongly supported the hypothesis that damage present
on the DNA template at the time of entry into the proliferative
cycles was responsible for cellular toxicity.   Further, the
results showed that the repair process was actually effective in
achieving biological recovery.

When, however, attempts have been made to relate inherent
drug sensitivity to repair capacity, clearcut results have not
always emerged.   Walker 256 carcinoma cells display unusual
sensitivity to difunctional alkylating agents and to cisplatin.
There is a subline of this tumour that shows a 30-fold increase
in resistance to cisplatin.   Nevertheless, the two sublines bind
the same amount of platinum on DNA following treatment with a
given dosage, they excise platinum lesions from their DNA at a
similar rate, and they remove DNA-protein crosslinks and DNA
interstrand crosslinks from DNA at a similar rate (74).   Following sulphur mustard treatment, nascent DNA synthesis on a damaged
template appears to be similar in both lines (75).   It is of
course possible that these lines might vary in their capacity to
remove a specific lesion that was not measured - an intrastrand
crosslink, for example - but if this is not the case, then some
target other than simply DNA exists in certain cells that confers
unusual sensitivity to bifunctional agents.   This could conceivably be at the level of chromatin or a DNA-nuclear matrix complex.

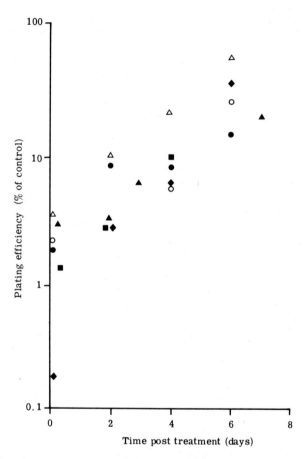

Figure 4a.   Recovery of nondividing human fibroblasts from cis-DDP toxicity. Stationary-phase human fibroblasts were treated with cis-DDP (△ ○, 32 μM; and ▲ ◆ ■ ●, 40 μM) and were either plated immediately or held in the nondividing state for various time periods and recovered from drug toxicity.

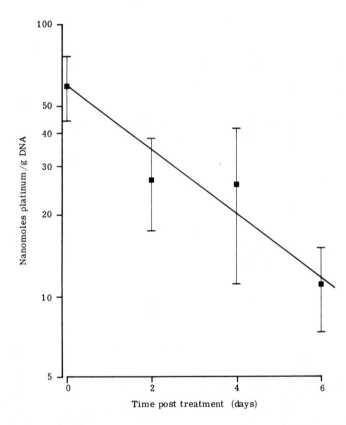

Figure 4b. Excision of Pt from DNA of nondividing human fibroblasts following cis-DDP treatment. The plot illustrates first-order loss of the Pt reaction products.

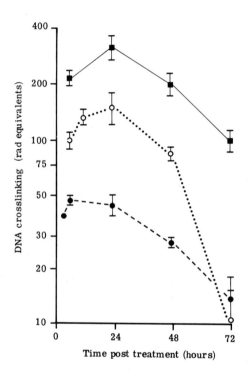

Figure 5.   Repair of cis-*DDP-induced DNA–protein crosslinks and DNA inter-strand crosslinks in human fibroblasts during holding in the nondividing state. Stationary cultures were treated with 40 μmol* cis-*DDP, and after various periods of holding in the nondividing state, crosslinking was measured by alkaline elution (■, DNA–protein crosslinks; and ○, DNA interstrand crosslinks) or by estimation of renaturable DNA in cell lysates (●, DNA interstrand crosslinks).*

Literature Cited

1. Rosenberg, B.; Van Camp, L.; Krigas, T. Nature 1965, 205,698.
2. Reslova, S. Chem.-Biol. Interact. 1971, 4, 66.
3. Kutinova, L.; Vonka, V.; Drobnik, J. Neoplasma 1972, 19, 453.
4. Reslova, S.; Srogl, M.; Drobnik, J. Advances in Antimicrobial and Antineoplastic Chemotherapy 1972, 2, 209.
5. Trosko, J.E. in "Platinum Coordination Complexes in Cancer Chemotherapy. Recent Results in Cancer Research, vol. 48", Springer-Verlag, Berlin, 1974, p.108.
6. Beck, D.J.; Brubaker, R.R. Mutation Res. 1975, 27, 181.
7. Monti-Bragadin, C.; Tamaro, M.; Banfi, E. Chem.-Biol. Interact. 1975, 11, 469.
8. Lecointe, P.; Macquet, J-P.; Butour, J-L.; Paoletti, C. Mutation Res. 1977, 48, 139.
9. Zwelling, L.A.; Bradley, M.O.; Sharkey, N.A.; Anderson, T.; Kohn, K.W. Mutation Res. 1979a, 67, 271.
10. Johnson, N.P.; Hoeschele, J.D.; Rahn, R.O.; O'Neill, J.P.; Hsie, A.W. Cancer Res. 1980, 40, 1463.
11. Turnbull, D.; Popescu, N.C.; DiPaolo, J.A.; Myhr, B.C. Mutation Res. 1979, 66, 267.
12. Fornace, A.J. Jr.; Little, J.B. Carcinogenesis 1980, 1, 989.
13. Leopold, W.R.; Miller, E.C.; Miller, J.A. Cancer Res. 1979, 39, 913.
14. Leopold, W.R.; Batzinger, R.P.; Miller, J.A.; Miller, E.C.; Earhart, R.H. Proc. Amer. Assoc. Cancer Res. 1981, 22, 108.
15. Rosenberg, B. Cancer Chemother. Rep. 1975, 59, 589.
16. Harrap, K.R.; Jones, M.; Wilkinson, C.R.; McD.Clink, H.; Sparrow, S.; Mitchley, B.C.V.; Clarke, S.; Veasey, A. in "Cisplatin: Current Status and New Developments", Academic Press, New York, 1980, p.193.
17. Tisdale, M.J.; Phillips, B.J. Biochem. Pharmacol. 1975a, 24, 1271.
18. Tisdale, M.J.; Phillips, B.J. Biochem. Pharmacol. 1975b, 24, 205.
19. Tisdale, M.J.; Phillips, B.J. Biochem. Pharmacol. 1975c, 24, 211.
20. Rosenberg, B. J. Clin. Hematol. Oncol. 1977, 7, 817.
21. Horacek, P.; Drobnik, J. Biochem. Biophys. Acta 1971, 254, 341.
22. Mansy, S.; Rosenberg, B.; Thomson, A.J. J. Amer. Chem. Soc. 1973, 95, 1633.
23. Stone, P.J.; Kelman, A.D.; Sinex, F.M. Nature 1974, 251, 736.
24. Munchausen, L.L.; Rahn, R.O. Biochem. Biophys. Acta 1975, 414, 242.
25. Goodgame, D.M.L.; Jeeves, I.; Phillips, F.L.; Skapski, A.C. Biochem. Biophys. Acta 1975, 378, 153.
26. Gellert, R.W.; Bau, R. J. Amer. Chem. Soc. 1975, 97, 7379.
27. Cramer, R.E.; Dahlstrom, P.L. J. Clin. Haematology and Oncology 1977, 7, 330.

28. Bau, R. in "International Conference on the chemistry of platinum group metals", Royal Society of Chemistry, Bristol, 1981, p.5.

29. Pascoe, J.M.; Roberts, J.J. Biochem. Pharmacol. 1974a, 23, 1345.

30. Pascoe, J.M.; Roberts, J.J. Biochem. Pharmacol. 1974b, 23, 1359.

31. Harder, H.C. Chem.-Biol. Interact. 1975, 10, 27.

32. Ganguli, P.K.; Theophanides, R. Eur. J. Biochem. 1979, 101, 377.

33. Roberts, J.J.; Pascoe, J.M. Nature 1972, 235, 282.

34. Zwelling, L.A.; Kohn, K.W.; Ross, W.C.; Ewig, R.A.G.; Anderson, T. Cancer Res. 1978, 38, 1762.

35. Thomson, A.J. in "Platinum Coordination Complexes in Cancer Chemotherapy: Recent Results in Cancer Res., vol. 48", Springer-Verlag, Berlin, 1974, p.38.

36. Roos, I.A.G.; Thomson, A.J.; Mansy, S. J. Amer. Chem. Soc. 1974, 96, 6484.

37. Kleinwachter, V.; Zaludova, R. Chem.-Biol. Interact. 1977, 16, 207.

38. Roos, I.A.G. Chem.-Biol. Interact. 1977, 16, 39.

39. Shooter, K.V.; Howse, R.; Merrifield, R.K.; Robbins, A.B. Chem.-Biol. Interact. 1972, 5, 289.

40. Filipski, J.; Kohn, K.W.; Bonner, W.M. Chem.-Biol. Interact. 1980, 32, 321.

41. Millard, M.M.; Macquet, J-P,; Theophanides, T. Biochem. Biophys. Acta 1975, 402, 166.

42. Macquet, J-P.; Butour, J-L. Eur. J. Biochem. 1978, 83, 375.

43. Tamburio, A.M.; Celotti, L.; Furcan, D.; Guantieri, V. Chem.-Biol. Interact. 1977, 16, 1.

44. Kelman, A.D.; Peresie, H.J.; Stone, P.J. J. Clin. Hematol. and Oncology 1977, 7, 440.

45. Macquet, J-P.; Butour, J-L. Biochimie 1978, 60, 901.

46. Cohen, G.L.; Bauer, W.R.; Barton, J.K.; Lippard, S.J. Science 1979, 203, 1014.

47. Cohen, G.L.; Ledner, J.A.; Bauer, W.R.; Ushay, H.M.; Caravana, C.; Lippard, S.J. J. Amer. Chem. Soc. 1980, 102, 2487.

48. Roberts, J.J.; Fraval, H.N.A. Biochimie 1978, 60, 869.

49. Roberts, J.J. in "Molecular Actions and Targets for Cancer Chemotherapeutic Agents", Academic Press, New York, p.17.

50. Pera, M.F.; Sessford, D.; Roberts, J.J. Biochem. Pharmacol. 1982 (in press).

51. Zwelling, L.A.; Anderson, T.; Kohn, K.W. Cancer Res. 1979b, 39, 365.

52. Roberts, J.J.; Friedlos, F. Biochim. Biophys. Acta 1981a, 655, 146.

53. Pera, M.F. Jr.; Rawlings, C.J.; Shackleton, J.; Roberts, J.J. Biochim. Biophys. Acta 1981a, 655, 152.

54. Zwelling, L.A.; Filipski, J.; Kohn, K.W. Cancer Res. 1979c, 39, 4989.

55. Zwelling, L.A.; Michaels, S.; Schwartz, H.; Dobson, P.O.; Kohn, K.W. Cancer Res. 1981, 41, 640.

56. Laurent, G.; Erickson, L.C.; Sharkey, N.A.; Kohn, K.W. Cancer Res. 1981, 41, 3347.

57. Erickson, L.C.; Zwelling, L.A.; DuCore, J.M.; Sharkey, N.A.; Kohn, K.W. Cancer Res. 1981, 41, 2791.

58. Strandberg, M.C.; Proc. Amer. Assoc. Cancer Res. 1981, 22, 202.

59. Rawlings, C.J.; Roberts, J.J. unpublished.

60. Harder, H.C.; Rosenberg, B. Int. J. Cancer 1970, 6, 207.

61. van den Berg, H.W.; Roberts, J.J. Chem.-Biol. Interact. 1976, 12, 375.

62. Fraval, H.N.A.; Roberts, J.J. Chem.-Biol. Interact. 1978a, 23, 99.

63. Fraval, H.N.A.; Roberts, J.J. Chem-Biol. Interact. 1978b, 23, 111.

64. Howle, J.A.; Gale, G.R. Biochem. Pharmacol. 1970, 19, 2757.

65. Taylor, D.M.; Tew, K.D.; Jones, J.D. Eur. J. Cancer 1976, 12, 249.

66. Johnson, N.P.; Hoeschele, J.D.; Kuemmerle, N.B.; Masker, W.E.; Rahn, R.O. Chem.-Biol. Interact. 1978, 23, 267.

67. Harder, H.C.; Smith, R.G.; Leroy, A.F. Cancer Res. 1976, 36, 3821.

68. Roberts, J.J. Adv. in Radiation Biol. 1978, 7, 211.

69. van den Berg, H.W.; Roberts, J.J. Chem.-Biol. Interact. 1975b, 11, 493.

70. Fraval, H.N.A.; Roberts, J.J. Cancer Res. 1979, 39, 1793.

71. Fraval, H.N.A.; Rawlings, C.J.; Roberts, J.J. Mutation Res. 1978, 51, 121.

72. Pera, M.F., Jr.; Roberts, J.J. unpublished results.

73. Pera, M.F.; Rawlings, C.J.; Roberts, J.J. Chem.-Biol. Interact. 1981b, 37, 245.

74. Rawlings, C.J.; Roberts, J.J. unpublished.

75. Roberts, J.J.; Friedlos, F. unpublished.

RECEIVED October 20, 1982

Biological Consequences of Platinum–DNA Crosslinks in Mammalian Cells

LEONARD A. ZWELLING

National Cancer Institute, Laboratory of Molecular Pharmacology, Developmental Therapeutics Program, Division of Cancer Treatment, Bethesda, MD 20205

Bifunctional DNA adducts or crosslinks can be formed by antineoplastic Pt-coordination complexes. 2 distinct DNA crosslinks can be produced in mammalian cells by cis-Diamminedichloroplatinum(II) (DDP) and its inactive isomer trans-DDP, DNA-protein crosslinks (DPC) and DNA interstrand crosslinks (ISC). Each can be quantified by using DNA alkaline elution, a technique based upon the size-dependent elution of DNA single strands from filters at pH 12. Proteolytic enzymes can be used to distinguish DPC from ISC. DPC form rapidly and are the major lesion produced by trans-DDP. ISC form over 6-12 hr following treatment and are more efficiently formed by cis-DDP. ISC correlated more closely with cytotoxicity than did DPC. This was confirmed using chemical blockade of ISC formation to enhance cell survival following cis-DDP treatment. Additionally, malignant cells resistant to cis-DDP in vitro and in vivo showed lower levels of ISC than their sensitive parent lines. Further studies in resistant and sensitive cells have led to a model in which the biological consequences of Pt-DNA damage result from the temporal and quantitative relationship between Pt-DNA damage and cellular repair at a given functional DNA site. The kinetics of this equilibrium between DNA damage and repair of various Pt-DNA adducts may determine the effect of cis-DDP treatment on cytotoxicity, mutagenicity and sister chromatid exchange frequency.

The consequences of damage to the DNA of living cells must result from three related factors; (1) the number of damaged sites, (2) the ability of the cell to repair the damage, and (3) the temporal relationship between damage production, damage repair and the normal cell functions with which unrepaired

damage could interfere. This scheme (Figure 1) suggests an
equilibrium between DNA damage and repair superimposed upon
ongoing DNA functions such as transcription and translation.
The state of the equilibrium at the time and at the site at
which a normal DNA function is to occur could determine the
consequences of the DNA damage. Therefore, differences between
the susceptibility of cell types to DNA damaging agents may
result from differences in the initial frequency of DNA damage,
differences in the cells' capacity to repair damage or
differences in the ability of the cell to tolerate damage either
through by-passing damage or abating normal function until damage
is repaired.

The DNA damage produced by Pt(II)-coordination complexes can
be included in such a schema. This discussion will be limited
to damage produced by cis- and trans-Diamminedichloroplatinum
(II). These isomers (Figure 2) are felt to interact with nucleophilic sites in intracellular macromolecules through the
displacement by these moieties of the chloride ligands (leaving
groups) of the Pt(II) complexes. From stereochemical
considerations the number and/or rate of macromolecular interactions would be different for Pt-complexes with leaving groups
in the cis vs. trans configuration (1). Each agent may elicit
different cellular responses with correspondingly different
consequences. We will present the results of work performed in
the Laboratory of Molecular Pharmacology over the past 5 years
using various cell systems. These data elucidate several Pt-DNA
interactions, the cellular DNA responses they elicit and the
consequences of the equilibrium between DNA damage and repair in
actively dividing mammalian cells.

Materials and Methods

In Vitro Cell Culture. Mouse leukemia L1210 cells (designated K25) were grown in RPMI 1630 medium supplemented with 20%
heat-inactivated fetal calf serum. V79 Chinese hamster lung
cells were grown in α-MEM medium with 5% fetal calf serum in
7.5% CO_2. The human cell lines were grown in Eagle's minimal
essential medium with 10% fetal calf serum.

Drug Treatments. Cis-Diamminedichloroplatinum(II) (NSC
119875) and trans-Diamminedichloroplatinum(II) (NSC 131558)
were obtained from the National Cancer Institute and were always
constituted in isotonic, aqueous solution just prior to use.
L-phenylalanine mustard (NSC 8806) was dissolved in 0.1 N HCl
and stored frozen.

Cell Survival Measurements. L1210 cell survival was quantified by colony forming ability in soft agar (2). V79 colony-
forming ability was measured using attached cells on plates of
initial plating densities of 300-3000/plate (3). The cyto-

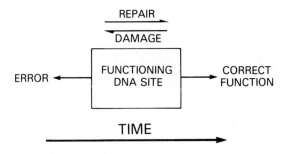

Figure 1.   *A schematic representation of the interaction between DNA damage and repair of a random, functioning DNA site.*

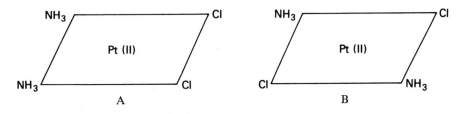

Figure 2.   *The structures of A,* cis-DDP *and B,* trans-DDP.

toxicity of cis-DDP in human cells is quantified by drug
inhibition of cell growth during 3 population doublings in
drug-free medium (4, 5).

Mutagenicity. V79 cells were back-selected to eliminate all
pre-existing HGPRT-mutants in medium containing hypoxanthine,
10^{-5}M, methotrexate 3.2 x 10^{-6}M, and thymidine, 5 x 10^{-6}M (3).
Following drug treatments cells were incubated in fresh medium
for 2 days and then subcultured at 2-5 x 10^6 cells/flask for an
additional 3-5 days of growth to allow mutant expression.
Following this, cells were seeded on plates and incubated in
6-thioguanine-containing medium. The fraction of thioguanine-
resistant cells (mutation frequency) was determined from the
plating efficiencies in the presence or absence of thioguanine.

Drug-Resistant L1210 Cells. The K25 L1210 cells were used as
a parent line to develop a line of cis-DDP-resistant L1210 cells.
The parent cells were treated with 10^{-4} methylnitrosourea for 1
hr, allowed to recover to exponential growth, treated with cis-
DDP for 1 hr and seeded in soft agar. A clone was selected from
the surviving cells, retreated with cis-DDP, reseeded in soft
agar and again a clone was selected. An additional methylnitrosourea treatment and 5 cycles of cis-DDP treatment and
colony formation yielded the cis-DDP resistant line (ZCR9).
These cells were cryopreserved and fresh aliquots unfrozen
approximately every 6 weeks. By this procedure resistance was
maintained and reproducibility of experiments over many months
was assured (6).
Murine L1210 tumor lines in vivo were obtained from 2
sources. Dr. J. Burchenal, Memorial Sloan-Kettering Institute,
provided the cis-DDP resistant line (L1210/PDD) and its
sensitive parent (L1210 (MSKI)). Dr. F. Schabel, Southern
Research Institute, derived the L-PAM-resistant line (L1210/
PAM). This tumor and its sensitive parent (L1210 (NCI)) were
obtained from Dr. D. Vistica, National Cancer Institute. These
tumors were obtained in either C57BL X DBA/2F$_1$ (called BD2F$_1$)
or DBA mice, but were maintained in male BD2F$_1$ mice only.
Tumor lines were passaged weekly by explanting ascites fluid
from tumored animals and inoculating 10^6 cells intraperitoneally
(i.p.) into mice. To maintain drug resistance, L1210/PDD and
L1210/PAM required drug treatments following inoculation (6).
Mice bearing L1210 cell tumors to be used in an experiment
were not treated with drugs to maintain tumor resistance during
the 7 days prior to explanation. 6-7 days following this tumor
inoculation, ascites tumor cells were explanted and either
inoculated into recipient animals upon whom survival studies
would be performed or explanted into RPMI 1630 medium + 20%
fetal calf serum, 50 µM 2-mercaptoethanol and either [2-^{14}C]
thymidine (0.02 µCi ml^{-1}) or [methyl-^{3}H]thymidine (0.2 µCi ml^{-1})
and incubated for 20 hr at 37°. The following day explanted

cells were washed free of radioactive label and 2-mercapto-
ethanol. Equal numbers of oppositely labeled sensitive and
resistant cells were mixed, treated with 20 μM cis-DDP, 20
μM L-PAM or no drug for 1 hr and then drug was removed.
Cells were resuspended in drug-free medium and DNA damage assays
(see below) were performed at various times thereafter.
        The animals into which these cells were inoculated were
either drug-treated or untreated controls. They were checked
daily for survival. It is critical to note that cells used for
DNA assays were aliquots of identical cells used for in vivo
survival measurements. Further, by mixing oppositely labeled
cells prior to drug treatment, uniform drug exposure was assured
(6).

        The Assessment of DNA Crosslinking by Alkaline Elution. DNA
damage, that is, interstrand crosslinks, DNA-protein crosslinks,
and strand breaks, was determined using the alkaline elution
technique (7, 8). Cells labeled with ^{14}C-thymidine for 20-24
hr were deposited on a membrane filter and lysed with a
detergent-containing solution. An alkaline solution (pH 12.1-
12.2) was then slowly pumped through the filter, and fractions
were collected to determine the rate of release of DNA from the
filter. For assay of crosslinks, the cells were exposed to
x-ray at 0°C prior to deposition on the filter. In order to
improve quantitation, control cells labeled with ^{3}H-thymidine
and x-irradiated at 0° were mixed with the experimental ^{14}C-
labeled cells prior to deposition on the filters. The elution
of ^{3}H-DNA serves as an internal reference for normalization of
the elution of ^{14}C-DNA.
        DNA strand breaks are measured by the increased elution rate
of shortened single strands. Crosslinks have the opposite
effect, and are measured by inserting a known frequency of strand
breaks by means of x-ray. Interstrand crosslinks reduce elution
rate by linking together two or more single strands. DNA-protein
crosslinks reduce elution because proteins tend to adsorb to the
filters under the alkaline conditions used. The effects of
DNA-protein crosslinks can be virtually eliminated by including
with the detergent lysis, proteolytic enzymes (8).
        Crosslinking is often expressed in rad-equivalents. This
simply indicates that the degree of alteration in DNA elution
rate [increase (strand breaks) or decrease (crosslinks)] produced
by the drug dose in question is equal in quantity to that which
would have been produced by that dose of x-radiation. A detailed
discussion of the quantitation of elution results can be found
in references 7 and 8. (Also see Figure 3 and legend).

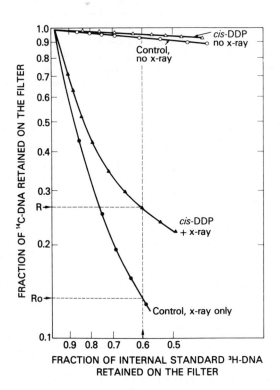

Figure 3. The alkaline elution kinetics of DNA from L1210 cells treated with cis-DDP (10 μM) for 1 h followed by 12 h incubation in a drug-free medium. L1210 cells were labeled with ^{14}C-thymidine for 20 h and were either cis-DDP treated (▲, △) or untreated (●, ○). (Reproduced with permission from Ref. 20. Copyright 1980, Academic Press.)

The two upper curves without irradiation indicate that cis-DDP produced no detectable DNA breakage. The two lower curves quantify DNA crosslinking as the DNA from cells treated with cis-DDP exhibiting slower elution kinetics than the DNA from control cells when both had received prior irradiation (600 R). The abscissa is generated by the coelution of oppositely labeled DNA from irradiated cells (internal standard cells). The point at which 60% of this ^{3}H-DNA remains on the filter is the point at which the retention (R) of ^{14}C-DNA is quantified and compared with that of controls (R_0).

Results

The Nature of the DNA Crosslinking Produced by Cis- and Trans-
Diamminedichloroplatinum(II) and its Relation to Cytotoxicity.
Initial Observations with L1210 Cells. Both compounds produced
proteinase-sensitive and proteinase-resistant crosslinks in
L1210 mouse leukemia cells as detected by alkaline elution
(Figure 4). Drug-induced crosslinking which is sensitive to
proteolytic digestion is taken as representative of DNA-protein
crosslinking (DPC). Crosslinking resistant to proteolytic
digestion is taken as interstrand crosslinking (ISC). As can be
seen in Figure 4, although both compounds produced DPC and ISC,
the contribution of DPC to the total crosslinking produced by
trans-DDP was greater than to the total crosslinking produced
by cis-DDP. Figure 4 also shows that the time course of
formation and disppearance of DPC vs. ISC is different with
trans-DDP, but similar with cis-DDP. That is both compounds
produced delayed ISC, but trans-DDP produced rapid DPC while the
majority of cis-DDP-DPC was delayed in formation. If the maximum
amount of the 2 types of crosslinking is compared with the subsequent ability of the cells to form colonies (Figure 5), DPC, the
major contributor to total crosslinking, was greater for trans-
than for cis-DDP at comparable toxicity. Comparing ISC and cell
survival brings the curves for the 2 drugs into line. This
result suggests a mechanistic relationship between ISC and cytotoxicity for these 2 agents (9).

This relationship was further substantiated by work in which
interstrand crosslink formation could be prevented by the avid
Pt binder thiourea. Thiourea was capable of blocking cis-DDP
cytotoxicity and interstrand crosslink formation in a similar
dose- (Figure 6) and time- (Figure 7) dependent fashion (10).

We have proposed a reaction scheme for cis-DDP with DNA bases
as a consequence of this work (Figure 8) (11). Cis-DDP could
undergo sequential activation to a positively charged species
capable of reaction with nucleophilic sites on DNA (N). Thiourea
could compete with DNA bases for Pt-binding and thus inactivate
cis-DDP directly (Reaction 5) or following cis-DDP activation
(Reaction 5'). Additionally thiourea could prevent monoadduct
conversion to ISC directly (Reaction 6) or following a second
activation (Reaction 6'). Reversal of ISC (Reaction 7), although
demonstrable in isolated chemical systems (12,13), was not
observed in living cells.

The ISC produced by cis-DDP or trans-DDP appears to indicate
the ultimate survival of treated cells.

In Vitro and In Vivo studies of sensitive and resistant
murine cells. A line of L1210 cells resistant to cis-DDP was
developed from the parent K25 line used in the previous studies.
Methylnitrosourea and cis-DDP treatments followed by soft-agar
colony formation were used to obtain this line designated ZCR9.
Equitoxic concentrations of cis-DDP were 2.4 times higher in
ZCR9 than in K25. This difference was reflected in the amount of
ISC but not DPC produced in each cell type (Figure 9). No dif-

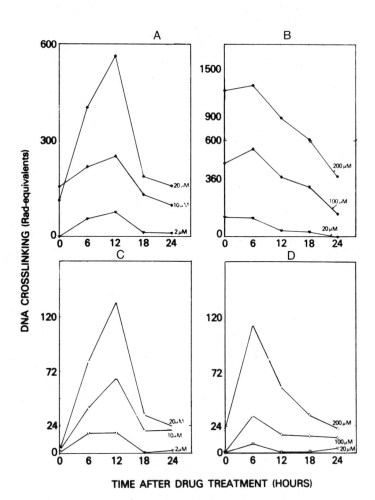

Figure 4. The kinetics of formation and disappearance of DNA–protein cross-linking (DPC) and DNA interstrand crosslinking (ISC) in L1210 cells treated with cis- or trans-DDP. Key to conditions: A, cis-DDP without proteinase (DPC and ISC); B, trans-DDP without proteinase (DPC and ISC); C, cis-DDP with proteinase (ISC only); and D, trans-DDP with proteinase (ISC only). (Reproduced with permission from Ref. 9.)

All drug treatments were for 1 h at indicated doses followed by incubation in drug-free medium for 0 to 24 h prior to crosslink quantification by alkaline elution.

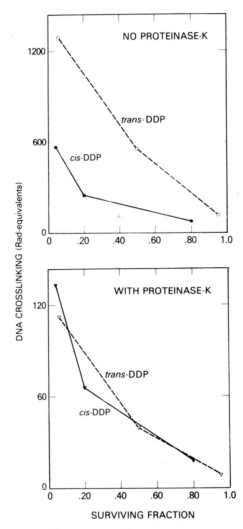

Figure 5. Relation between DNA interstrand crosslinking and DNA–protein crosslinking and survival of L1210 cells as measured by soft-agar colony formation. Key to conditions: top, without proteinase-K (DPC + ISC); and bottom, with proteinase-K (ISC only). (Reproduced with permission from Ref. 9.)

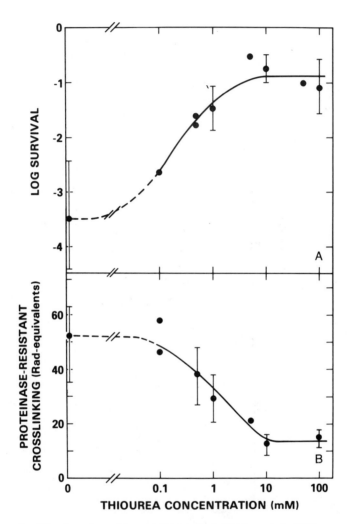

Figure 6.   The dose dependence of thiourea's inhibition of cis-DDP *cytotoxicity (A) and interstrand crosslinking (B) in L1210 cells. (Reproduced with permission from Ref. 10.)*

Cells were treated with 20 µM cis-DDP for 1 h, washed, and then treated for 1 h with various concentrations of thiourea in medium after which colony formation in soft agar was quantified immediately (A) or delayed 6–12 h before proteinase-resistant crosslinking (ISC) was quantified (B).

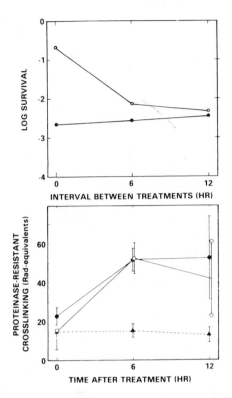

Figure 7.   The effect of varying the time interval between cis-DDP *treatment and thiourea treatment on cytotoxicity (top) and ISC formation (bottom). (Reproduced with permission from Ref. 10.)*

L1210 cells were treated for 1 h with cis-DDP *(20 μM), washed, and then treated immediately, 6 h, or 12 h later with thiourea (100 μM) for 1 h. Cytotoxicity and ISC were then quantified. Key: ●, no thiourea; ○, 100 mM thiourea for 1 h just prior to inoculation into soft agar or ISC measurement; and ▲, thiourea immediately following* cis-DDP *with ISC quantification 0, 6, or 12 h later.*

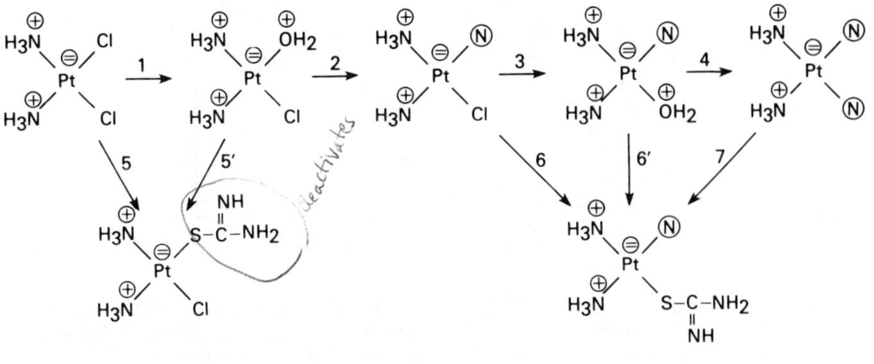

Figure 8.   Scheme for reactions of cis-DDP *with nucleophilic site (N) or thiourea at various points in the formation of a* cis-DDP–DNA *crosslink. (Reproduced with permission from Ref. 11. Copyright 1981, Academic Press.)*

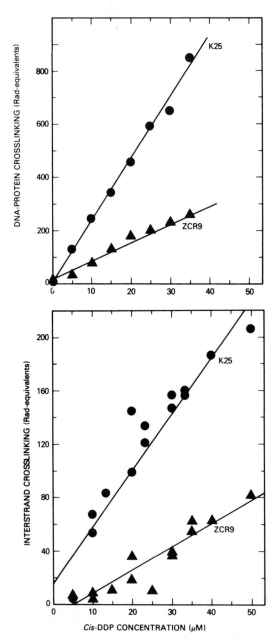

Figure 9. Concentration dependence of cis-*DDP DNA–protein crosslinking (top, 3000 R) and DNA interstrand crosslinking (bottom, 300 R) in sensitive (K25) and resistant (ZCR9) L1210 cells. (Reproduced with permission from Ref. 6.)*

All treatment times were 1 h. DPC was quantified immediately after treatment; ISC, 6 h later. The ratios of the slopes of these lines (K25/ZCR9) are 3.0 for DPC and 2.5 for ISC. The ratio for relative colony formation (survival) was 2.4 (ZCR9/K25). These ratios represent the ratios of cis-DDP doses producing equal effects in each assay.

ferences were noted in the kinetics of cis–DDP crosslink
formation and repair in these 2 lines (6). These studies were
then extended to tumors in mice. Sensitive-resistant pairs of
L1210 cells were obtained (see Materials and Methods) in mice.
Animal survival in tumor-bearing mice was compared with DNA
crosslinking in explants from aliquots of the identical tumor
used to inoculate these mice. Lines were selected for resistance
to the bifunctional alkylating agent L-phenylalanine mustard
(L-PAM) as well as to cis–DDP. The results are summarized in
Table I.

In the cis–DDP sensitive-resistant pair (L1210 (MSKI) and
L1210/PDD), cis–DDP resistance was confirmed in L1210/PDD
and cis–DDP-induced ISC was almost absent. L1210/PDD was not
cross-resistant to L-PAM. Comparable ISC was produced by L-PAM
in explants of both lines. In the L-PAM sensitive-resistant
pair (L1210 (NCI) and L1210/PAM), L-PAM resistance was confirmed
in L1210/PAM and ISC was appropriately depressed. However,
L1210/PAM was strikingly resistant to cis–DDP, but cis–DDP-ISC
was only partially depressed. Thus, although all our data to
this point indicated delayed, ISC would predict for cis–DDP
cytotoxicity, an exception had been found (6). This exception
was then studied in further detail.

A Mechanism of Cis-DDP Resistance in L1210/PAM. Malignant
ascites cells were explanted from mice bearing L1210 (NCI) and
L1210/PAM into soft-agar cloning tubes and colonies allowed to
form (2). Single colonies of each cell line were selected,
subcultured and tested for resistance to cis–DDP. The resistance
of L1210/PAM to cis–DDP in vivo was maintained in vitro.

ISC assays revealed a peak of ISC 6–12 hr following a 1-hr
exposure to cis–DDP in both cell lines. The magnitude of this
crosslinking in L1210/PAM was 60% of that in L1210 (NCI) for any
given drug dose. This difference was not sufficient to explain
the marked difference in cis–DDP sensitivity between these cell
lines (14).

Following peak ISC, ISC declined in both cell lines, but the
rate was 1.7-fold faster in L1210/PAM than L1210 (NCI). This
difference could arise if crosslinks were more rapidly removed
or more slowly formed in L1210/PAM. By preventing further ISC
with thiourea 5–6 hr following cis–DDP treatment (10), the
removal of interstrand crosslinks could be examined with no
contribution from ongoing ISC formation. The 2 lines removed
formed crosslinks at comparable rates following blockade of
additional ISC formation by thiourea. The removal of ISC
appears normal in L1210/PAM, but the conversion of monoadducts
to crosslinks is decreased. This could be due to enhanced
monoadduct removal or inactivation. Initial Pt–DNA adducts are
likely to be comparable in these cells as DPC was comparable
immediately following cis–DDP treatment (14).

Table I. The Survival of L1210-Bearing Mice vs. Quantified

Interstrand Crosslink Formation in Identical Explanted Tumors[a]

Tumor Line	Cis-DDP			L-PAM		
	%ILS[b]	ISC[c]		%ILS[b]	ISC[c]	
		6 hr	12 hr		6 hr	12 hr
L1210 (MSKI)	151	0.20	0.21	94	0.23	0.20
L1210/PPD	11	0.01	0.01	76	0.18	0.17
L1210 (NCI)	66	0.30	0.26	96	0.17	0.18
L1210/PAM	6	0.19	0.16	25	0.07	0.08

[a]Survival compared with untreated, tumor-bearing mice. Recipient mice were inoculated with 1-3 x 10^6 tumor cells i.p. and treated with either cis-DDP, 4.5 mg kg^{-1} i.p. on days 1, 5, 9 and 13 following tumor inoculation or 13 mg kg^{-1} L-PAM on day 1 following tumor inoculation. Crosslinking measurements were made on aliquots of the identical cells used for tumor inoculation which were explanted into tissue culture rather than inoculated into recipient mice. (From Reference 6).

[b]% Increased life span.

[c]Interstrand crosslinking: crosslinking coefficient = $(\dfrac{1-r_0}{1-r})^{1/2} -1$

where r and r_0 are the fraction of DNA retained on the filter from drug-treated or untreated cells respectively in the alkaline elution assay with proteinase. The time of elution at which r and r_0 were measured was usually 10 hr. 6 hr and 12 hr indicate the time following a 1 hr drug treatment at which ISC was quantified.

The resistance of L1210/PAM to cis-DDP may reside in a combination of events which can be fit into the equilibrium scheme in Figure 1. It appears that initial Pt-DNA interactions are comparable in these 2 cell lines. ISC progresses to a higher peak in L1210 (NCI) than in L1210/PAM because the equilibrium between damage and repair (or inactivation) in Figure 1 is shifted further to the right (repair) in L1210/PAM. As cell doubling times were comparable in these cells, the time axis of critical cellular events involving DNA is probably similar in L1210 (NCI) and L1210/PAM. Therefore, the increased resistance of L1210/PAM arises as a result of a lower number of critical lesions (ISC) which in turn results from cellular inactivation or repair of the precursor (monoadduct) of that lesion.

Pt-DNA Damage and Repair in Human Cells. Erickson et al. have recently demonstrated a correlation between the capability of several human cell types to repair methylation damage (Mer[+] phenotype) and cell survival following treatment with chloroethylnitrosoureas (15). These cell lines were also examined for their sensitivity or resistance to cis-DDP. Although the magnitude of cis-DDP ISC again correlated with cytotoxicity, no correlation was found between survival or crosslinking and the presence or absence of the Mer[+] phenotype. This Mer repair mechanism is probably not involved in the cellular response to Pt-DNA damage (4, 5).

The Relationship between Pt-DNA Crosslinking and Mutagenicity. V79 Chinese hamster cells were used to compare DNA damage with 2 different consequences of that damage. Colony forming ability was again used to quantify the lethality of cis- and trans-DDP. Additionally, mutagenicity was quantified in these cells at the hypoxanthine-guanine phosphoribosyltransferase locus (3) (Table II).

Again, as had been seen in L1210 cells, ISC peaked 6-12 hr following drug treatment, and DPC was a greater contributor to total crosslinking following trans-DDP compared with cis-DDP. Once again, at equitoxic concentrations of each agent, ISC was comparable whereas DPC was much greater in trans-DDP-treated cells. However, trans-DDP was virtually non-mutagenic (Figure 10); while cis-DDP was quite mutagenic. At doses of each agent producing comparable cytotoxicity and comparable ISC, trans-DDP produced more DPC and was not mutagenic. Neither ISC nor DPC are therefore necessarily mutagenic (3).

To further explore the relationship between these DNA effects and their biological consequences in V79 cells, we expanded the examined parameters to include measurement of Pt-induced sister chromatid exchanges (SCE) (a visibly detectable indication of reciprocal exchanges of chromosomal DNA). Bradley et al. showed that both compounds can produce SCE, thus SCE production can be dissociated from mutagenicity (16).

Table II. Cytotoxicity, Mutagenicity and DNA Crosslinking in V79

Cells Treated with Cis-DDP or Trans-DDP

Concentration (μM)	Treatment time (hr)	Post Incubation time (hr)	Survival fraction[a]	Mutation frequency[b]	Crosslinking (rad equivalents)	
Cis-DDP					−ProK	+ProK
11	2	0	0.1	3×10^{-4}	124	6
		6			270	46
		12			311	94
					187	41
		18			101	33
Trans-DDP						
320	2	0	0.19	$<10^{-5}$	1303	40
		6			2300	99
		12			880	79
					1200	116
		18			522	106

Source: Reference 3.

[a]Survival of colony-forming ability.

[b]HGPRT locus.

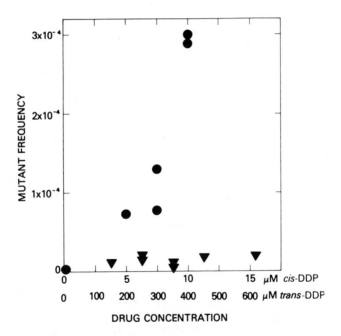

Figure 10.   The mutation frequency produced by a 2-h treatment of V79 cells with ●, cis- or ▲ trans-DDP. (Reproduced with permission from Ref. 3.)

Finally, to understand the processes relating cis-DDP DNA
damage to the various measured biological consequences, we
utilized thiourea in a fashion similar to that used in L1210
cells (vide supra - Figure 8). As had been seen in L1210 cells,
the treatment of V79 cells with thiourea immediately following
cis-DDP treatment, completely blocked the cytotoxic effect even
at drug concentrations capable of producing 97% cell kill.
Mutagenicity could also be blocked when cis-DDP treatment was
immediately followed by thiourea however the thiourea inhibition
of mutagenicity diminished over the same cis-DDP dose range
wherein cytotoxicity was totally preventable by thiourea (Figure
11). Additionally if the thiourea treatment was delayed for 4.5
hr after cis-DDP, some cytotoxicity was still prevented, but
mutagenicity had escaped thiourea blockade. The mutagenic
process becomes fixed more rapidly and at lower cis-DDP doses
than the cytotoxic process (17).

SCE production by cis-DDP was also affected by thiourea
(Figure 12). However over a dose range where immediate thiourea
completely blocked both cytotoxicity and mutagenicity, SCE
formation could only partially be prevented. This SCE formation
escaped thiourea blockade within 4.5 hr. The order of susceptibility of cis-DDP effects to immediate thiourea blockade is SCE
formation < mutagenicity < cytotoxicity (17).

A model connecting these various biological consequences of
cis-DDP in V79 cells with potential Pt-induced DNA lesions can
be constructed (Figure 13). Substantiating the data accrued in
L1210 cells, V79 cytotoxicity appeared to be most closely associated with delayed interstrand crosslink formation. Equitoxic
doses of cis- and trans-DDP produced comparable ISC and thiourea,
a known blocker of delayed ISC formation in L1210 cells, blocked
cis-DDP cytotoxicity in a fashion consistent with the results of
the L1210 work.

Trans-DDP has leaving groups stereochemically disposed to
make the formation of crosslinks at adjoining base pairs within
one strand of DNA (intrastrand crosslinking) unlikely (see Figure
2). It is not mutagenic. Cis-DDP, which can potentially form
intrastrand crosslinks, is mutagenic. If cis-DDP intrastrand
crosslinking forms to a greater magnitude or more rapidly than
ISC, then the decreased ability of thiourea to block cis-DDP
mutagenicity compared with its ability to block cytotoxicity
suggests mutagenicity may result from intrastrand crosslink
formation.

SCE formation probably derives from neither the mutagenic
nor cytotoxic cis-DDP lesion. The non-mutagenic trans-DDP can
form SCE's. Immediate thiourea can only block SCE formation at
very low cis-DDP doses and delaying thiourea allows almost total
escape of SCE formation from thiourea blockade. DNA monoadduct
formation may induce SCE formation. What little effect thiourea
does have on SCE formation may derive from thiourea's binding of
unreacted, intracellular Pt prior to its binding to DNA at all.

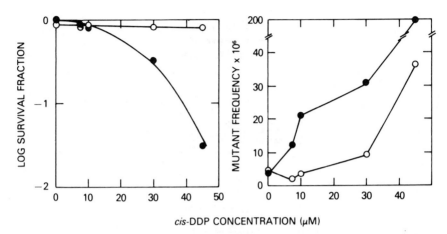

Figure 11.   *The effect of thiourea on* cis-*DDP cytotoxicity and mutagenicity in V79 Chinese hamster cells. Cells were treated with various concentrations of* cis-*DDP for 1 h followed by a 1 h incubation in the presence (○) or absence (●) of 100 mM thiourea. (See Ref. 17).*

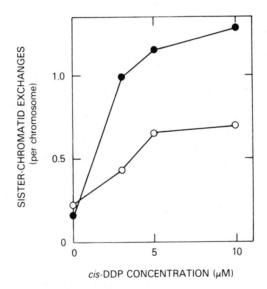

Figure 12.   *The effect of thiourea on* cis-*DDP sister-chromatid exchange production in V79. Conditions are outlined in Fig. 11 legend.*

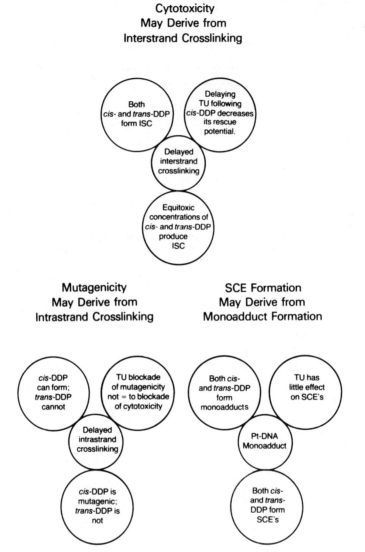

Figure 13.   The biological consequences of different DNA–Pt interactions in V79 cells. The appropriate DNA lesion is surrounded by the evidence relating it to the particular biological response it produces.

Discussion

The scheme in Figure 1 has implicit within it a kinetic approach to the study of DNA damage and repair and its relationship to desirable and toxic consequences of antineoplastic, DNA reactive drugs. In this paper the stepwise approach to the study of this scheme for one agent, cis–DDP, is presented. The initial selection of cis–DDP was made because of its clinical efficacy and the availability of an inactive isomer (1). We had hoped that some critical DNA lesion would be more efficiently produced by the active compound. The development of the alkaline elution technique incorporating enzymatic deproteinization to distinguish between interstrand and DNA–protein crosslinking was critical for this analysis (7, 8).

The results of our initial studies in L1210 cells indicated that ISC may be a key DNA lesion produced by cis–DDP (9). The studies with thiourea (10) and resistant L1210 cells (6) confirmed this idea. However, the example of the resistance of L1210/PAM to cis-DDP despite high levels of crosslinking emphasized the necessity of studying the kinetics of lesion formation and repair (14) as well as the magnitude of DNA damage at any one point in time. The studies with V79 confirmed this as the susceptibility of these cells to various consequences of cis–DDP was altered in different dose- and time-dependent fashions by thiourea (3, 17). These studies demonstrate the type of information obtainable in well-defined cellular systems with techniques which can quantify certain cell functions and drug-induced DNA lesions.

How can such an approach be extended in the future? Erickson et al. have shown with their work in human cells one important step. The results of studies using human material as a target for cis–DDP may reveal differences from results obtained in rodent systems. These results may have more bearing on clinical problems (4, 5). Erickson et al. have also developed a fluorometric alkaline elution assay requiring no labeled DNA (18). Patient material explanted into culture or obtained during therapy could be analyzed for DNA damage with this assay and conceivably could be correlated with plasma drug concentrations, other in vitro assays, or clinical tumor response.

The identification of critical DNA lesions in cells could also aid in new drug development. Analogs of promise could be compared with parent compounds in a manner similar to our comparison of cis- and trans-DDP as to DNA damage and its resultant effects. An initial test of this approach vs. animal screening could be made to see if similar results were obtained. If so, the in vitro approach would be more rapid and less costly.

Perhaps of greatest importance to future endeavors is the directions in which this current work moves us on a more basic level. In particular, the results with L1210/PAM and its cis-DDP-resistance raise more questions than they answer. What

kind of process would explain Pt-monoadduct inactivation? Could
it be a naturally-occuring substance which resembles thiourea in
its inactivating effect? Recent work suggests metallothionein
could play such a role (19). Or, is a specific platinum adduct
DNA repair mechanism extant? The human cell work would indicate
if so, it differs from that which responds to DNA methylation
(4, 5, 15). If such a repair process exists, is it inducible,
and why would a cell possess a system which responds to metal-DNA
adduct formation as distinguished from organic adduct formation?
The answers to these questions should impact not only on the
field of antineoplastic drug development but also on normal and
malignant cell biology and physiology.

Abbreviations used: DDP, Diamminedichloroplatinum(II); L-PAM,
L-phenylalanine mustard; i.p., intraperitoneal; RPMI 1630, Roswell
Park Memorial Institute medium 1630; DPC, DNA-protein crosslinking; ISC, DNA interstrand crosslinking; SCE, sister-chromatid
exchanges.

Acknowledgments

Thanks to our numerous collaborators in this work: Drs.
Mattews O. Bradley, Leonard C. Erickson, Kenneth Micetich,
Warren Ross, Tom Anderson, Guy Laurent and Jonathan Ducore; the
technical assistance of Stephen Michaels, Regina A. G. Ewig,
Nancy Sharkey, Irene Clark, Suzanne Patterson, Patricia P. Dobson
and Howard Schwartz; and the secretarial efforts of Ms. Madie
Tyler. A special thanks to Dr. Kurt W. Kohn, Chief of the
Laboratory of Molecular Pharmacology, who has supported all of
this work with advice in experimental design and expert data
analysis and interpretation, as well as valuable critique of
this and all past manuscripts.

Literature Cited

1. Zwelling, L. A.; Kohn; K. W. In Pharmacologic Principles of
    Cancer Treatment; Chabner, B. A., Ed; W. B. Saunders:
    Philadelphia, 1982; pp. 309-339.
2. Chu, M. Y.; Fisher, G. A. Biochemical Pharmacology, 1968, 17,
    753-767.
3. Zwelling, L. A.; Bradley, M. O.; Sharkey, N. A.; Anderson,
    T.; Kohn, K. W. Mutation Research 1979, 67, 271-280.
4. Erickson, L. C.; Zwelling, L. A.; Ducore, J. M.; Sharkey, N.
    A.; Kohn, K. W. Cancer Research 1981, 41, 2791-2794.
5. Laurent, G.; Erickson, L. C.; Sharkey, N. A.; Kohn, K. W.
    Cancer Research 1981, 41, 3347-3351.
6. Zwelling, L. A.; Michaels, S.; Schwartz, H.,; Dobson, P. P.;
    Kohn, K. W. Cancer Research 1981, 41, 640-649.

7. Kohn, K. W. "Methods in Cancer Research"; DeVita, V. T., Jr.; Busch, H., Ed.; Academic Press: New York, 1979; Vol. XVI, pp. 291–345.

8. Kohn, K. W.; Ewig, R. A. G.; Erickson, L. C.; Zwelling, L. A. "DNA Repair. A Laboratory Manual of Research Procedures"; Friedberg, E. C.; Hanawalt, P. C., Ed.; Marcel Dekker: New York, 198; pp. 379–401.

9. Zwelling, L. A.; Anderson, T.; Kohn, K. W. Cancer Research 1979, 39, 365–369.

10. Zwelling, L. A.; Filipski, J. and Kohn, K. W. Cancer Research 1979, 39, 4989–4995.

11. Kohn, K. W. "Molecular Actions and Targets for Cancer Chemotherapeutic Agents", Academic Press: New York, 1981; pp. 3–16.

12. Deutsch, W. A.; Spierina, A. L.; Newkome, G. R. Biochem. Biophys. Res. Commun., 1980, 97, 1220–1226.

13. Filipski, J.; Kohn, K. W.; Prather, R.; Bonner, W. M. Science 1979, 204, 181–183.

14. Micetich, K.; Michaels, S.; Jude, G.; Kohn, K.; Zwelling, L. Proc. Amer. Assoc. Cancer Research, 1981 22, 252.

15. Erickson, L. C.; Bradley, M. O.; Ducore, J. M.; Ewig, R. A. G.; Kohn, K. W. Proc. Natl. Acad. Sci. USA, 1980, 77, 467–471.

16. Bradley, M. O.; Hsu, I. C.; Harris, C. C. Nature, 1979, 282, 318–320.

17. Bradley, M. O.; Patterson, S.; Zwelling, L. A. Mutation Research, in press.

18. Erickson, L. C.; Osieka, R.; Sharkey, N. A.; Kohn, K. W. Analytical Biochemistry, 1980, 106, 169–174.

19. Bakka, A.; Endresen, L.; Johnsen, A. B. S.; Edminson, P. D.; Rugstad, H. E. Toxicology and Applied Pharmacology, 1981 61, 215–226.

20. Zwelling, L. A.; Kohn, K. W. "Cisplatin. Current Status and New Developments"; Prestayko, A. W.; Crooke, S. T.; Carter S. K. Ed.; Academic Press: New York, 1980; pp. 21–35.

RECEIVED October 4, 1982

Structural Chemistry of Platinum–DNA Adducts

THOMAS D. TULLIUS, H. MICHAEL USHAY, CAROLYN M. MERKEL, JOHN P. CARADONNA, and STEPHEN J. LIPPARD

Columbia University, Department of Chemistry, New York, NY 10027

Aspects of the binding of the antitumor drug, cis-diamminedichloroplatinum(II) (cis-DDP), and other platinum complexes to DNA are reviewed. This work was undertaken because DNA is widely regarded as the cellular target for cis-DDP and because of our interest in heavy metal reagents as specific stains for biological specimens. cis-DDP unwinds the double helix when it binds to DNA through covalent attachment to the bases. It also substantially shortens the DNA. These structural effects are revealed by gel electrophoretic study of closed circular, superhelical plasmid DNAs and by electron microscopy. When cis-DDP is allowed to react with DNA in the presence of the intercalating drug ethidium bromide, duplex unwinding still occurs but the shortening effect is substantially diminished. Ethidium can also switch the cis-DDP binding sites that are sensitive to digestion by nucleases. In the absence of ethidium, cis-DDP inhibits both restriction enzymes and exonuclease III digestion of DNA, and the latter has been used to demonstrate that cis-DDP is especially effective at stopping the enzyme when bound at oligo(dG) sequences. When platinum is bound in the presence of ethidium, however, different oligo(dG) regions are exposed. These results are used to rationalize the synergism observed when cis-DDP is used in combination chemotherapy with intercalating drugs. Using radiolabeled $[^{14}C]$methylamine it has been shown that cis-$[Pt(NH_2CH_3)_2Cl_2]$ does not release its amine ligands upon binding to DNA. An intrastrand GpG crosslink involving N7 atoms of guanine is currently regarded as the most likely structure for the cytotoxic cis-DDP-DNA linkage. The compound $[(dien)Pt-Cl]Cl$ promotes the B→Z conformational transition of poly(dG-dC)·poly(dG-dC).

0097-6156/83/0209-0051$07.00/0

Heavy metals, especially the third row transition elements, are useful reagents in biology and biochemistry. The high electron density of these elements (notably tungsten, osmium, platinum and gold) makes them well suited for revealing aspects of supramolecular structures in electron microscopic images (1). More recently, simple platinum complexes have become widely used in cancer chemotherapy (2).

We wish to understand the interactions of heavy metal compounds with biological materials at a molecular level. Little is known about the structural chemistry of heavy metal stains attached to macromolecules, and the chemical basis of the tumor killing ability of cis-diamminedichloroplatinum(II) (cis-DDP) is still obscure. By studying the chemistry of heavy metal complexes of biological macromolecules we can design better, more specific staining reagents. Finding out how the platinum antitumor drugs bind to their cellular target, DNA, could help us design effective drugs with fewer of the toxic side effects which limit the clinical efficacy of cis-DDP.

In this chapter we summarize some recent results from our laboratory which bear on the question of the structural chemistry of platinum-DNA complexes. We find the local structure of DNA, as well as the nature of the platinum compound, to affect in a profound way the structure of the resulting platinum-DNA complex.

Levels of DNA Structure. A DNA molecule has several levels of structure ranging from the primary structure of the sequence of bases to the secondary structure of the Watson-Crick double helix to the tertiary structure resulting from folding or supercoiling the double helix to even higher order structures involved in the condensation of DNA in the cell nucleus. To serve as a basis for understanding the interaction of platinum complexes with DNA, we first describe some of the more important features of DNA structure.

A supercoiled double helix apparently is necessary for many cellular processes involving DNA (3). DNA is found to be supercoiled in the simplest procaryotes, as well as in the cells of higher organisms. In cells with nuclei, the DNA double helix is wrapped in shallow superhelices around complexes of eight histone proteins. This structural unit is termed the nucleosome (4). It repeats along a chain of DNA to form the well known "beads on a string" structure (5) seen in electron micrographs of chromatin spread on a grid.

From procaryotes, such as E. coli, much simpler supercoiled DNA molecules can be isolated. These molecules, called plasmids (6), consist of a few thousand DNA base pairs joined in a closed circle. The double helix of such a circular molecule is supercoiled upon itself, to form a condensed structure, called "form

I." The topological constraints inherent in such a structure result in linking the number of superhelical turns to the winding of the Watson-Crick double helix (7). For example, an intercalating drug causes the DNA double helix to unwind when the drug binds by insertion between base pairs. Ethidium bromide, a commonly used intercalator, unwinds the DNA helix by 26° per bound drug molecule (8). If such a molecule is bound to closed circular, supercoiled DNA, the local unwinding of the double helix results in removal of negative superhelical turns, to maintain the same total number of turns (Watson-Crick + supercoil) in the DNA. If, however, the closed circular DNA has a break in one of its chains, these topological constraints are relieved, there are no supercoils, and the molecule exists in a relaxed, open circular form. This structure is termed "form II." The advantage of studying the binding of platinum complexes to such plasmid molecules is that very subtle changes in the winding of the double helix or in the density of supercoiling translate to easily observed shifts in the mobility of the DNA on electrophoresis gels. Thus structural changes that occur upon platinum binding are amplified many times in the experimentally observable event.

At the level of primary structure, several recent experiments have shown the effect of base sequence on the local structure of DNA. A dramatic example is the crystal structure of $d(CpG)_3$ as determined by Rich and coworkers (9). This molecule crystallizes in a left-handed double helical form called Z-DNA, which is radically different in its structural properties from the familiar right-handed B-DNA structure. Dickerson and Drew (10) showed in the crystal structure of the dodecanucleotide d(CGCGAATTCGCG) that the local twist angle of a DNA double helix varies with sequence. Deoxyribonuclease I cuts the phosphodiester backbone of the dodecanucleotide preferentially at sites of high twist angle (11). From these and other (12,13) experiments we see that the structure of DNA varies with base sequence, and that enzymes are sensitive to these details of structure.

Platinum Binding to DNA. How do simple platinum complexes bind to DNA? What are the effects of the primary, secondary and tertiary structures of DNA on this binding? We have approached these questions experimentally over the last several years (14). Our results and the results of others will be summarized in this section.

An important early observation was that cis-DDP, the antitumor drug, binds covalently and not by intercalation to DNA (15). We present evidence to support this conclusion later in the section describing the effects of ethidium bromide on platinum binding. Since platinum(II), when bound to nitrogen ligands, is rather inert kinetically (16), platinum-DNA adducts may be isolated and studied without appreciable platinum loss.

As a model for how platinum complexes might interact with the DNA of higher organisms, we have studied the binding of the active

antitumor drug cis-DDP and the inactive trans stereoisomer with
the nucleosome core particle (17). We were interested to learn
whether the platinum complexes would bind to the DNA, the protein,
or both, of the core particle. We found that cis-DDP, at low
platinum to nucleotide ratios (r_b), interacted almost exclusively
with nucleosomal DNA, while trans-DDP formed specific histone-
histone and DNA-histone crosslinks. This experiment was one of
the first to demonstrate a clear, qualitative difference in the
way in which the two platinum complexes bind DNA in an in vitro
system.

We (18) and others (19,20,21) have studied the effect of
platinum complexes on the conformation of covalently closed, circular supercoiled DNA using agarose gel electrophoresis. Both
cis- and trans-DDP were found to unwind the Watson-Crick double
helix, resulting in removal of negative supercoils from these
topologically constrained DNA molecules (see above). An unwinding
angle of 22° per bound cis-DDP molecule was measured (22). We
observed with pSM1 (18) and pBR322 (22,23) plasmids that both cis-
and trans-DDP could remove all supercoils, resulting in a closed
circular DNA molecule which comigrated on gels with relaxed
(nicked) circular DNA. In contrast to subsequent results of
Scovell and coworkers (20,21), we found (18) that equivalent
amounts of bound cis- and trans-DDP caused equivalent changes in
DNA conformation. For example, at comigration of relaxed- and
closed-circular platinated pBR322, the r_b was 0.050 + 0.005 for
both isomers (22). In addition, again in contrast to Scovell's
(20,21) work, we observed that both cis- and trans-DDP cause
further positive winding of supercoiled DNA, resulting in an
increase in gel mobility of the DNA, at platinum binding levels
greater than that necessary to cause comigration of closed and
relaxed circular DNA (18).

A second effect of platination was noted (18) on the electrophoretic mobility of relaxed circular DNA. The mobility of this
form increased with increasing platinum binding, as opposed to the
initial decrease and subsequent increase in mobility of supercoiled DNA. This behavior was attributed to a shortening of the
DNA due to platinum induced crosslinks. Further evidence was
obtained from electron micrographs of the platinated DNA samples
(18,24), which showed a dramatic decrease in contour length of
relaxed plasmid molecules upon platination (see Figure 6 below).

Effect of Bound Platinum on DNA Processing Enzymes. With some
of the effects of platination on DNA structure now defined, we can
ask whether and how these changes in DNA conformation will affect
enzymes which process DNA.

Type II restriction endonucleases (25) are enzymes isolated
from procaryotes which recognize and make double-stranded cuts at
specific DNA sequences. We investigated how platination of plasmid pBR322 would affect the ability of the enzyme Bam HI to cut at
its single recognition sequence in this plasmid (23). Bam HI

cleaves the sequence

$$\downarrow$$
$$-\overline{GG}ATCC-$$
$$-CCTA\overline{GG}-$$
$$\uparrow$$

at the phosphodiester bonds between the pairs of guanines as shown. Previous work on bacteriophage λ DNA had suggested (26) that cis-DDP might crosslink the adjacent guanine bases in the enzyme cutting site, but still allow the enzyme to cleave the DNA backbone. The crosslinked, cut DNA would appear as uncut DNA on gels, but if the platinum were removed by cyanide treatment before running the gel, the cuts would be evident. There are several Bam HI sites in λ DNA, however, making the analysis of the results difficult. Our experiment (23) using pBR322 DNA with a single Bam HI site showed conclusively that crosslinking of the guanines by cis-DDP with concomitant cutting of the DNA backbone does not occur. We found that Bam HI cutting was progressively inhibited by increasing amounts of bound cis-DDP, with total inhibition occurring at r_b = 0.050 ± 0.005. Cyanide treatment did not produce linear DNA from the samples which were apparently not cut by Bam HI, as would have been predicted from the previous study (26).

Some restriction endonucleases have several cutting sites on a particular DNA molecule. In an experiment (27) with such an enzyme we used Pst I, which cleaves plasmid pSM1 at four sites. We asked whether cis-DDP binding to any of one these sites, which necessarily have identical enzyme recognition sequences, would render it more difficult to cut than the others. The cutting at one of these sites, the D-B junction, was indeed inhibited at a lower platinum binding level than the others. Consideration of the sequences of bases flanking the four sites showed that the D-B junction has $d(G)_4 \cdot d(C)_4$, $d(GAG) \cdot d(CTC)$ and $d(G)_2 \cdot d(C)_2$ sequences surrounding the enzyme recognition sequence. None of the other three sites has oligo(dG)·oligo(dC) sites nearby. The conclusion was made that cis-DDP bound at oligo(dG)· oligo(dC) (or perhaps $d(GAG) \cdot d(CTC)$ (28)) sites causes a more profound change in DNA structure and inhibits the restriction enzyme. A greater amount of bound cis-DDP would then be necessary to inhibit enzyme digestion at other sites lacking these sequences.

Sequence Specificity of cis-DDP Binding to DNA. Previous experiments had also indicated that oligo(dG)·oligo(dC) sequences might be preferred binding sites for cis-DDP. A greater buoyant density change was seen for platinated poly(dG)·poly(dC) than for platinated poly(dG-dC) when compared to the unplatinated polymers (29). To study in more detail this effect of the primary structure of DNA on platinum binding, our group (30) as well as that of Haseltine (31) developed a method for detecting platinum binding at specific sequences in DNA.

This assay used the enzyme exonuclease III (32) which digests

DNA exonucleolytically from its 3ʼ ends. Bound cis-DDP stops this exonucleolytic degradation.[32] If the platinated DNA substrate is radioactively labeled with ^{32}P at one 5ʼ end (as for DNA sequencing ([33])), denaturation of the exonuclease III-produced fragments, separation by size on a DNA sequencing electrophoresis gel, and autoradiography will reveal the stopping points of the enzyme. The sequences at these stopping points are determined by comparing the fragment lengths with the lengths of DNA molecules produced by sequencing reactions. Since the bases at the 3ʼ ends of the sequencing reaction products are known, this method allows the determination of the base sequences at the sites where platination stopped exonuclease III digestion. It was found that cis-DDP bound to oligo(dG) sites stopped the enzyme; stopping at other base sequences was not detected ([30]). We concluded that either cis-DDP binds preferentially to these oligo(dG) sites to the exclusion of other sequences, or that the structure resulting from cis-DDP bound at oligo(dG) sequences is singularly efficient at stopping exonuclease III.

Ethidium Bromide Alters the Mode of Binding of cis-DDP to DNA

The antitumor activity of platinum drugs is very sensitive to changes in the stereochemistry of the platinum complex. For example, while cis-DDP is an effective antitumor agent, the corresponding trans isomer is not ([2]). We wanted to study how changing the tertiary and secondary structure of plasmid DNA would affect the reactivity of cis-DDP toward the DNA. Several of the drugs used in a clinical regimen with cis-DDP to improve its efficacy are also able to alter the structure of DNA ([2]). We chose to study ethidium bromide (EtdBr), a well characterized DNA intercalating agent ([8]), as a model for other drugs which are used with cis-DDP.

Previous work has shown that DNA which had been platinated with cis-DDP cannot bind as much EtdBr by intercalation as unplatinated DNA ([15]). Figure 1 is a fluorescence Scatchard plot of the binding of EtdBr to calf thymus DNA to which varying amounts of cis-DDP were bound. Upon increased platinum binding, the slope of the fluorescence Scatchard plot remained constant. Therefore cis-DDP does not competitively inhibit the binding of ethidium. This result demonstrates that the platinum drug does not intercalate into the DNA duplex, but binds covalently. The change in abscissa, however, reveals that platinum bound to DNA reduces the number of sites available for ethidium binding.

We then asked how binding ethidium to DNA before platination would affect the ability of cis-DDP to bind. Figure 2 shows the results of atomic absorption measurements of platinum binding to pBR322 DNA. The kinetics of binding are unchanged when ethidium is present during platination. The ability of cyanide to remove bound platinum is greatly enhanced, however. For example, with no ethidium present and more than approximately one platinum atom

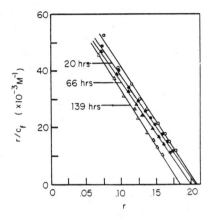

Figure 1. Fluorescence Scatchard plot of the binding of EtdBr to calf-thymus DNA in the absence (○) and the presence (●, 20 h; ▲, 66 h; and △, 139 h) of cis-DDP in Tris–HCl (50 mM) and sodium chloride (0.2 M) at pH 7.5. Conditions: [DNA phosphate] = 1.05 × 10⁻⁵ M; [EtdBr] = 2.2 × 10⁻⁶ – 1.7 × 10⁻⁵ M; and r_f = 0.83. (Reproduced from Ref. 15. Copyright 1976, American Chemical Society.)

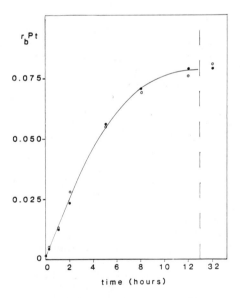

Figure 2. Binding of cis-DDP to pBR322 DNA at 37 °C in sodium phosphate (1 mM) and sodium chloride (3 mM) at pH 7.4. Conditions: [Pt] = 2.50 × 10⁻⁵ M; [DNA phosphate] = 2.50 × 10⁻⁴ M; and r_f = 0.10. Key: ○, no ethidium present; and ●, 7.5 × 10⁻⁶ M ethidium present.

bound per five base pairs, 8-10% of the platinum cannot be removed by cyanide treatment (23). When saturating amounts of ethidium are present during platination, all bound platinum could be removed from the DNA upon cyanide treatment.

The ability of cis-DDP to unwind the DNA duplex is unaffected by the presence of ethidium during platination. Figure 3 depicts the changes in gel mobilities that occur when increasing amounts of platinum are bound to DNA forms I and II. Note that, whether ethidium is present or not, there is at first a diminution in the mobility of the form I band upon platinum binding due to duplex unwinding (and concomitant introduction of positive supercoils). There is then a subsequent increase in mobility in the form I band past the point where it comigrates in the gel with the form II band as platinum continues to bind and increase the number of positive supercoils.

The ability of cis-DDP to decrease the effective length of the plasmid is greatly reduced, however, when platinum is bound in the presence of ethidium. Figure 4 shows that the presence of ethidium during platination decreases the mobility of platinated form II DNA when compared with the mobility of control platinated DNA. This difference in mobility is not due to a difference in the amount of bound platinum (see Figure 2), and it depends upon the amount of ethidium present during platination.

A plot of gel mobility versus the amount of platinum bound, Figure 5, demonstrates this difference. We compare gel mobilities of samples platinated with a formal ratio of one cis-DDP per nucleotide, for samples containing either no ethidium or three ethidium molecules per ten nucleotides. The gel mobilities are normalized to 0 for form II and 1.0 for form I DNA in the control sample. Note that there is about a 35% decrease in mobility where forms I and II comigrate in the gel when platinum is bound in the presence of saturating amounts of ethidium.

These changes in gel mobility can be correlated to changes in the physical structure of the DNA, as seen in Figure 6. The uppermost electron micrograph of unplatinated pBR322 DNA clearly shows nicked and supercoiled molecules. The center micrograph is of pBR322 DNA platinated with cis-DDP to a level of 28 platinum atoms per 100 nucleotides. The contour length of the relaxed circular DNA is greatly decreased, as has been seen previously (18).

The bottom micrograph is of pBR322 platinated to a level of 23 platinum atoms per 100 nucleotides in the presence of saturating amounts of ethidium. It is clear that this DNA is more similar to control DNA than are the samples platinated with no ethidium present. There is some compacting and "shrinking" seen, but not to the extent seen in the sample platinated in the absence of ethidium.

In summary, ethidium bromide does not alter the kinetics of platinum binding. This result is not surprising since these binding kinetics have been shown to be comparable to the pseudo-

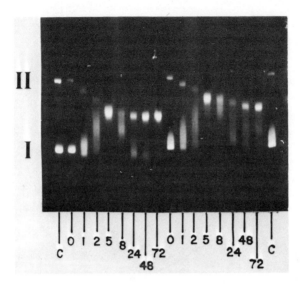

Figure 3. Electrophoresis in a 1.5% agarose gel (Tris–acetate–EDTA buffer) of approximately 0.5 μg of forms I and II pBR322 DNA following incubation with cis-DDP for the times indicated. Conditions: [Pt] = 4.25 × 10⁻⁵ M; [DNA phosphate] = 2.83 × 10⁻⁴ M; and cis-DDP r_f = 0.150. Key: left side, no EtdBr present; and right side, 8.5 × 10⁻⁶ M EtdBr present.

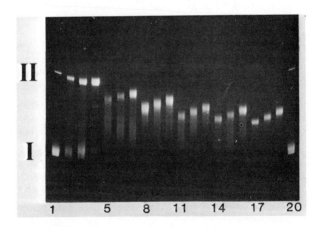

Figure 4. Electrophoresis in a 1.5% agarose gel of forms I and II pBR322 DNA following incubation with cis-DDP. Key to [EtdBr]: 0 M for lanes 1, 2, 5, 8, 11, 14, and 17; 2.7 × 10⁻⁶ M for lanes 3, 6, 9, 12, 15, and 18; and 5.4 × 10⁻⁶ M for lanes 4, 7, 10, 13, 16, 19, and 20. Key to incubation time: lanes 1–4, 0 h; lanes 5–7, 1 h; lanes 8–10, 2 h; lanes 11–13, 5 h; lanes 14–16, 8 h; and lanes 17–20, 26 h. Conditions: [Pt] = 2.70 × 10⁻⁵ M; [DNA phosphate] = 1.80 × 10⁻⁴ M; and cis-DDP r_f = 0.150.

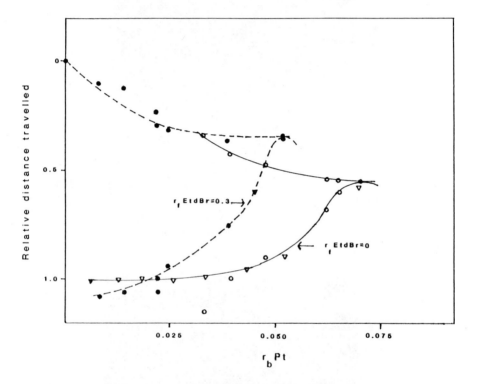

Figure 5. Gel mobilities for forms I and II pBR322 DNA as a function of the amount of bound cis- *or* trans-DDP. *Distances traveled in the gel are normalized so that in the control the mobility of form I DNA is 1.0 and the mobility of form II DNA is 0.0. Conditions: [Pt]* $= 2.34 \times 10^{-4}$ M; *[DNA phosphate]* $= 2.34 \times 10^{-4}$ M; *and platinum* $r_f = 1.0$. *Key:* ○, cis-DDP, *no ethidium;* ●, cis-DDP, *ethidium* $r_f = 0.3$; △, trans-DDP, *no ethidium; and* ▲, trans-DDP, *ethidium* $r_f = 0.3$.

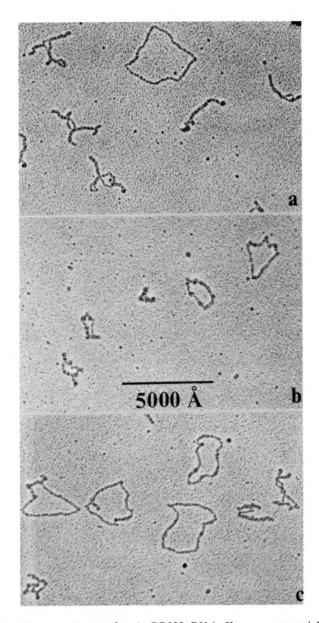

Figure 6. Electron micrographs of pBR322 DNA. Key: a, untreated DNA; b, no EtdBr and cis-DDP $r_b = 0.28$; c, EtdBr $r_f = 0.3$ and cis-DDP $r_b = 0.23$. Conditions in the platination mixture: [Pt] = 2.50 × 10⁻⁴ M; [DNA phosphate] = 2.68 × 10⁻⁴ M; cis-DDP $r_f = 0.90$; and an incubation time of 18 h (35).

first order rate of aquation of the platinum complex (34), and ethidium and cis-DDP do not react with each other in solution (35). The ability of the platinum complex to unwind the duplex causing concomitant winding of the superhelix is also unchanged.

The ability of cyanide ion to remove bound platinum is greatly enhanced when ethidium is present during platination. This finding implies that the platinum is more accessible to cyanide treatment either through an easily available coordination site on the platinum, or by the platinum being bound to DNA in some entirely different manner. The DNA duplex shortening that is induced upon platinum binding is greatly reduced when ethidium is present, also implying some different manner of binding. The extent of reduction depends directly upon the amount of ethidium present during platination.

We conclude that the presence of ethidium during platination blocks a long range inter- or intra-strand crosslink from occurring, probably by stabilizing and stiffening the DNA duplex. This effect would keep the duplex from collapsing and compacting the DNA.

Ethidium Switches the Nuclease-Detectable Binding Sites of cis-DDP on DNA

In examining further this effect of ethidium, we found that the exonuclease III method described above detected different cis-DDP binding sites on a DNA molecule of known sequence when platination was carried out in the presence of ethidium (36).

The original exonuclease III experiment (30) had presented us with an apparent anomaly. Although cis-DDP binding to $(dG)_n$ sites (n = 2,3,5) in the 165 base pair DNA molecule was detected by the enzyme, a $5'-(dG)_6-dC-(dG)_2-3'$ sequence seemed to have little bound platinum. This site is located only 29 bases from the 3' end, so its proximity to the origin of exonuclease III digestion coupled with its extensive run of adjacent guanines led us to expect intense bands on sequencing gels corresponding to exonuclease III stopping points caused by platination. Lanes 1 and 8 in Figure 7 show, however, that only weak bands appear in this region of the gel. But if ethidium is present in the platination reaction mixture, a dramatic change in the gel pattern is observed. Lanes 2-5 and 9-12 illustrate the effect of increasing amounts of ethidium on the intensity of the bands in the G_6-C-G_2 region. These bands become the most intense in the autoradiograph due to platination.

A higher resolution gel, Figure 8, shows an interesting effect of this ethidium titration. The first bands to appear are those due to platination of the $3'-(dG)_2$ site; the $(dG)_6$ sequence shows little detectable platination at the lowest level of ethidium. As the amount of ethidium in the reaction mixture is increased, the $(dG)_6$ site shows more platination, and platination at the $(dG)_2$ site appears relatively to decrease.

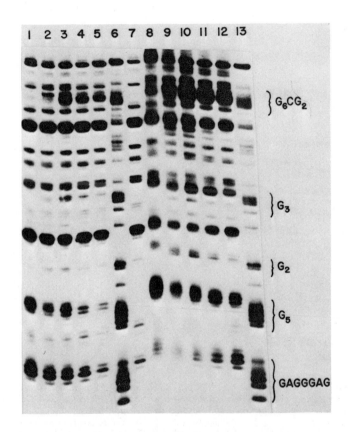

Figure 7. Autoradiograph of an 8% polyacrylamide/7 M urea electrophoresis gel showing the effect of ethidium bromide on exonuclease III-detected cis-DDP binding sites on a 165-base-pair DNA molecule.

Key to cis-DDP r_f: lanes 1–5, 0.01; and lanes 8–12, 0.05. Key to ethidium bromide r_f: lanes 1 and 8, 0; lanes 2 and 9, 0.012; lanes 3 and 10, 0.057; lanes 4 and 11, 0.12; and lanes 5 and 12, 0.23. Lanes 6 and 13 show Maxam–Gilbert guanine-specific reaction products for sequencing. Lane 7 contains products of exonuclease III digestion of unplatinated, end-labeled 165-base-pair DNA. Platination was carried out for 3 h at 37 °C. Electrophoresis was for 2 h at 1800 V (36).

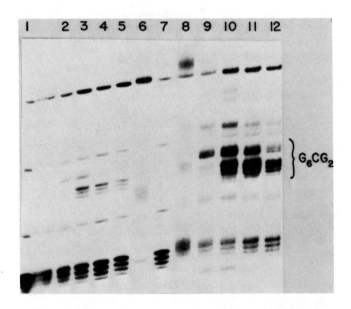

Figure 8.   Autoradiograph of an 8% polyacrylamide/7 M urea electrophoresis gel showing the effect of ethidium bromide on exonuclease III-detected cis-DDP *binding sites on a 165-base-pair DNA molecule.*

Key to cis-DDP r_f: lanes 1–5, 0.01; and lanes 8–12, 0.05. Key to ethidium bromide r_f: lanes 1 and 8, 0; lanes 2 and 9, 0.012; lanes 3 and 10, 0.057; lanes 4 and 11, 0.12; and lanes 5 and 12, 0.23. Lane 6 shows Maxam–Gilbert guanine-specific reaction products for sequencing. Lane 7 contains products of exonuclease III digestion of unplatinated, end-labeled 165-base-pair DNA. Platination was carried out for 3 h at 37 °C. Electrophoresis was for 4 h at 1800 V (36).

What is the reason for the effect of ethidium on the sites where exonuclease III detects platination? It is not simply due to increased platinum binding in the presence of ethidium; the results presented in Figure 2 rule out this explanation. We think that this experiment shows that cis-DDP binding is sensitive to the local structure of DNA. We consider two limiting cases. The first is that cis-DDP might bind only rarely to the G_6-C-G_2 site in the absence of ethidium, perhaps because the structure of the helix is unsuitable. Ethidium then would alter the DNA structure such that this site becomes a good binding site for cis-DDP. The second case is that cis-DDP might bind to the G_6-C-G_2 sequence to the same extent in the presence or absence of ethidium, but the mode of binding is different in these two circumstances. Without ethidium, cis-DDP might bind in a manner to which exonuclease III is insensitive, so the enzyme detects no platinum binding. With ethidium in the platination mixture, however, cis-DDP could now bind in a way which will stop exonuclease III digestion, so that intense bands are seen in the sequencing gel. We are presently attempting to determine which of these explanations is correct.

More important, though, are the potential implications of these results for the mechanism of synergism in combination chemotherapy. We have shown that one drug can alter the biochemically detectable binding site of another drug. This rationalization at the molecular level is in contrast to the more common explanation of synergism as resulting from action of two drugs at different phases in the cell cycle.

Amine Ligands Are Not Lost From Platinum Upon Binding to DNA

There is now considerable evidence from work described in this paper, others in this volume (37), and recent NMR papers ($38,39,40$), that cis-DDP reacts in a bifunctional manner with DNA. An interesting question is whether cis-DDP can interact with DNA using more than two of its coordination sites. Hydrogen bonding between the protons on the ammine ligands and oxygen atoms of the DNA phosphate backbone is one possibility. Another is that, after hydrolysis of one or both chloride ligands and subsequent binding of platinum to a DNA base, the trans labilizing ability of the heterocyclic purine or pyrimidine ring nitrogen atom attached to the $Pt(NH_3)_2^{2+}$ fragment would promote displacement of an ammine ligand. As a result, a third and possibly a fourth coordination site could be made available for platinum-DNA binding ($41,42$). This mechanism, in which two sites in addition to the easily hydrolyzable chloride sites are opened up for possible metal-DNA coordination, is not possible for trans-DDP and would explain in terms of ligand substitution kinetics the greater efficacy of cis- versus trans-DDP as an antitumor drug.

Evidence to support this mechanism comes from studies (43) showing that $[Pt(NH_3)_3Cl]Cl$ can crosslink poly(A) bifunctionally. Such a phenomenon could only occur if one or more of the ammine ligands were labilized. Preliminary experiments carried out in our laboratory (44) indicated the loss of two ammonia molecules per molecule of cis-DDP bound to DNA at very low binding levels. Mass spectroscopic studies also suggested loss of ammonia but this result could have been due to the conditions under which the mass spectrum was obtained (45). Indirect support for an ammonia release mechanism comes from the existence of cis-DDP bound to DNA which is resistant to removal by cyanide ion (23,46). The inability of cyanide to remove platinum may be explained by coordination of platinum to DNA through three or four Pt-DNA bonds.

When dichloroethylenediamineplatinum(II), $[Pt(en)Cl_2]$, doubly labeled with ^{195m}Pt and ^{14}C, was allowed to react with nucleotides, both labels remained together (47). Subsequent work (48) revealed that, when doubly labeled $[Pt(en)Cl_2]$ was injected into tumor bearing mice, the two labels became unequally distributed with respect to different biochemical fractions. The former result does not preclude ammonia release from cis-DDP since ethylenediamine coordination is stabilized by the chelate effect. Moreover, reaction of cis-DDP with DNA may differ from its reactions with nucleotides because a platinum bound to a guanine base in a region of locally high guanine content in DNA could encounter a locally very high concentration of other guanine bases resulting in a "DNA chelate effect."

In order to determine whether or not monodentate amine ligands could be released from a platinum complex upon binding to DNA, we studied the reaction of ^{14}C-labeled cis-$[PtCl_2(NH_2CH_3)_2]$ with T7 and M. luteus DNAs. The compound cis-$[PtCl_2(NH_2CH_3)_2]$ has antitumor activity (49,50) with a therapeutic index 15% that of cis-DDP. After platinum incubation followed by dialysis to remove unbound reagents the amount of bound platinum was assayed by atomic absorption spectroscopy (AAS) and the amount of methylamine ligand on the DNA was determined separately by liquid scintillation counting (LSC). From the level of platinum binding determined by AAS and the radioactivity associated with the DNA it is possible to determine whether platinum binding followed by loss of methylamine has occurred.

Figure 9 shows the result of two such experiments. From the AAS and LSC data it is clear that, within experimental error, no release of methylamine occurs upon binding of cis-$[PtCl_2(NH_2CH_3)_2]$ to DNA. Neither increasing the amount of platinum complex added nor increasing the incubation time at a fixed amount of added platinum leads to loss of the amine ligands. Experiments carried out with M. luteus as well as T7 DNA show the results to be unaffected by increasing the G+C content (73% vs 47%, respectively) of the DNA. To determine whether DNA-bound platinum that is resistant to cyanide treatment is attached through more than two linkages, we allowed $[^{14}C]$cis-$[PtCl_2(NH_2CH_3)_2]$ to react with T7 DNA. The DNA was then treated with NaCN as reported previously (23) and binding levels were determined by AAS and LSC. The data show very

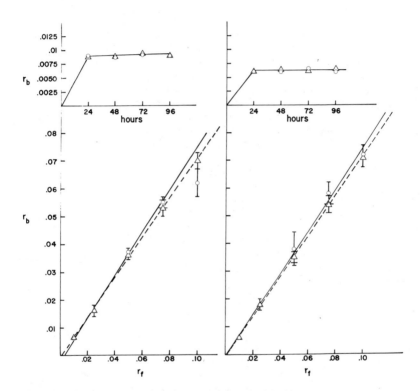

Figure 9. Plots of r_b vs. time (top) and r_b vs. r_f (bottom) for the binding of [^{14}C]cis-[$PtCl_2(NH_3CH_3)_2$] to T7 DNA (left) and M. luteus DNA (right). Key: ○, r_b determined by AAS; and △, r_b determined by LSC. In the plots of r_b vs. r_f, error bars are 2σ and the calculated best straight lines are drawn through the AAS (—) and the LSC (– – –) data.

clearly that two moles of amine ligand per mole of platinum remain with the DNA. These results thus demonstrate that only two Pt-DNA bonds are required for cyanide resistant platination and point to bifunctional crosslinking as being most important.

Robins (48), however, has shown that, in vivo, the ethylenediamine ligand can be separated from $[\overline{Pt(en)Cl_2}]$ and we now address this observation. Although the trans effect of the purine or pyrimidine ring nitrogen atoms is not strong enough to labilize the amine ligand trans to it when cis-$[PtCl_2(NH_2CH_3)_2]$ and, by analogy, cis-DDP and $[Pt(en)Cl_2]$ bind to DNA, it is possible that other compounds present in the cell could bind to these platinum complexes to displace the amine ligands. Sulfhydryl containing compounds are prime candidates and glutathione (51), the most abundant intracellular sulfhydryl containing molecule in mammalian cells, is a major contender. Binding studies, as described above, were carried out in the presence of glutathione at the physiologically relevant concentration of 1 mM. This amount of glutathione does not diminish the amount of platinum bound to DNA. Approximately 20-30% of the radioactivity due to methlyamine molecules is lost, however. This result is not surprising in view of the recent study of Sadler (this volume) and previously reported work (16) showing that methionine and methionine containing peptides can labilize the ammine ligands upon binding to cis-diamminedichloroplatinum(II). The infrared spectrum and chemical analysis (52) of a 2:1 complex of glutathione and cis-DDP are consistent with the loss of the ammine ligands. Studies are currently in progress to determine whether glutathione remains bound to platinum on the DNA. Interestingly, preliminary studies in this laboratory point toward glutathione enhancing the rate at which cis-DDP alters the tertiary structure of superhelical DNA (53).

Finally, as a word of caution, it should be remembered that cis-$[PtCl_2(NH_2CH_3)_2]$ has only 15% of the antitumor activity of cis-DDP. It would be very interesting indeed if this difference in antitumor activity was due to the ability of cis-DDP to liberate ammonia upon binding to DNA.

Binding $[(dien)PtCl]Cl$ to poly(dG-dC)· poly(dG-dC) Facilitates the B→Z Conformational Transition

In the course of studying the effects of cis-DDP on DNA structure and reactivity the compounds trans-DDP and $[(dien)PtCl]Cl$ are often used in parallel control experiments. The trans isomer possesses the same charge, ligand composition, and bifunctional binding ability as cis-DDP but is ineffective as a drug owing to its different stereochemistry. When hydrolyzed, the compound $[(dien)PtCl]Cl$ has the same charge as the drug but can only bind monofunctionally to DNA, since the other three sites are blocked by the tridentate diethylenetriamine (dien) ligand. While investigating changes in the spectroscopic properties of the synthetic polymers poly(dG)· poly(dC) and poly(dG-dC)· poly(dG-dC) upon platinum binding, we observed that the $[(dien)PtC\ell]C\ell$ compound could facilitate the right- to left- handed, B→Z, conformational transition in poly(dG-dC)·poly(dG-dC). Interestingly, cis-DDP, the primary subject of our investigation, was unable to induce or facilitate the B→Z transition and actually prevented it from occurring even under very favorable conditions (54). The same was found to be true for trans-DDP.

The changes in the circular dichroism (CD) spectrum of poly-(dG-dC)·poly(dG-dC) which occur upon cis-DDP binding are very similar to those reported for calf thymus (24), M. luteus (55), and salmon sperm (55) DNAs. Whereas $[(dien)PtC\ell]C\ell$ has little effect on the CD spectrum of calf thymus DNA (24), drastic changes are observed upon the binding of this complex to poly(dG-dC)·poly-(dG-dC), as shown in Figure 10. At r_b < 0.1 there is little change in the long wavelength part of the spectrum but the 250 nm band is reduced in intensity. At r_b = 0.1 and above, the positive absorbance at 295 nm, which is a shoulder in the spectrum of the unmodified polymer, increases dramatically in intensity up to a saturation binding level of approximately r_b = 0.33. A plot of molar ellipticity at 295 nm versus r_b (not shown) reveals a sigmoidal shape characteristic of a cooperative transition. The cooperative nature of the binding and the fact that the saturation binding level of $[(dien)Pt]^{2+}$ is one per three nucleotides indicate the formation of a stable, regular structure. This structure appears to be related to the monofunctional nature of $[(dien)Pt]^{2+}$ since neither cis- nor trans-DDP produce the effect.

The spectral changes noted above are not consistent with the transition from right(B)- to left(Z)-handed DNA (56), however. Under the salt and buffer conditions used in these experiments we were unable to induce the B→Z transition in the absence of ethanol which lowers the water activity. Malfoy et al. (57) could bring about the transition with $[(dien)Pt]^{2+}$ alone by using very low salt buffers and excluding EDTA. When $[(dien)Pt]^{2+}$ binds to poly(dG-dC)·poly(dG-dC) at r_b = 0.054 and 0.093, for instance, the amount of ethanol necessary to bring about the Z conformation is reduced from 55% for unmodified polymer to 36% and 25%, respectively (54). Interestingly, samples with r_b values greater than 0.1 and which showed the large positive CD absorption at 295 nm could not be converted to Z-DNA, even at very high ethanol concentrations. Moreover, when poly(dG-dC)·poly(dG-dC) in the Z conformation (55% ethanol) was allowed to react with saturating amounts of $[(dien)PtC\ell]C\ell$, the CD spectrum showed the large absorbance at 295 nm after removal of ethanol. Therefore, the polymer could not be "locked into" the Z conformation by the platinum reagent. Independent evidence supporting the occurrence of Z-DNA was obtained by ^{31}P NMR spectroscopy (56) as shown in Figure 11. The conformational changes induced by $[(dien)Pt]^{2+}$ are completely reversible as shown by experiments in which the platinated DNA was treated with NaCN. Following removal of the platinum the normal amount of ethanol (55%) was necessary to induce the Z conformation.

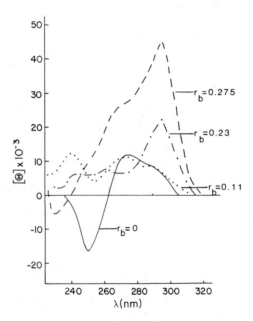

Figure 10.   The circular dichroism spectra of poly(dG–dC) • poly(dG–dC) modified
at the indicated levels with [(dien)PtCl]Cl (54).

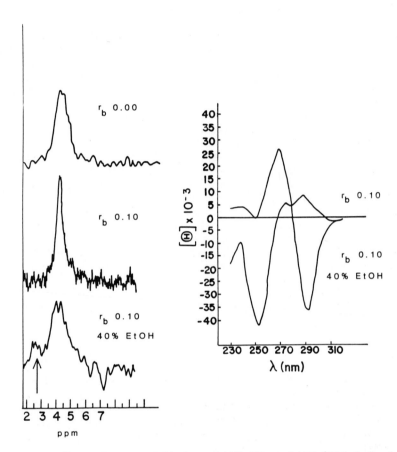

Figure 11. ³¹*P-NMR spectra (left) of a, poly(dG–dC) • poly(dG–dC) in buffer, b, poly(dG–dC) • poly(dG–dC) modified to* r_b *= 0.10 with [(dien)PtCP]Cl; and c, sample in b after raising the ethanol concentration to 40%. The arrow designates the resonance characteristic of* Z *-DNA. Circular dichroism spectra (right) of the samples in b and c (54).*

The ability of $[(\text{dien})\text{PtCl}]\text{Cl}$ to promote the Z conformation could be due to several factors. The addition of a bulky substituent to the N7 atom of guanosine would help rotate the base from the anti conformation, found in B-DNA, to the syn conformation of Z-DNA. Studies with the carcinogen acetylaminofluorene, which binds to C8 of guanine, showed it to induce the Z conformation through a similar mechanism (58). Moreover, the addition of a +2 charge to the guanine base would help stabilize the higher charge density of the Z-DNA helix caused by the increased proximity of the two phosphate chains. This effect would be similar to that evoked to explain why methylation at N7 of guanine facilitates the B→Z transition (59). Finally, examination of space filling models of Z-DNA shows that $[(\text{dien})\text{Pt}]^{2+}$ bound to N7 of guanine forms good hydrogen bonding contacts between the amino protons of the diethylenetriamine ligand and phosphate and cytosine O2 oxygen atoms of the flanking nucleotides.

The N7 atom of guanine is located on the outside of the Z-DNA helix and, as such, may be more available for platinum binding. We attempted to test this point by comparing the amount of bound $[(\text{dien})\text{Pt}]^{2+}$ on poly(dG-dC)·poly(dG-dC) in both the B and Z conformations. After 24 h and at shorter times the binding levels were approximately equal for both conformations. This result may be due to the fact that the kinetics of platinum binding are determined by the rate of chloride hydrolysis and therefore are not a function of DNA structure.

Acknowledgment

The work described here was supported under a grant from the National Cancer Institute, No. CA-15826, PHS.

Literature Cited

1.   Hayatt, M.A. "Positive Staining for Electron Microscopy;" van Nostrand, 1975.
2.   "Cisplatin, Current Status and New Developments;" Prestayko, A.W.; Crooke, S.T.; Carter, S.K., Eds.; Academic Press, 1980.
3.   Cozzarelli, N.R. Science (Washington, D.C.) 1980, 207, 953-960.
4.   McGhee, J.D.; Felsenfeld, G. Ann. Rev. Biochem. 1980, 49, 1115-1156.
5.   Olins, A.L.; Olins, D.E. Science (Washington, D.C.) 1974, 183, 330-332.
6.   Novick, R.P. Sci. Amer. 1980, 243, 102-127.
7.   Bauer, W.R. Ann. Rev. Biophys. Bioeng. 1978, 7, 287-313.
8.   Wang, J.C. J. Mol. Biol. 1974, 89, 783-801.
9.   Wang, A.H.J.; Quigley, G.J.; Kolpak, F.J.; Crawford, J.L.; van Boom, J.H.; van der Marel, G.; Rich, A. Nature (London) 1979, 282, 680-686.
10. Dickerson, R.E.; Drew, H.R. J. Mol. Biol. 1981, 149, 761-785.
11. Lomonossoff, G.P.; Butler, P.J.G.; Klug, A. J. Mol. Biol. 1981, 149, 745-760.

12. Kabsch, W.; Trifonov, E.N. Nucleic Acids Res. 1982, 10, 1097-1104.
13. Dingwall, C.; Lomonossoff, G.P.; Laskey, R.A. Nucleic Acids Res. 1981, 9, 2659-2673.
14. Lippard, S.J. Accounts Chem. Res. 1978, 11, 211-217.
15. Howe-Grant, M.; Wu, K.C.; Bauer, W.R.; Lippard, S.J. Biochemistry 1976, 15, 4339-4346.
16. Howe-Grant, M.E.; Lippard, S.J.; in "Metal Ions in Biological Systems;" Sigel, H., Ed.; Marcel Dekker, 1980; pp.63-125.
17. Lippard, S.J.; Hoeschele, J.D. Proc. Natl. Acad. Sci. USA 1979, 76, 6091-6095.
18. Cohen, G.L.; Bauer, W.R.; Barton, J.K.; Lippard, S.J. Science (Washington, D.C.) 1979, 203, 1014-1016.
19. Mong, S.; Prestayko, A.W.; Crooke, S.T.; in "Cisplatin, Current Status and New Developments;" Prestayko, A.W.; Crooke, S.T.; Carter, S.K., Eds.; Academic Press, 1980; p. 213-226.
20. Scovell, W.M.; Kroos, L.R. Biochem. Biophys. Res. Comm. 1982, 104, 1597-1603.
21. Scovell, W.M.; Kroos, L.R.; Capponi, V.J., chapter in this book.
22. Ushay, H.M., Lippard, S.J.; unpublished.
23. Ushay, H.M.; Tullius, T.D.; Lippard, S.J. Biochemistry 1981, 20, 3744-3748.
24. Macquet, J.P.; Boutour, J.L. Biochimie 1978, 60, 901-914.
25. Wells, R.D.; Klein, R.D.; Singleton, C.K.; in "The Enzymes;" Boyer, P.D., Ed.; Academic Press, 1981; pp. 157-191.
26. Kelman, A.D.; Buchbinder, M. Biochimie 1978, 60, 893-899.
27. Cohen, G.L.; Ledner, J.A.; Bauer, W.R.; Ushay, H.M.; Caravana, C.; Lippard, S.J. J. Amer. Chem. Soc. 1980, 102, 2487-2488.
28. Brouwer, J.; van de Putte, P.; Fichtinger-Schepman, A.M.J.; Reedjijk, J. Proc. Natl. Acad. Sci. USA 1981, 78, 7010-7014.
29. Stone, P.J.; Kelman, A.D.; Sinex, F.M. Nature (London) 1974, 251, 736-737.
30. Tullius, T.D.; Lippard, S.J. J. Amer. Chem. Soc. 1981, 103, 4620-4622.
31. Royer-Pokora, B.; Gordon, L.K.; Haseltine, W.A. Nucleic Acids Res. 1981, 9, 4595-4609.
32. Rogers, S.G.; Weiss, B. Methods Enzymol. 1980, 65, 201-211.
33. Maxam, A.M.; Gilbert, W. Methods Enzymol. 1980, 65, 499-560.
34. Johnson, N.P.; Hoeschele, J.D.; Rahn, R.O. Chem.-Biol. Interactions 1980, 30, 151-169.
35. Merkel, C.M.; Lippard, S.J. Cold Spring Harbor Symp. Quant. Biol., in press.
36. Tullius, T.D.; Lippard, S.J. Proc. Natl. Acad. Sci. USA 1982, 79, 3489-3492.
37. See in particular chapters by Macquet, Chottard, Scovell, Roberts, and their coworkers in this book.

38. Girault, J.-P.; Chottard, G.; Lallemand, J.-Y.; Chottard, J.-C. Biochemistry 1982, 21, 1352-1356.
39. Caradonna, J.P.; Lippard, S.J.; Gait, M.; Singh, M. J. Amer. Chem. Soc., in press.
40. Marcelis, A.T.M.; den Hartog, J.H.J.; Reedijk, J. J. Amer. Chem. Soc. 1982, 104, 2664-2665.
41. Barton, J.K.; Lippard, S.J. Ann. N.Y. Acad. Sci. 1978, 313, 686-700.
42. Barton, J.K.; Lippard, S.J.; in "Nucleic Acid-Metal Ion Interactions;" Spiro, T.G., Ed.; Wiley, 1980; pp. 32-113.
43. Wherland, S.; Deutsch, E.; Eliason, J.; Sigler, P.B. Biochem. Biophys. Res. Comm. 1973, 54, 662-668.
44. Barton, J.K. Ph.D. Dissertation, Columbia University, 1978.
45. Roos, I.A.G.; Thomson, A.J.; Eagles, J. Chem.-Biol. Interactions 1974, 8, 421-427.
46. Bauer, W.; Gonias, S.; Kam, S.; Wu, K.; Lippard, S. Biochemistry 1978, 17, 1060-1068.
47. Robins, A.B. Chem.-Biol. Interactions 1973, 6, 35-45.
48. Robins, A.B., personal communication.
49. Gale, G.; Rosenblum, M.; Atkins, L.; Walker Jr., E.; Smith, A.; Meischen, S. J. Natl. Cancer Inst. 1973, 51, 1227-1234.
50. Braddock, P.; Connors, T.; Jones, M.; Khokhar, A.; Melzack, D.; Tobe, M. Chem.-Biol. Interactions 1975, 11, 145-161.
51. Meister, A.; Tate, S.S. Ann. Rev. Biochem. 1976, 45, 559-604.
52. Odenheimer, B.; Wolf, W. Inorganica Chimica Acta 1982, 66, L41-L43.
53. Ushay, H.M.; Pascopella, L.G.; Lippard, S.J.; unpublished data.
54. Ushay, H.M.; Santella, R.M.; Caradonna, J.P.; Grunberger, D.; Lippard, S.J. Nucleic Acids Res. 1982, 10, 3573-3588.
55. Srivasta, R.C.; Froelich, J.; Eichhorn, G.L. Biochimie 1978, 60, 879-891.
56. A thorough review of the current status of Z-DNA research is found in "Biomolecular Stereodynamics;" Sarma, R.H., Ed.; Adenine Press, 1981; Vol. I.
57. Malfoy, B.; Hartman, B.; Leng, M. Nucleic Acids Res. 1981, 9, 5659-5669.
58. Santella, R.M.; Grunberger, D.; Weinstein, I.B.; Rich, A. Proc. Natl. Acad. Sci. USA 1981, 78, 1451-1455.
59. Moller, A.; Nordheim, A.; Nichols, S.R.; Rich, A. Proc. Natl. Acad. Sci. USA 1981, 78, 4777-4781.

RECEIVED October 4, 1982

Physicochemical and Structural Studies of the In Vitro Interactions between Platinum(II) Compounds and DNA

J. P. MACQUET, J. L. BUTOUR, and N. P. JOHNSON

Laboratoire de Pharmacologie et de Toxicologie Fondamentales, CNRS, 205, Route de Narbonne, 31400 Toulouse, France

Perturbations of DNA secondary structure and stability induced by cis-[Pt(NH$_3$)$_2$Cl$_2$] (cis-DDP), $trans$-DDP and [Pt(dien)Cl]Cl at low levels of DNA binding (r_b) are summarized and preliminary characterization of the corresponding platinum-DNA adducts is presented. For $r_b \leqslant 0.01$ both cis- and $trans$-DDP form interstrand crosslinks, shorten the DNA and exclude stoichiometric amounts of intercalating agents. However, cis-DDP destabilizes DNA at this r_b while $trans$-DDP stabilizes the polymer and only the cis isomer causes an increase in the circular dichroism of DNA. [Pt(dien)Cl]Cl does not form crosslinks ; it changes neither the length of DNA, the CD spectra nor the intercalation of ethidium bromide. Fixation of [Pt(dien)Cl]Cl stabilizes DNA at $r_b \leqslant 0.01$. Two major products of the reaction of cis-DDP with salmon sperm DNA have been isolated and both contain guanine. [Pt(dien)Cl]Cl fixes primarily at N^7 of guanine for $r_b < 0.1$; in addition, fixation at N^7 of adenine for $r_b > 0.1$ and at N^1 and N^7 of adenine for $0.3 < r_b < 0.4$ was observed.

Although cis-DDP binds covalently to proteins, RNA and other nucleophiles in the cell (1), it is fixation on DNA which seems to be responsible for the antitumor activity of this compound (2). The toxicity of cis-DDP seems to be associated with an inhibition of DNA synthesis rather than an inhibition of RNA or protein synthesis (3, 4, 5) ; similarly, mammalian cells (6) and bacteria (5, 7, 8) deficient in DNA repair are more sensitive to killing by cis-DDP. This argument implies that inhibition of DNA synthesis is responsible for the general cytotoxicity of cis-DDP, but it does not explain why tumor cells are killed more read-

ily than healthy ones without invoking a special sensitivity of
tumor cells, such as lack of DNA repair capability (9). The
antitumor activity of a series of platinum compounds is generally
correlated with their ability to perturb various functions of DNA
such as enhancement of mutagenesis (10, 11, 12), inhibition of DNA
synthesis (8, 13, 14, 15) and induction of lysogenic bacteria (10,
16).

Platinum compounds without antitumor activity (17) such as
trans-DDP and [Pt(dien)Cl]Cl (Figure 1) covalently bind to DNA
in vivo. Several studies have compared the biological effects
which result when equal amounts of these three platinum compounds
are fixed on DNA (typically r_b = 10^{-4}-10^{-6}). Cis-DDP is 5-10 times
more toxic toward E. coli (8) and mammalian cells (1, 11) than
trans-DDP. The relative toxicity is correlated with the ability
of these two isomers to inhibit DNA replication (8, 13, 14). The
cis isomer is repaired more efficiently by E. coli (8) and is at
least 750 times more mutagenic in mammalian cells (11) than the
trans isomer. The compound [Pt(dien)Cl]Cl binds covalently to the
DNA of E. coli and seems not to be repaired ; nevertheless this
compound does not inhibit DNA synthesis or kill the bacteria (8).
Repair of platinum compounds by E. coli may be under the control
of the SOS system ; cis-DDP induces 5-10 times more recA protein
in treated E. Coli than an equal amount of trans-DPP or
[Pt(dien)Cl]Cl fixed on the DNA (18). It seems that different
modes of fixation on DNA are responsible for the different mutagenicity, toxicity and DNA repair of these platinum complexes.
These results suggest that the antitumor activity of platinum(II)
compounds may also depend on the formation of particular platinum-
DNA lesions.

To test this hypothesis we have measured the penetration and
DNA binding in L1210 leukemia cells grafted in mice which have
received equitoxic doses of the drugs (Table I). [Pt(en)$_2$]Cl$_2$ has
four platinum-nitrogen bonds and should not react with DNA ; for
this negative control, platinum fixation on the DNA was not detectable (r_b < 5x10^{-6}). Results in Table I show that cis-DDP, trans-
DDP and [Pt(dien)Cl]Cl enter the cancer cell and bind to its DNA,
but only cis-DDP is antitumoral. Fixation of 25 times more trans-
than cis-DDP on the DNA of L1210 leukemia cells does not cause
antitumor activity for the trans isomer. From bacterial studies
mentioned above, a 25 fold excess of trans-DDP on the DNA ought
to inhibit DNA synthesis more efficiently than the smaller amount
of bound cis-DDP suggesting that, for L1210 leukemia, inhibition
of DNA synthesis may not be the mechanism of antitumor activity.
If DNA is the cellular target of these drugs, the antitumor activity of cis-DDP nevertheless appears to require a platinum-DNA
lesion with a particular structure.

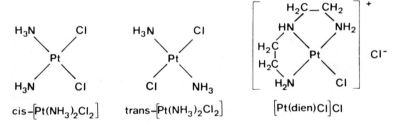

Figure 1. Structures of the three platinum compounds.

TABLE I. PENETRATION AND DNA BINDING of Pt(II)
COMPOUNDS IN L1210 LEUKEMIA CELLS (19).

10^6 cells were grafted i.p. in DBA/2 mice on day 0 and animals
were treated by i.p. injection with the maximum non-toxic dose
(LD_0) of the drug on day 3. For the penetration and DNA binding
experiments, the animals were sacrified 2 h after treatment, the
leukemia cells were removed and washed until no platinum was detected in the supernatant after centrifugation. The cells were
counted and the platinum covalently fixed *per* cell was determined
by atomic absorption. DNA was isolated from these cells by phenol
extraction and the r_b was determined. For the antitumor experiments, animals were grafted with 10^5 L1210 cells and observed
for 30 days. The results are expressed as the mean survival time
of treated animals (T) divided by the mean survival time of non-
treated animals (C). T/C $\geqslant$ 125 % is considered as significant
antitumor activity.

Compound	LD_0 (μmol/kg)	T/C (%)	Pt fixed to cells (% treatment dose)	r_b
cis-DDP	30	200	0.4	1/30,000
trans-DDP	167	116	1.5	1/1,200
[Pt(dien)Cl]Cl	203	100	0.1	1/10,000
[Pt(en)$_2$]Cl$_2$	> 2,600	98	0.02[a]	< 1/200,000[b]

[a]after 4 washings some free compound is still present due to the
large amount injected ; [b]limit of detection.

If the fixation of Pt(II) compounds on DNA is responsible
for the various biological activities of these compounds, then
the relative potencies of *cis*-DDP, *trans*-DDP and [Pt(dien)Cl]Cl
must be a consequence of their modes of binding on the DNA rather
than the stoichiometry of fixation. The objective of this paper
is to determine whether or not the different biological activities
of these compounds are associated with particular deformations of
DNA. To accomplish this goal we will first try to quantitate the
alterations of DNA conformation and stability by these compounds
in vitro at the lowest possible r_b. The limit of detection for
most of the physicochemical techniques which will be considered
is $r_b = 0.005$. The level of DNA binding which produces most biological effects is one or two orders of magnitude less and so we
will emphasize results from studies with $0.005 \leqslant r_b \leqslant 0.05$. Since
the kinetics of fixation of these compounds are different and the
amount of platinum bound to DNA will change if side reactions are
possible, we will limit our discussion to physicochemical studies
which have measured the platinum on the DNA. Generally platinum
concentration has been determined by flameless atomic absorption
or by using radioactive ^{195m}Pt, both which have a limit of detection of $r_b = 1-5 \times 10^{-6}$. Secondly, some preliminary results from our

laboratory concerning the isolation and characterization of the platinum-DNA adducts formed by these compounds will be presented. Finally, we will discuss briefly how the observed structures of the platinum-DNA lesions may be responsible for the altered structure and stability of DNA *in vitro*.

ALTERATIONS OF DNA SECONDARY STRUCTURE AND STABILITY BY Pt(II) COMPOUNDS, $r_b \leqslant 0.05$

Before examining the conformation and stability of the platinum-DNA complex formed *in vitro*, it is worth briefly considering the mechanism of the reaction between Pt(II) chloroammines and DNA. *Cis*-[Pt(NH$_3$)$_2$Cl$_2$] does not react with DNA but the aquated forms, [Pt(NH$_3$)$_2$(H$_2$O)Cl]$^+$ and [Pt(NH$_3$)$_2$(H$_2$O)$_2$]$^{2+}$, bind covalently to the polynucleotide (20) and the overall reaction liberates 2 Cl$^-$ (21).

[Pt(NH$_3$)$_2$Cl$_2$]

$-$Cl$^-$ $\updownarrow$ $+$Cl$^-$

$$[Pt(NH_3)_2(H_2O)Cl]^+ \underset{+H^+}{\overset{-H^+}{\rightleftharpoons}} [Pt(NH_3)_2Cl(OH)]$$

$-$Cl$^-$ $\updownarrow$ $+$Cl$^-$ $-$Cl$^-$ $\updownarrow$ $+$Cl$^-$

$$[Pt(NH_3)_2(H_2O)_2]^{2+} \underset{+H^+}{\overset{-H^+}{\rightleftharpoons}} [Pt(NH_3)_2(H_2O)(OH)]^+ \underset{+H^+}{\overset{-H^+}{\rightleftharpoons}} [Pt(NH_3)_2(OH)_2]$$

If aqueous solutions of *cis*- or *trans*-DDP are allowed to equilibrate, the kinetics of the reactions of these aquated species with DNA can be measured. At low r_b the reaction is pseudo-first-order with respect to platinum concentration. For *cis*-DDP, the half-life of the reaction of the diaquo species with 10^{-4} M DNA at 25°C, pH = 5-6 is 0.8 min and the monoaquo species, *cis*- and *trans*-[Pt(NH$_3$)$_2$(H$_2$O)Cl]$^+$, have half-lives of 6 h and 2 h respectively. The forms [Pt(NH$_3$)$_2$Cl(OH)] and [Pt(NH$_3$)$_2$(OH)$_2$] do not react with DNA and *cis*-[Pt(NH$_3$)$_2$(H$_2$O)(OH)]$^+$ reacts with the same kinetics as the diaquo form (20). However, if freshly dissolved solutions of platinum compounds are added to the DNA, formation of the monoaquo species is the rate limiting step (22). Figure 2 shows the reactions of fresh solutions of the three compounds with DNA at 37°C. Under these conditions the half-lives of the reactions were 3.9, 2.5 and 0.65 h for *cis*-DDP, *trans*-DDP and [Pt(dien)Cl]Cl respectively (19).

It has been proposed that Pt(II) compounds bind to DNA in three different ways, *cis*-bidentate, *trans*-bidentate and monodentate, and that the compounds in Figure 1 are representative of these three classes of binding (23). We will now consider the effect of the fixation of these compounds *in vitro*, $0.005 \leqslant r_b \leqslant 0.05$, on the structure and the stability of DNA.

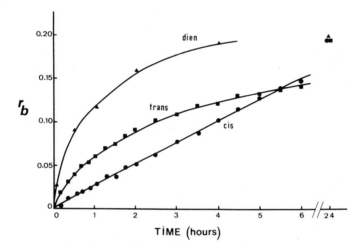

*Figure 2.   Kinetics of the reaction between salmon-sperm DNA and cis-DDP (●),
trans-DDP (■), or [Pt(dien)Cl]Cl (▲); $r_i = 0.2$.*

Aliquots of cis- or trans-DDP were taken at different times and added to a solution of EtdBr.
Fluorescence measurements were performed as previously described (32), and platinum bound
to DNA was determined from standard curve of r_b vs. fluorescence. For [Pt(dien)Cl]Cl, aliquots
were taken at different times, and the reaction was stopped by increasing the Cl⁻ concentration
to 1 M. These samples were then passed through Sepharose-6B columns in order to remove the
unreacted platinum, and the concentration and the r_b of the platinum–DNA complexes were
determined.

Fixation of Pt(II) compounds on DNA does not cause chain breaks. A single chain break in supercoiled PM2 DNA converts the polymer from a compact closed circular conformation to a relaxed open circular form. This conformational change is an extremely sensitive measure of chain scission and it has been used to detect the nicking of DNA by Pt(II) compounds (24, 25, 26). Table II shows the percentage of nicked PM2 DNA molecules which were observed by electron microscopy after fixation of various amounts of the three platinum compounds on the DNA (25). It can be seen that below r_b = 0.1 none of the compounds cause chain breaks in the DNA.

TABLE II. RATIOS BETWEEN SUPERCOILED AND NICKED
PM2 DNA MOLECULES IN THE DIFFERENT PLATINUM-DNA
COMPLEXES VISUALIZED BY ELECTRON MICROSCOPY.

Compound	r_b	Supercoiled molecules (%)	Nicked molecules (%)
DNA	0	81(78-84)	19
cis-Pt(NH$_3$)$_2$-DNA	10^{-4}	78(72-84)	22
	10^{-3}	73(69-77)	27
	10^{-2}	78(77-79)	22
	10^{-1}	48(42-54)	52
trans-Pt(NH$_3$)$_2$-DNA	10^{-4}	77(75-79)	23
	10^{-3}	80(78-82)	20
	10^{-2}	79(76-82)	21
	10^{-1}	82(80-84)	18
Pt(dien)-DNA	10^{-4}	82(79-85)	18
	10^{-3}	80(77-83)	20
	10^{-2}	78(74-82)	22
	10^{-1}	69(68-70)	31

Values in parentheses give the range. 200 molecules of each complex were visualized at different places on the grid.

Cis- and *trans*-DDP but not [Pt(dien)Cl]Cl form interstrand crosslinks. The best characterized of the *cis*-Pt(NH$_3$)$_2$-DNA lesions is the interstrand crosslink which has been deduced from the appearance of high molecular weight DNA in denaturing conditions (27), enhanced thermal renaturation (22) and a diminished rate of alkaline elution (28). It is evident from thermal renaturation

experiments (Figure 3) that *cis*- and *trans*-DDP, but not
[Pt(dien)Cl]Cl form interstrand crosslinks permitting the reforma-
tion of the double helical structure of heat-denatured DNA which
is subsequently cooled (25). Recently Roberts (29) has quantitated
the number of interstrand crosslinks formed by $\overline{cis}$-DDP for
$1 \times 10^{-5} \leqslant r_b \leqslant 5 \times 10^{-4}$. Exposure of either purified DNA or DNA in
mammalian cells to *cis*-DDP for 2 hours produced about 1 crosslink
per 150 bound platinum molecules as determined by the percentage
of high molecular weight DNA observed in alkaline sucrose gradients. In both cases the crosslinking frequency increased to about
1/30 when the platinum–DNA complex was stored in buffer for
24 hours after treatment. Assuming a crosslinking frequency of
1/30, the data in Figure 3 indicates that a single crosslink *per*
500-1000 base pairs is necessary for complete renaturation of the
DNA.

Cis- and *trans*-DDP but not [Pt(dien)Cl]Cl shorten DNA. The
length of PM2 DNA which has been treated by the three compounds
has been measured using electron microscopy (23). This technique
appears to be more sensitive than migration during gel electrophoresis which did not change appreciably for $r_b <$ 0.05 (30). In
contrast, for $r_b \leqslant 0.05$ electron microscopy revealed a linear
relationship between the decrease in the length of PM2 DNA and the
quantity of bound *cis*- or *trans*-DDP. Fixation of [Pt(dien)Cl]Cl
did not change the size of the DNA (Figure 4). Judging from the
slopes of the curves in Figure 4, fixation of a single *cis*-DDP
shortened the DNA by 17 Å while each *trans*-DDP decreased the
length by 10 Å. Alterations of the viscosity (25) of DNA as a
function of r_b (Figure 5) are remarkably similar to the change in
the length of DNA observed using electron microscopy. The drop in
viscosity is not caused by chain breaks and is consistent with the
hypothesis that these compounds shorten DNA.

Fixation of *cis*- and *trans*-DDP, but not [Pt(dien)Cl]Cl,
disrupts DNA base stacking. Spectroscopic studies such as UV
hyperchromism and circular dichroism reflect the immediate
environment of the base and are sensitive probes of conformational
changes involving, at most, several nucleic acid bases. Between
$0.01 \leqslant r_b \leqslant 0.05$ *cis*-DDP increased the positive CD band of DNA at
270 nm by about 40 % (Figure 6) unlike *trans*-DDP and [Pt(dien)Cl]Cl
which had no effect (31). UV hyperchromism was not observed after
fixation of any of the three compounds in this range of r_b (23).

A more direct measurement of the disruption of base-base
interactions by fixation of these molecules is their ability to
prevent the association of EtdBr with DNA. EtdBr intercalates
between base pairs and the number of intercalated molecules can be
determined using fluorescence spectroscopy (32). *Cis*- and *trans*-DDP
each prevented the intercalation of one EtdBr molecule *per*
platinum bound to DNA while [Pt(dien)Cl]Cl had no effect (Figure 7).

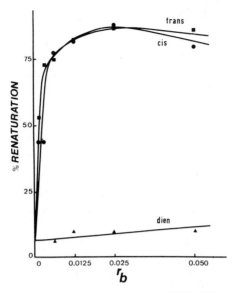

Figure 3. The percentage of renaturation of cis-DDP *(●),* trans-DDP *(■), and [Pt(dien)Cl]Cl (▲) at low* r_b.

Platinum–T7 DNA complexes (25 µg/mL) in NaClO₄ (10 mM) were denatured by raising the temperature to 100°C and then renatured by decreasing the temperature at a rate of 1 °C/min to 25 °C.

$$\% \text{ renaturation} = (A_f - A) \times 100/(A_f - A_0)$$

where A_0 is the absorbance at 260 nm before denaturation, A_f is the absorbance at 260 nm corresponding to the maximum of hyperchromicity, and A is the absorbance at 260 nm after renaturation.

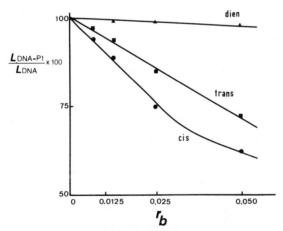

Figure 4. Shortening of PM2 DNA as a function of r_b. *Key:* ●, cis-DDP; ■, trans-DDP; *and* ▲, [Pt(dien)Cl]Cl.

Nicked circular PM2 DNA (0.02 mg/mL) was incubated in NaClO₄ (10 mM) with platinum compounds at 20 °C in the dark for 8 d. After dialysis against NaClO₄ (10 mM) and platinum determination by atomic absorption spectrophotometry, the complexes were absorbed on carbon-coated copper grids and observed using a Philips 301 electron microscope. The average length of control DNA (L_{DNA}) and of platinum–DNA complexes (L_{DNA-Pt}) were determined from an observation of at least 60 molecules.

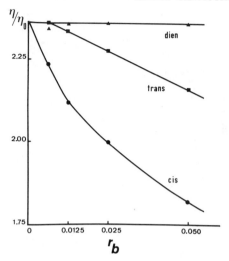

Figure 5. Relative viscosity of sonicated salmon sperm DNA complexed with cis-DDP (●), trans-DDP (■), or [Pt(dien)Cl]Cl (▲) vs. r_b. The viscosity of the platinum–DNA complex is η; the solvent viscosity is η_0.

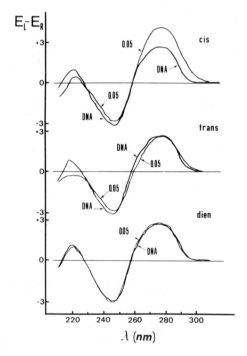

Figure 6. Circular-dichroism spectra of salmon sperm DNA alone and complexed with cis-DDP (top), trans-DDP (middle), or [Pt(dien)Cl]Cl (bottom) for $r_b = 0.05$.

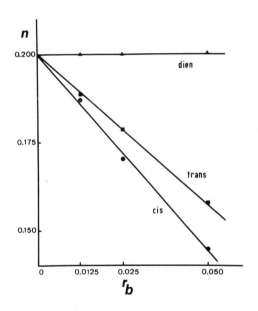

Figure 7.   Number of EtdBr binding sites (n) in salmon sperm DNA complexed with cis-DDP (●), trans-DDP (■), or [Pt(dien)Cl]Cl (▲) at low r_b. Scatchard plots of EtdBr binding to different platinum–DNA complexes were used to determine n.

For $r_b < 0.01$, cis-DDP destabilizes DNA while trans-DDP and [Pt(dien)Cl]Cl stabilize DNA. Alteration of the melting temperature of DNA by fixation of the three platinum compounds at low r_b is shown in Figure 8. In all cases the changes in T_m were a linear function of the quantity of bound platinum. For the fixation of 5 platinum per 1000 bases (30 platinum per T7 DNA molecule), trans-DDP and [Pt(dien)Cl]Cl increased the melting temperature by 0.7°C and 1.7°C respectively while cis-DDP decreased the T_m by 1.7°C (25).

Single stranded regions of DNA are not detected for cis-DDP, trans-DDP or [Pt(dien)Cl]Cl for $r_b < 0.025$. In order to see if single stranded DNA is formed by the fixation of Pt(II) compounds on DNA we have measured the nuclease Sl digestion of salmon sperm DNA which had been treated at low r_b by the three compounds in Figure 1. The reaction was followed by the release of acid soluble UV absorbing material, limit of detection 1 % digestion. Nuclease Sl from Aspergillus oryzae did not digest DNA which had been treated with any of the compounds below $r_b = 0.025$. At $r_b = 0.05$ cis-DDP but not trans-DDP or [Pt(dien)Cl]Cl induced single stranded regions which were sensitive to this enzyme. At higher r_b values Sl nuclease was able to partially digest DNA which had been treated by all three compounds. In all cases the extent of Sl nuclease digestion increased nonlinearly as a function of r_b. It appears that the formation of single stranded DNA may be a cooperative phenomenon which requires the participation of several fixed platinum (33).

Summary. Physicochemical studies of the alteration of DNA conformation and stability by the fixation of cis-DDP, trans-DDP and [Pt(dien)Cl]Cl at $0.005 \leqslant r_b \leqslant 0.05$ reveal that each compound alters the DNA in a characteristic manner. Table III represents an attempt to quantify these effects for $r_b = 0.01$.

At this r_b, the fixation of cis-DDP excludes one EtdBr molecule per bound platinum, implying a change in the conformation which prevents intercalation. Hydrogen bonding between the DNA strands is weakened, as indicated by the decrease in the melting temperature of DNA, but it is not weakened sufficiently to produce single stranded regions which are a substrate for Sl nuclease. Fixation of a single cis-DDP on DNA shortens the polymer by 17 A. The shortening of DNA by fixation of cis-DDP has been attributed to the formation of microloops caused by a crosslink between two bases far apart from each other (23). Conceivably, DNA shortening could be the result of noncovalent charge-charge interactions between the positive platinum-base adduct and a negative phosphate, but in this case [Pt(dien)Cl]Cl should also shorten the DNA, which is not observed.

TABLE III. CHANGES IN THE CONFORMATION
AND STABILITY OF DNA AFTER FIXATION OF
Pt(II) CHLOROAMINES *IN VITRO*, r_b = 0.01.

Compound	*cis*-DDP	*trans*-DDP	[Pt(dien)Cl]Cl
DNA chain breaks[a]	0	0	0
Interstrand crosslinks *per* bound platinum	1/30[b]	ND	0[c]
ΔT_m[a]	-2.4°C	1.3°C	3,3°C
S1 sensitive single stranded DNA[d]	0	0	0
DNA shortening (Å/Pt)[e]	17	10	0
EtdBr/Pt[f]	1	1	0

a. ref. 25 ; b. ref. 29, 0.00005 ⩽ r_b ⩽ 0.0004 ; c. ref. 25,
0.001 ⩽ r_b ⩽ 0.01 ; d. ref. 33, r_b ⩽ 0.025 ; e. ref. 23 ;
f. number of excluded EtdBr molecules per bound platinum, ref. 32.

Fixation of *trans*-DDP on DNA at r_b = 0.01 also prevents the
intercalation of an equimolar quantity of EtdBr. As in the case
of the *cis* isomer, bidentate complexation at two sites on complementary bases or between well separated bases could account for
the formation of interstrand crosslinks and microloops respectively. However, unlike *cis*-DDP, the *trans* isomer stabilizes rather
than destabilizes the DNA at low r_b. *Trans*-DDP also stabilizes
PolyI : PolyC and, in this case, the stabilization was decreased
by increasing the ionic strength (34) implying that charge-charge
interactions are likely responsible for the stabilization. *Trans*-
DDP binds to yeast tRNA[phe] by a covalent bond at N^7 guanine and
hydrogen bonds between an ammine ligand and a phosphate group (35).
Hence, charge-charge interactions, hydrogen bonds or water bridges
(34) may be responsible for the stability of the *trans*-DDP-DNA
complex relative to DNA at low rb.

Fixation of [Pt(dien)Cl]Cl does not cause crosslinks or microloops because this compound can not make a bidentate complex with
DNA. Below r_b = 0.1 the Pt(dien)-DNA complex is more stable than
DNA, probably because of charge-charge interactions or hydrogen
bonds between the platinum complex and adjacent nucleotides.

It is worth noting that the alterations of DNA conformation
and stability for r_b = 0.01 which have just been described are

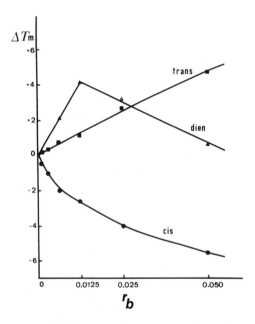

Figure 8. The melting-temperature variations of platinum–T7 DNA complexes at low r_b (ΔT_m = T_m of the complex − T_m of DNA). Key: ●, cis-DDP; ■, trans-DDP; and ▲, [Pt(dien)Cl]Cl. Melting curves of platinum–T7 DNA complexes (25 µg/mL) in NaClO$_4$ (10 mM) were recorded by measuring the hyperchromicity at 260 nm. The rate of temperature increase was 1 °C/min. In these conditions T7 DNA had a T_m of 73.0 ± 0.2 °C.

based on certain physicochemical parameters, such as DNA length, EtdBr intercalation and melting temperature, which appear to be linear functions of the amount of bound platinum from $r_b = 0.05$ to $r_b = 0.005$, the limit of detection. In the next section we shall see that no new platinum-DNA adducts are formed between $0.0005 < r_b < 0.1$. Hence, it seems likely that the changes in DNA structure and stability which have been observed for $r_b = 0.01$ (Table III) are also present at lower levels of platinum binding.

STRUCTURES OF THE PLATINUM-DNA ADDUCTS

Spectroscopic and crystallographic studies of platinum-base complexes give some insight into the reactivity of the platinum compounds and their possible binding sites on DNA. The reactions of the different nucleosides or nucleotides with the chloro and aquo derivatives of *cis*- and *trans*-DDP have been studied by UV spectroscopy (36), raman difference spectrophotometry (37) and high pressure liquid chromatography (38). For both chloro isomers, the rates of the reactions with various nucleic acid monomers show the following trend : GMP > AMP > CMP and dG > dA > dC >> T. The dichloro and diaquo derivatives react slowly with thymidine and UMP (37) or not at all (38, 39).

The stoichiometry of the platinum-base complex depends on the Pt:base ratio and also on the pH. For instance, it has been shown that the *cis*-diaquo species reacts with adenine, adenosine and AMP to give 1:1, 1:2 and 2:1 (Pt:base) complexes. Similar results have been observed for the *trans* isomer except that the 1:2 complexes with adenosine and AMP were not formed (40). The diaquo and dichloro species of *cis*- and *trans*-DDP bind to GMP and dGMP to give 1:1 and 1:2 complexes as shown by raman spectroscopy (41) and NMR (42). *Cis*-$[Pt(NH_3)_2(H_2O)_2]^{2+}$ forms a 1:2 complex with cytidine or uridine at acid pH whereas under neutral conditions the 1:1 complex is formed (43). It also reacts with GpG and GpC forming a bidentate complex with the two bases (44).

The platinum binding sites on nucleic acid bases have been elucidated by x-ray crystallography (45, 46, 47), NMR (37, 43, 48, 49) and raman spectroscopy (37, 41, 43). The reported sites of fixation of *cis*-DDP are the N^7 of guanosine, AMP, GMP and GpG (37, 41, 44, 45, 49) and the N^3 of CMP and cytidine (43, 47). *Trans*-DDP forms mono and bis complexes with 5'-GMP at N^7 for $r_i = 1$ and at N^1 and N^7 at pH > 9 for $r_i = 2$ (41). It also reacts at N^1 and N^7 of adenosine and at N^3 of cytidine (39). The only crystal structure (35) reported for a *trans*-DDP base complex is the structure of yeast tRNA in which platinum is bound to N^7 of guanine 34. Hydrogen bonds were observed between one of the ammine groups and O^6 of the same base and between the other ammine and the three oxygen atoms belonging to the 5'-phosphate of this nucleotide. The main binding sites of [Pt(dien)Cl]Cl complexed with nucleosides and nucleotides as shown by x-ray crystallography and NMR are the N^7 position of guanine (46, 48), N^7 and N^1 of adenine

(48, 49, 51), N^3 of cytosine (48, 51) and N^3 of thymidine (49, 52).
No evidence for binding at the phosphate group has yet been demonstrated even with a large excess of [Pt(dien)Cl]Cl (48). Judging
from NMR results, [Pt(dien)Cl]Cl gives three types of complexes
with adenosine or 5'-AMP corresponding to binding at N^7, at N^1 or
at N^7 and N^1 simultaneously ; N^7 is the kinetically preferred
binding site (48, 51).

GC base pairs appear to be the preferred site of fixation of
platinum(II) compounds on DNA. This conclusion is supported by
three types of arguments. First, the rate of fixation of *cis*-DDP
to DNA is correlated with its GC content (53). Hence, if *cis*-DDP
is mixed with two DNAs of different GC content, it will fix
preferentially to the DNA with highest percentage of guanine (54,
55). Second, the quantity of purine bases which have not reacted
with platinum can be determined by means of paper chromatography
of the depurinated platinum-DNA complex. This experiment shows
that *cis*-DDP reacts with guanine before it binds to adenine (56).
Finally, raman spectroscopy of platinum-DNA complexes reveals
that fresh aqueous solutions of *cis*-DDP react preferentially
with guanine at r_i = 0.2 and also with adenine at r_i = 0.4 whereas
no reaction with cytosine or thymine was observed (37).

Isolation and preliminary characterization of the platinum-
DNA adducts. Recently we have developped a method to separate the
platinum-DNA adducts (*i.e.*, complexes formed on DNA between the
platinum compound and one or two bases) from the DNA (57). Since
the purpose of this experiment was to determine the structure of
these adducts, it seemed important not to modify them during the
isolation. Enzymatic digestion, such as has been used to cut
alkylated bases from DNA (58) might be the gentlest technique, but
there is increasing evidence that the platinum-DNA lesion is
resistant to nuclease digestion (59, 60, 61). Alkylated purines
detach spontaneously from damaged DNA (58, 62), but heating the
platinum-DNA complex formed by the three complexes in Figure 1
did not release platinum. In fact, we have recently observed that,
unlike alkylating agents, fixation of a platinum on the N^7 position of guanosine stabilizes the bond between the sugar and the
base (63).

For these reasons we have used depurinating conditions
(15 min, 100°C, 90 % HCOOH) which separated adenine, guanine and
the platinum-DNA adducts from apurinic acid. These products were
resolved by high voltage paper electrophoresis at pH 2. The paper
was cut into 1 cm strips which were eluted in water and the profile of platinum concentration was determined by flameless atomic
absorption. Under these conditions, the apurinic acid migrated
toward the positive electrode while the purine bases and the
adducts migrated toward the negative electrode. For all three
compounds, less than 10 % of the platinum was detected on the
apurinic acid, even at r_b = 0.4. The electrophoresis profiles of
hydrolysed platinum-DNA complexes formed by *cis*-DDP, *trans*-DDP and

[Pt(dien)Cl]Cl at r_b = 0.1 are shown in Figure 9. Subsequent paper chromatography of the major peaks gave a single UV absorbing spot which contained platinum. This evidence suggests that each major peak in Figure 9 represents a single platinum-base(s) complex (57). The structures of several of these complexes have been determined.

[Pt(dien)Cl]Cl. We have first investigated the Pt(dien)-DNA adducts because monofunctional fixation of platinum on DNA was expected to be simpler than bidentate fixation. In addition, complexes of [Pt(dien)Cl]Cl with nucleic acid bases which could serve as model compounds for the identification of the Pt(dien)-DNA adducts have been previously synthesized and well characterized.

Hydrolysis of DNA which had been reacted with [Pt(dien)Cl]Cl at $0.0005 \leqslant r_b < 0.1$ liberated a single product which migrated 26 cm (Figure 9). Above this r_b a second peak at 30 cm became apparent and a small peak near 34 cm was observed at $0.3 \leqslant r_b \leqslant 0.4$. Paper chromatography revealed that each peak contained a single product. The material in each peak was eluted in water and its UV absorption was measured. Each adduct was then reacted with thiourea to displace the platinum from the base which was subsequently identified. The sites of platinum fixation were determined by comparison of the UV spectra, mass spectra and electrophoretic and chromatographic mobility of the adducts with hydrolysed [Pt(dien)(nucleoside)]$^{2+}$ complexes of known structure.

The results support the following mechanism for the reaction of [Pt(dien)Cl]Cl with DNA *in vitro*. The platinum compound binds exclusively to N^7 of guanine below r_b = 0.1. Above this r_b it also fixes at N^7 of adenine. Above r_b = 0.3 denaturation of the DNA exposes the N^1 position of adenine and [Pt(dien)]$_2$A, with fixation at N^1 and N^7, is formed (63).

Cis-DDP. The electrophoresis profile of *cis*-DDP-DNA, r_b = 0.1, had platinum-containing peaks which migrated 2, 14, 23 and 27 cm toward the negative electrode (Figure 9). At r_b = 0.4 a fifth peak appeared at 32 cm. The relative intensity of the material at 14 cm remained constant within experimental error from r_b = 0.006 to 0.4. In contrast, the relative sizes of the peaks at 23 cm(I) and 27 cm(II) varied from approximately equal intensities for $0.1 < r_b < 0.4$ to a ratio of I/II = 3.5 ± 1 at r_b = 0.0005, the limit of detection for these peaks (57).

The two major peaks of the platinum profile each contained a single product judging by paper chromatography. Reaction of the eluted material with thiourea released guanine from both adducts. Hydrolysis of *cis*-[Pt(NH$_3$)$_2$(dG)$_2$]$^{2+}$ in which the platinum is complexed at the N^7 of two guanine bases (45, 50), gave platinum-containing peaks which migrated 14 and 23 cm (Figure 9). Paper chromatography revealed that the material in these peaks had the same R_f as that found in the corresponding *cis*-DDP-DNA hydrolysis products. Hence, the material at 14 and 23 cm in Figure 9 appears

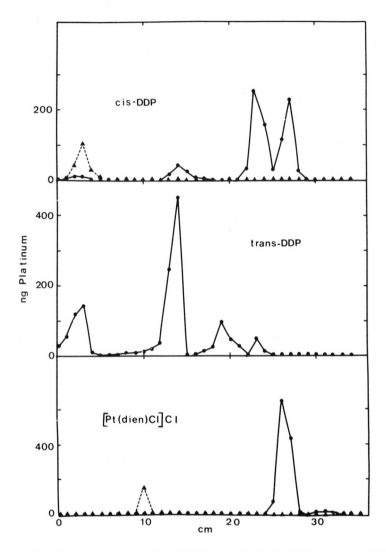

Figure 9. *Electrophoresis profiles of DNA treated with* cis-DDP *(top),* trans-DDP *(middle), and [Pt(dien)Cl]Cl (bottom). Key: —, hydrolyzed platinum–DNA complex, $r_b = 0.1$; and – – –, hydrolyzed platinum–DNA complex isolated from treated* E. coli, $r_b = 0.0005$ *(intensity × 2). The origin is at zero and the abscissa is the distance migrated toward the negative electrode after 45 min of electrophoresis at 100 mA (7000 V).*

to come from the acid hydrolysis of cis-[Pt(NH$_3$)$_2$(dG)$_2$]$^{2+}$. The peaks at 27 and 32 cm have not yet been identified.

Trans-DDP. For the hydrolysed *trans*-DDP-DNA complex, r_b = 0.1, the electrophoresis profile had peaks at 3, 14, 19 and 23 cm (Figure 9) whose relative intensities did not change between r_b = 0.003, the limit of detection of the peak at 23 cm, and r_b = 0.3. Above this r_b a peak near 26 cm appeared (57). Experiments are in progress to determine the structures of the adducts which correspond to the peaks of the electrophoresis profile.

Platinum-DNA adducts *in vivo*. In order to compare the adducts formed by these compounds with DNA *in vivo* and *in vitro*, DNA was isolated from *E. coli* which had been treated with either *cis*-DDP or [Pt(dien)Cl]Cl. After hydrolysis and electrophoresis, all of the platinum from the DNA of *E. coli* which had been treated with *cis*-DDP remained at the origin while adducts from bacteria treated with [Pt(dien)Cl]Cl migrated about 10 cm (Figure 9). Similar results were obtained for DNA isolated from L1210 leukemia cells which had been treated with [Pt(dien)Cl]Cl in culture (57).

Recent immunochemical studies have shown that antibodies against the *cis*-Pt(NH$_3$)$_2$-DNA complex formed *in vitro* do not recognize the platinum-DNA complex isolated from rats which have been treated with *cis*-DDP (64). The present results show that the platinum-DNA adducts isolated from treated bacteria and mammalian cells do not give the same electrophoresis patterns after acid hydrolysis as the corresponding adducts formed *in vitro*. It seems that, *in vivo*, some of the modes of fixation of platinum compounds to DNA may be different than those found *in vitro*.

In summary, the preliminary structures of the platinum-DNA adducts indicate that, in DNA, [Pt(dien)Cl]Cl and *cis*-DDP both bind to the N^7 position of guanine. In the case of [Pt(dien)Cl]Cl, this adduct is the only detectable mode of fixation below r_b = 0.1. *Cis*-DDP forms two guanine-containing adducts with DNA at r_b = 0.0005. One of these appears to be *cis*-[Pt(NH$_3$)$_2$(dG)$_2$]$^{2+}$ which was present at 3.5 ± 1 times the concentration of the other adduct at this r_b. The structure of the second adduct has not yet been determined. In the next section we will briefly consider how each of these lesions might cause the alteration of DNA structure and stability which have been observed (Table III).

HOW THE OBSERVED PLATINUM-DNA ADDUCTS MIGHT ALTER DNA CONFORMATION AND STABILITY *IN VITRO*

Fixation of platinum compounds at the N^7 position of guanine labilizes the proton at N^1. Table IV summarizes the changes in pK of the guanine N^1 proton upon fixation of *cis*-DDP, *trans*-DDP or [Pt(dien)Cl]Cl at the N^7 position. The decrease in the pK of the N^1 proton is comparable for the fixation of [Pt(dien)Cl]Cl, for the 5'-GMP : *trans*-DDP complexes and for the 2:1 5'-GMP : *cis*-DDP complex, but only *cis*-DDP destabilizes the DNA (Table III). Fixation of platinum at N^7 of guanine may not sufficiently change the hydrogen bonding with the complementary cytosine to destabilize the DNA.

Unusual base pairing has been observed in the crystal structure of a platinum-guanosine complex and it has been suggested that fixation of platinum at N^7 may labilize the N^1 proton and thereby cause mispairing during DNA replication (68) which would lead to mutations. This hypothesis seems unlikely since the pK of [7-methylguanosine]$^+$ and [Pt(dien)G]$^{2+}$ are significantly lower than for guanosine, but [7-methylguanosine]$^+$ does not cause mispairing (69) and [Pt(dien)Cl]Cl is, at best, a very weak mutagen (70).

TABLE IV. VARIATION OF THE pK OF THE GUANINE
N^1 PROTON BY FIXATION OF PLATINUM(II)
COMPOUNDS AT THE N^7 POSITION.

Compound	Δ pK	Reference
cis-[Pt(NH$_3$)$_2$(5'-GMP)$_2$]$^{2-}$	- 0.3[a]	41
cis-[Pt(NH$_3$)$_2$(GpG)]$^+$	- 1.3[c]	44
cis-[Pt(NH$_3$)$_2$(9-EtG)(1-MeC)]$^{2+}$	- 1.6[b]	66
cis-[Pt(NH$_3$)$_2$(5'-GMP)(H$_2$O)]$^+$	- 2.8[a,d]	41
trans-[Pt(NH$_3$)$_2$(5'-GMP)$_2$]$^{2-}$	- 0.6[b]	41
trans-[Pt(NH$_3$)$_2$(5'-GMP)(H$_2$O)]$^+$	- 1.0[b]	41
[7-methylguanosine]$^+$	- 2.1[c]	67
[Pt(dien)G]$^{2+}$	- 1.2[b]	63

a. raman spectroscopy ; b. ultraviolet absorption ; c. NMR ;
d. precipitation for $5 \leqslant pH \leqslant 7.5$.

It has been previously suggested that chelation of *cis*-DDP on positions N^7 and O^6 of guanine might labilize the N^1 proton sufficiently to induce mispairing and base pair substitution mutations (9). Such a complex might also be responsible for the destabilization of DNA at low r_b which was observed for *cis*-DDP but not for *trans*-DDP or [Pt(dien)Cl]Cl.

Fixation of platinum compounds at N7 position of guanine stabilizes the glycosyl linkage. Methylation of the N7 position
of guanine labilizes the glycosyl linkage (62) and the spontaneously created apurinic sites on DNA *in vivo* can be recognized and
repaired by a specific endonuclease (71). In addition, the loss
of a purine base could lead to a single strand break in the DNA.
For these reasons we have investigated the influence of platinum
at the N^7 position of guanosine on the stability of the glycosyl
linkage.

Guanosine, [7-methylguanosine]$^+$ and [Pt(dien)G]$^{2+}$ were reacted at 37°C in 1 M HCl and the hydrolysis of the glycosyl bond
was followed by changes in the UV absorbance. The reaction was
first order with half-lives of 11.5 ± 1 h for guanosine, 8.5 ± 1 h
for [7-methylguanosine]$^+$ and 135 ± 25 h for [Pt(dien)G]Cl$_2$. Similarly, the half-life for the hydrolysis of the glycosyl linkage of
dG and [Pt(dien)dG]Cl$_2$ were about 4 min and 2.5 h respectively.
These results indicate that, unlike alkylating agents, fixation of
platinum at the N^7 position of guanine nucleosides stabilizes the
bond between the sugar and the base (55).

There may be a simple explanation for the different behavior
of the alkyl group and the platinum compound. In the case of
[7-methylguanosine]$^+$, the N^7 position carries a formal 1+ charge
which, judging from resonance structures, can be delocalized to
the N^9 position. In contrast, the 2+ charge of the platinum complex is shared by the four nitrogen atoms which bind to the dsp^2
orbitals of the platinum. Hence, in the case of alkylation the
positive charge may reside on the imidazole ring and destabilize
the glycosyl linkage while for platination, the charge would be
delocalized on the platinum moiety.

Does fixation of platinum(II) chloroamines on DNA *in vitro*
labilize the amine ligands ? Fixation of *cis*-DDP on 1-methylcyto-
sine rearranges the platinum complex to form a *trans* isomer which
indicates fixation on a base may labilize the NH$_3$ ligand (72). It
has been proposed that fixation of *cis*-DDP on a heterocyclic
nitrogen atom of DNA may liberate NH$_3$ by means of the *trans* effect
(73, 74). Such an eventuality would permit this platinum compound
to bind to DNA by 3 or 4 sites and consequently introduce a number
of adducts in DNA which might not be found in reactions with isolated nucleic acid bases. Although the reaction of *cis*-
[Pt[^{14}C](en)Cl$_2$] with nucleic acid bases does not liberate
[^{14}C]en (75), a different mode of binding in DNA might weaken the
platinum-nitrogen bond to a greater extent.

For this reason we synthesized *cis*-[Pt[^{14}C](en)Cl$_2$] (76) and
measured the [^{14}C] and Pt on the DNA. For r_b = 0.1, 2091 ± 82 and
2127 ± 76 cpm were found on the DNA before and after exhaustive
dialysis of the reaction mixture, respectively. Hence, fixation
of [Pt(en)Cl$_2$] (which is an active antitumor agent (17)) on DNA
in vitro does not labilize the ethylenediamine ligand. In the
absence of published studies on the lability of NH$_3$ ligand of

platinum chloroammines fixed on DNA, perhaps these results may be cautiously extrapolated to *cis*-DDP.

Fixation of [Pt(dien)Cl]Cl at N^7G favors the B $\longrightarrow$ Z conformational transition. At r_b = 0.05 [Pt(dien)Cl]Cl, but not *cis*- or *trans*-DDP, favors the B $\longrightarrow$ Z transition of poly(dG-dC). poly(dG-dC). Monofunctional fixation of platinum at the N^7 might favor the *syn* conformation of guanine which is found in Z DNA (77).

Cis-DDP may form intrastrand crosslinks and microloops. Preliminary characterization of the mode of fixation of *cis*-DDP on DNA indicates the formation of *cis*-[Pt(NH_3)_2(dG)_2]^{2+} which appears to be the major adduct at r_b = 0.0005. For $0.1 < r_b < 0.3$ this adduct represents 47 ± 7 % of the platinum fixed on the DNA (57). Such an adduct may be a result of intrastrand crosslinks between adjacent guanine bases (54, 55). However, no more than 0.04 Pt/DNA nucleotide can be fixed on adjacent guanine bases (78) in salmon sperm DNA. Hence, *cis*-DDP likely forms bis-complexes with non-nearest neighbor guanine bases. Such complexes may be implicated in the formation of microloops (23) or guanine separated by one or more bases such as in GAG or GCG sequences (79).

A HYPOTHESIS CONCERNING THE MECHANISM OF THE REACTION BETWEEN *CIS*-DDP AND DNA.

Recent evidence suggests that, *in vitro* and *in vivo*, the formation of interstrand crosslinks proceeds by two steps in which the attachment of the two strands of DNA occurs much slower than the initial fixation of platinum on DNA (29). Similarly, the formation of intrastrand crosslinks *in vitro* appears to occur in two steps (80). This mechanism of reaction implies the initial formation of a reactive intermediate which subsequently could make either interstrand crosslinks, intrastrand crosslinks or perhaps microloops (23) depending on whether it reacted with the base complementary to the initial site of fixation, the nearest neighbor base or with a base farther away.
        Several arguments suggest that covalent binding of *cis*-Pt(NH_3)_2 - at the N^7 position of guanine and fixation at O^6 (either through a water bridge, a hydroxyl group or by direct Pt-O^6 coordination) would be an attractive candidate for this intermediate. The N^7 position of guanine is apparently the initial site of fixation for the *cis*-DDP-DNA adduct whose structure has been determined. A second metastable bond between O^6 and the platinum moiety might reasonably delay the crosslinking reaction of *cis*-DDP. Liberation of the N^1 proton in the N^7-O^6 complex has been previously suggested to account for the mutagenicity of *cis*-DDP (9). Zwelling (this symposium) reports that thiourea simultaneously inhibits mutagenicity and the formation of crosslinks in mammalian cells. It may be that thiourea replaces the Pt-O^6 linkage with a platinum-sulfur bond thereby depleting this

metastable intermediate which is necessary for both mutagenicity and crosslink formation.

Abbreviations. DDP = [Pt(NH$_3$)$_2$Cl$_2$] ; dien = diethylenetriamine, (NH$_2$-CH$_2$-CH$_2$)$_2$NH ; en = ethylenediamine, (NH$_2$-CH$_2$)$_2$; EtdBr = ethidium bromide, 3-8-diamino-6-phenyl-5-ethylphenanthridinium bromide ; r$_i$ = molar ratio Pt introduced/DNA nucleotide ; r$_b$ = number of Pt covalently bound/DNA nucleotide ; T$_m$ = temperature at which DNA is half denatured ; i.p. = intraperitoneal.

Acknowledgments   This work was supported by grants from D.G.R.S.T. (décision d'aide n° 77.7.1348) and l'Association pour le Développement de la Recherche sur le Cancer. The comments of Drs. M. Leng, B. Malfoy (Orléans) and of J.C. Chottard (Paris) are appreciated.

Literature Cited

1. Pascoe, J. M.; Roberts, J. J. Biochem. Pharmacol. 1974, 23, 1345-1357.
2. Roberts, J. J.; Thomson, A. J. "Progress in Nucleic Acid Research and Molecular Biology"; Cohn, W. E., Ed. ; Academic Press : New York, 1979; Vol. 22, 71-133.
3. Howle, J. A.; Gale, G. R. Biochem. Pharmacol. 1970, 19, 2757-2762.
4. Harder, H. C.; Rosenberg, B. Int. J. Cancer 1970, 6, 207-216.
5. Beck, D. J.; Brubaker, R. R. J. Bacteriol. 1973, 116, 1247-1252.
6. Fraval, H. N. A.; Rawlings, C. J.; Roberts, J. J. Mutation Res. 1978, 51, 121-132.
7. Drobnik, J.; Urbankova, M.; Krekulova, A. Mutation Res. 1973, 17, 13-20.
8. Alazard, R.; Germanier, M.; Johnson, N. P. Mutation Res. 1982, 93, 327-337.
9. Rosenberg, B. Biochimie 1978, 60, 859-867.
10. Lecointe, P.; Macquet, J. P.; Butour, J. L. Biochem. Biophys. Res. Commun. 1979, 90, 209-213.
11. Johnson, N. P.; Hoeschele, J. D.; Rahn, R. O.; O'Neill, J. P.; Hsie, A. W. Cancer Res. 1980, 40, 1463-1468.
12. Plooy, A. C. M.; Lohman, P. H. M. Toxicology 1980, 17, 169-176.
13. Harder, H. C.; Smith, R. G.; Leroy, A. F. Cancer Res. 1976, 36, 3821-3829.
14. Johnson, N. P.; Hoeschele, J. D.; Kuemmerle, N. B.; Masker, W. E.; Rahn, R. O. Chem.-Biol. Interactions 1978, 23, 267-271.
15. Kohl, H. H.; Haghighi, S.; McAuliffe. C. A. Chem.-Biol. Interactions 1980, 29, 327-333.
16. Reslova, S. Chem.-Biol. Interactions 1971/72, 4, 66-70.
17. Cleare, M. J.; Hoeschele, J. D. Bioinorg. Chem. 1973, 2, 187-210.
18. Salles, B.; Lesca, C. Biochem. Biophys. Res. Commun. 1982, 105, 202-208.

19. Butour, J. L. Thesis, Paul Sabatier University, Toulouse, France, 1980.
20. Johnson, N. P.; Hoeschele, J. D.; Rahn, R.O. Chem.-Biol. Interactions 1980, 30, 151-169.
21. Macquet, J. P.; Theophanides, T. Bioinorg. Chem. 1975, 5, 59-66.
22. Horacek, P.; Drobnik, J. Biochim. Biophys. Acta 1971, 254, 341-347.
23. Macquet, J. P.; Butour, J. L. Biochimie 1978, 60, 901-914.
24. Howe-Grant, M.; Wu, K. C.; Bauer, W. R.; Lippard, S. J. Biochemistry 1976, 15, 4339-4346.
25. Butour, J. L.; Macquet, J. P. Biochim. Biophys. Acta 1981, 653, 305-315.
26. Mong, S.; Daskal, Y.; Prestayko, A. W.; Crooke, S. T. Cancer Res. 1981, 41, 4020-4026.
27. Roberts, J. J.; Pascoe, J. M. Nature (London) 1972, 235, 282-284.
28. Zwelling, L. A.; Anderson, T.; Kohn, K. W. Cancer Res. 1979, 39, 365-369.
29. Roberts, J. J.; Friedlos, F. Chem.-Biol. Interactions 1982, in press.
30. Cohen, G. L.; Bauer, W. R.; Barton, J. K.; Lippard, S. J. Science 1979, 203, 1014-1016.
31. Macquet, J. P.; Butour, J. L. Eur. J. Biochem. 1978, 83, 375-387.
32. Butour, J. L.; Macquet, J. P. Eur. J. Biochem. 1977, 78, 455-463.
33. Butour, J. L. in preparation.
34. Hermann-Teyssie, D. Thesis, University of Liege, Belgium, 1980.
35. Jack, A.; Ladner, J.E.; Rhodes, D.; Brown, R. S.; Klug, A. J. Mol. Biol. 1977, 111, 315-328.
36. Scovell, W. M.; O'Connor, T. J. Am. Chem. Soc. 1977, 99 120-126.
37. Mansy, S.; Chu, G. Y. H.; Duncan, R. E.; Tobias, R. S. J. Am. Chem. Soc. 1978, 100, 607-616.
38. Inagaki, K.; Tamaoki, N.; Kidani, Y. Inorg. Chim. Acta 1980, 46, L93-L95.
39. Mansy, S.; Rosenberg, B.; Thomson, A.J. J. Am. Chem. Soc. 1973, 95 , 1633-1640.
40. Kleinwächter, V.; Zaludova, R. Chem.-Biol. Interactions 1977, 16, 207-222.
41. Chu, G. Y. H.; Mansy, S.; Duncan, R. E.; Tobias, R. S. J. Am. Chem. Soc. 1978, 100, 593-606.
42. Marcelis, A. T. M.; Van Kralingen, C. G.; Reedijk, J. J. Inorg. Biochem. 1980, 13, 213-222.
43. Chu, G. Y. H.; Duncan, R. E.; Tobias, R. S. Inorg. Chem. 1977, 16, 2625-2636.
44. Chottard, J. C.; Girault, J. P.; Chottard, G.; Lallemand, J. Y.; Mansuy, D. J. Am. Chem. Soc. 1980, 102, 5565-5572.

45. Cramer, R. E.; Dahlstrom, P. L.; Seu, M. J. T.; Norton, T.; Kashiwagi, M. Inorg. Chem. 1980, 19, 148–154.
46. Melanson, R.; Rochon, F. D. Can. J. Chem. 1979, 57, 57–61.
47. Wu, S. M.; Bau, R. Biochem. Biophys. Res. Commun. 1979, 88, 1435–1442.
48. Kong, P. C.; Theophanides, T. Bioinorg. Chem. 1975, 5, 51–58.
49. Lim, M. C.; Martin, R. B. J. Inorg. Nucl. Chem. 1976, 38, 1915–1918.
50. Kong, P. C.; Theophanides, T. Inorg. Chem. 1974, 13, 1167–1170.
51. Kong, P. C.; Theophanides, T. Inorg. Chem. 1974, 13, 1981–1985.
52. Inagaki, K.; Kidani, Y. Bioinorg. Chem. 1978, 9, 333–343.
53. Mansy, S. Ph. D. Thesis, University of Michigan, 1972.
54. Stone, P. J.; Kelman, A. D.; Sinex, F. M. Nature (London) 1974, 251, 736–737.
55. Stone, P. J.; Kelman, A. D.; Sinex, F. M.; Bhargava, M. M.; Halvorson, H. O. J. Mol. Biol. 1978, 104, 793–801.
56. Munchausen, L. L.; Rahn, R. O. Biochim. Biophys. Acta 1975, 414, 242–255.
57. Johnson, N. P. Biochem. Biophys. Res. Commun. 1982, 104, 1394–1400.
58. Singer, B. "Progress in Nucleic Acid Research and Molecular Biology"; Cohn, W. E., Ed.; Academic Press : New York, 1975; Vol. 15, 219–332.
59. De Pauw-Gillet, M. C.; Houssier, C.; Fredericq, E. Chem.-Biol. Interactions 1979, 25, 87–102.
60. Tullius, T. D.; Lippard, S. J. J. Am. Chem. Soc. 1981, 103, 4620–4622.
61. Royer-Pokora, B.; Gordon, L. K.; Haseltine, W. A. Nucl. Acids Res. 1981, 9, 4595–4609.
62. Lawley, P. D.; Brookes, P. Biochem. J. 1963, 89, 127–138.
63. Johnson, N. P.; Macquet, J. P.; Wiebers, J. L. in preparation.
64. Malfoy, B.; Hartmann, B.; Macquet, J. P.; Leng, M. Cancer Res. 1981, 41, 4127–4131.
65. Izatt, R. M.; Christensen, J. J.; Rytting, J. H. Chem. Revs. 1971, 71, 439–481.
66. Lippert, B. J. Am. Chem. Soc. 1981, 103, 5691–5697.
67. "Handbook of Biochemistry", 2nd ed.; Sober, H., Ed.; CRC Press : Cleveland, 1970; G-38.
68. Faggiani, R.; Lock, C. J. L.; Lippert, B. J. Am. Chem. Soc. 1980, 102, 5418–5419.
69. Ludlum, D. B. J. Biol. Chem. 1970, 245, 477–482.
70. Lecointe, P.; Macquet, J. P.; Butour, J. L.; Paoletti, C. Mutation Res. 1977, 48, 139–143.
71. Lindahl, T. Ann. Rev. Biochem. 1982, in press.
72. Lippert, B.; Lock, C. J. L.; Speranzini, R. A. Inorg. Chem. 1981, 20, 808–813.
73. Wherland, S.; Deutsch, E.; Eliason, J.; Sigler, P. B. Biochem. Biophys. Res. Commun. 1973, 54, 662–668.

74. Lippard, S. J. Accts. Chem. Res. 1978, 11, 211-217.
75. Robins, A. B. Chem.-Biol. Interactions 1973, 6, 35-45.
76. Johnson, G. L. "Inorganic Syntheses"; Holtzclaw, H. F., Ed.;
    McGraw Hill : New-York, 1966; Vol. VIII, 242-244.
77. Malfoy, B.; Hartmann, B.; Leng, M. Nucleic Acids Res. 1981,
    9, 5659-5669.
78. Josse, J.; Kaiser, A. D.; Kornberg, A. J. Biol. Chem. 1961,
    236, 864-875.
79. Brouwer, J.; Van de Putte, P.; Fichtinger-Schepman, A. M. J.;
    Reedijk, J. Proc. Natl. Acad. Sci. USA 1981, 78, 7010-7014.
80. Filipski, J.; Kohn, K. W.; Bonner, W. M. Chem.-Biol. Inter-
    actions 1980, 32, 321-330.

RECEIVED October 4, 1982

Model for the Interaction of *cis*-Diamminedichloroplatinum(II) with Simian Virus 40 DNA

WILLIAM M. SCOVELL, LEE R. KROOS[1], and VINCENT J. CAPPONI

Bowling Green State University, Department of Chemistry,
Bowling Green, OH 43403

Physico-chemical and nuclease probes which are
sensitive to modifications of DNA clearly indicate
that both cis- and trans-$PtCl_2(NH_3)_2$ bind to (G+C)
rich regions of DNA, although they exhibit different
modes of binding. Both electrophoretic profiles of
$PtCl_2(NH_3)_2$ treated SV40 DNA and the extent of S1
nuclease digestions on the modified DNAs emphasize
that the isomers exert different effects on DNA
structure. However, the isomers are comparable in
inhibiting site specific cleavage by a particular
restriction enzyme, with the relative inhibition for
a series of five restriction endonucleases paralleling
the number and relative position of guanines in and
adjacent to the recognition site. These data suggest
that the Bgl 1 site, which is in the regulatory region
of the SV40 genome, is a hyper-reactive site to
$PtCl_2(NH_3)_2$ binding. This may be directly related to
the impairment of biological functions of SV40 virus
in infected cells by cis-DDP treatment.

Perhaps the two most prominent differences between cis- and
trans-DDP[+] are the (1) geometrically different structures and (2)
the therapeutic efficacy of cis-DDP as an anti-neoplastic agent,
while trans-DDP is inactive (1,2,3). The chemotherapeutic action
of cis-DDP is thought to result from a direct covalent binding to
DNA, which manifests selective inhibition of DNA synthesis, both
in vitro and in vivo (4,5,6). Notwithstanding that both isomers
may form a number and variety of different DNA or DNA-protein
crosslinked adducts, only one or more of the cis-DDP adducts is
responsible for the desired therapeutic effects. This significant difference must be related, in part, to the different

[1] Current address: Stanford University Medical School, Department of Biochemistry, Stanford, CA 94305

stereochemical bonding constraints inherent in the isomeric
structures. With this in mind, we have felt that it is essential
to compare the effect that both cis- and trans-DDP binding exerts
on DNA or chromatin structure and/or function. Although both
isomers are expected to bind preferentially to (G+C) rich regions
of DNA (7,8,9) and may bind monofunctionally or produce interstrand crosslinks (10,11), a mode of binding to DNA which is
stereochemically unique to cis-DDP involves an intrastrand crosslink to adjacent guanines on native DNA or to other nucleotide
bases (G,A or C) in denatured regions. Stone et al (9) originally offered the former proposal and a number of recent findings
are consistent with it (12-16).

As with similar biological problems, a major dichotomy surfaces in defining a biological system in which one attempts to
relate the chemical interactions in the genome to the impairment
of biological function. Ideally this system would not only be of
sufficient simplicity to make this goal within reach, but on the
other hand, complex enough to be of relevance in human
(eukaryotic) cells.

We have therefore focused much of our efforts on comparing
the effect that cis- and trans-DDP exerts on SV40 DNA and the
SV40 minichromosome. In this communication, we shall summarize
recent findings from our laboratory which help to shape a working
model for discerning how cis- and trans-DDP binding may modify
the DNA structure and therefore disrupt the normal biological
functions of SV40 virus.

The SV40 Genome

As a result of an intensive effort in the last decade, the
oncogenic animal virus, simian virus 40 (SV40), is perhaps one
of the most widely used models for studies on the molecular mechanisms of gene expression and regulation in eukaryotic cells (17,
18,19). There is good reason for its popularity. The small DNA
genome, shown schematically in Figure 1, is entirely sequenced
(5,243 b.p.) (20,21,22) contains only five known genes (denoted t,
T, VP1, VP2, and VP3) and a regulatory region (shown stippled),
the locations of which have been precisely mapped (17,18, 19).
The location of cleavage sites (in map units) for the restriction
endonucleases Bgl 1, Kpn I, Hpa II, Eco RI and Bam HI, all of
which cut SV40 DNA at a single, unique site, are shown in the
circular SV40 map. The temporal order of viral gene expression
in a lytic infection is divided into the "early" and "late"
regions. Replication is initiated at the origin of replication
(Ori) at about 0.66 (23) and proceeds bidirectionally to ter-
minate at approximately 0.17. T antigen is synthesized early and
then its site specific binding to DNA at 0.66 is thought to be
involved in both control of further T antigen transcription and
the initiation of viral DNA synthesis (24), the latter of which
proceeds at the same time that the "late" genes are expressed.

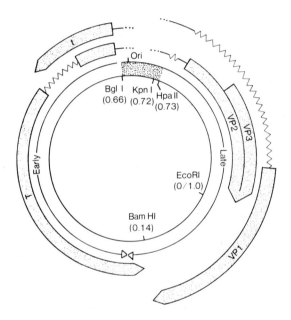

Figure 1. Schematic representation of SV40 genome indicating the locations of principal features (19).

The genome is represented as a circle with the origin of replication (Ori) at the top (See Ref. 63 for details about the origin of DNA replication). Restriction endonuclease cutting sites are shown for Bgl 1, Kpn I, Hpa II, Eco RI, and Bam HI with Eco RI at 0/1.0. The genome is divided into coding sequences for the early genes (large T, small t) and the late genes (VP1, VP2, and VP3). Shaded arcs with arrowheads indicate coding positions of mRNA molecules with arrowheads pointing in the 5' → 3' direction. The stippled area contains the regulatory region of the genome.

Of particular note for our purposes, Kutinova et al (25) have reported that in SV40 infected African green monkey kidney cells, cis-DDP inhibits SV40 replication and the production of the late proteins, while exhibiting no observable effect on T antigen production.

Cis-DDP Unwinds SV40 DNA Twice As Effectively As Trans-DDP (15)

The binding of a variety of molecules, ions, or biomacromolecules to DNA is known to change the local structure of DNA (26,27,28). Gel electrophoresis provides a sensitive method to monitor such alterations in tertiary structure in supercoiled (c^3s) DNA since the mobility of the DNA is proportional to the absolute number of supercoils, $|\tau|$ (29). Figure 2 shows generally that binding to DNA may produce structural changes which result in the unwinding of the DNA backbone. As increasing amounts of molecules or ions bind to the DNA, the negative supercoils are unwound until the intact relaxed form ($\Delta\alpha$ =0, τ =0) is produced. On further binding, the DNA usually unwinds further to the positively supercoiled form.

Figure 3 outlines the experimental protocol for this aspect of the study, together with that for the subsequent investigation with restriction endonucleases. The time dependent effect of trans-DDP binding on the electrophoretic mobility of supercoiled and nicked SV40 DNA is shown in Figure 4a (15). Four observations are of primary interest. The trans-DDP binds to and unwinds c^3s DNA. At low levels of binding, there is little or no decrease in the mobility of c^3s DNA indicating very little effect on unwinding of the DNA or altering its tertiary structure. A decreased mobility is apparent at ca. 3 hours. The intact relaxed form of DNA is observed at 24 hours, its mobility being coincident with that of nicked DNA. Under these reaction conditions, and at elevated (trans-DDP/DNA(N)) mole ratios 4 times greater, there was no evidence that trans-DDP unwound the DNA further to a positively supercoiled form.

The electrophoretic profile for the cis-DDP reaction under identical conditions is compared in Figure 4b. Three aspects of the profile reveal differences between the effect that cis- and trans-DDP exert on the structure of SV40 DNA. The cis-DDP binds to and unwinds the supercoiled DNA to the intact relaxed form in ca. 6 hours, a factor of 4 times faster than the trans-DDP. At 24 hours, the mobility of the DNA has reversed and is now greater than that of the intact relaxed form, indicative of formation of the positively supercoiled form. As noted above, the electrophoretic pattern indicates that trans-DDP binding cannot unwind the DNA to a similar extent. Analysis of the rate of DDP binding to DNA as measured by the atomic absorption of bound Pt indicates that cis-DDP binds to DNA slightly faster than trans-DDP. At the point of the intact relaxed form, the (DDP/DNA(N)) mole ratios for cis- and trans-DDP are 0.08 and 0.15, respectively. These

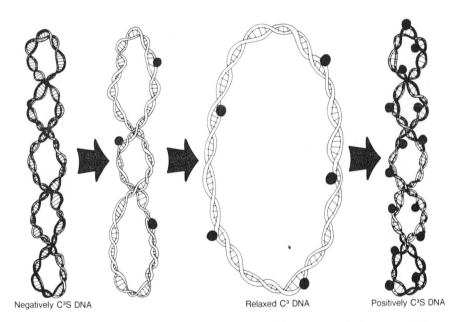

Negatively C³S DNA   Relaxed C³ DNA   Positively C³S DNA

Figure 2.   Schematic representation of the unwinding of negatively supercoiled DNA caused by the binding of increasing amounts of drugs (dark circles). In the unwinding process, the topological linking number (α) remains invariant while the number of supercoils (τ) changes. The DNA is shaded also to denote different degrees of superhelicity.

INTERACTION OF CIS- AND TRANS-DDP WITH SV40 DNA

Effect of the Covalent Binding on:

   1.   Effective Unwinding of DNA

   2.   Cleavage by Restriction Endonucleases

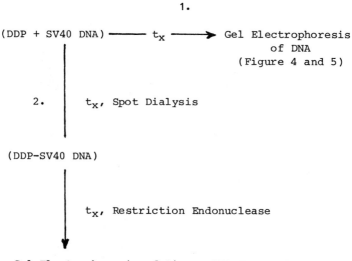

Gel Electrophoresis of Linear DNA Fragments
(Figure 7)

Figure 3.   Experimental protocols: Path 1 is used to compare the relative influence of cis- *and* trans-*DDP binding on unwinding c³s SV40 DNA (15). Path 2 is used to determine the relative distribution of* cis- *and* trans-*DDP at specific sites in the SV40 genome (16).*

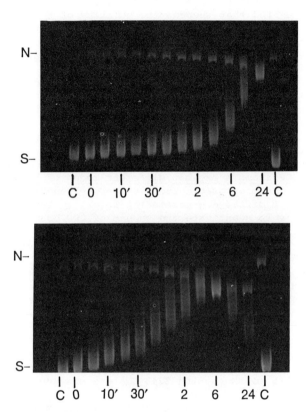

Figure 4. Electrophoretic profile of supercoiled (S) and nicked (N) SV40 DNA incubated with trans-*DDP (top) and* cis-*DDP (bottom) both at [DDP/DNA(N)]ᵢₙcᵤbₐₜₑd = 1.0 for various times at 25 °C. The outermost lanes contain control (C) SV40 DNA after incubation for 0 min (left) and 24 h (right). Lanes 2–13 contain DNA reacted with* trans-*DDP or* cis-*DDP for times (left to right) of 0, 3, 10, 20, 30, 50, and 85 min and 2, 3, 6, 12, and 24 h. (Reproduced with permission from Ref. 15. Copyright 1982, Academic Press.)*

ratios indicate that the <u>cis-DDP</u> <u>is</u> <u>twice</u> <u>as</u> <u>effective</u> as
<u>trans-DDP</u> in unwinding the DNA to the intact relaxed form.

Possibly the most significant difference between the binding
characteristics of the two isomers is observed at very short
reaction times, which corresponds to very low levels of DDP
binding. We find that whereas the mobility of the trans-DDP
modified DNA exhibits very little decrease in mobility at t $\approx$ 0
(i.e., mix DDP with DNA and freeze immediately), the cis-DDP
modified DNA, on the other hand, has a comparatively large
decrease in mobility. This latter effect is more clearly evident
in Figure 5 which compares the mobilities of the cis- and
trans-DDP modified DNAs for the first 30 minutes of reaction.
Although the cis-DDP binding reduces the DNA mobility at t$\approx$0,
the mobility of the trans-DDP modified DNA is not comparably
reduced until at least 30 minutes. Clearly the pronounced difference at low levels of binding, perhaps a factor of 50 or more
as expressed by the different mobilities, indicates that the <u>cis-</u>
and <u>trans-DDP</u> <u>isomers</u> <u>exhibit</u> <u>different</u> <u>modes</u> <u>of</u> <u>binding</u>, while
the overall electrophoretic profile for the reaction is con-
sistent with a difference persisting at all r_b levels. Although
we are unable to quantitate the amount of DDP bound at these very
short reaction times, we estimate the (DDP/DNA(N)) mole ratio to
be probably ca. 5 x 10^{-4}, which is equivalent to only a few DDP
bound to the SV40 genome.

These findings do not agree with those of Cohen et al (30)
who have reported that the binding of cis- or trans-DDP to pSMI
DNA produced essentially identical unwinding of the DNA. The
results presented here clearly demonstrate a number of well
defined differences in the manner in which these isomers alter
the tertiary structure and unwind SV40 DNA. Although further
work is required to resolve the factors responsible for the differences in the two studies, we can report that results (not
shown) similar to those with SV40 DNA are observed using ϕX174RF
DNA.

Of the modes of binding which the cis-DDP may exhibit, the
monodentate binding would be expected to produce unwinding of the
DNA comparable to that of the trans-DDP. However, the
intrastrand crosslinking of cis-DDP to adjacent guanines, a mode
of binding stereochemically unique to the cis-DDP isomer, and
which could explain why cis-DDP unwinds the SV40 DNA twice as
effectively as does trans-DDP, should be regarded as a primary
candidate for producing this effect. While this cannot be
regarded as a unique interpretation of the data, a number of studies support it (12-16). Another binding mode which cannot be
rigorously excluded, the cis-DDP chelation at 0-6 and N-7 on
guanine, is a possibility, but there are no studies which we feel
currently substantiate it. The "cis-DDP pinching" of the DNA
backbone, as a result of forming the intrastrand crosslink to
adjacent guanines, may be expected to exert a pronounced

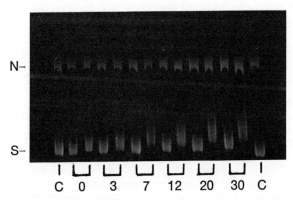

Figure 5. Comparative electrophoretic profile of supercoiled (S) and nicked (N) SV40 DNA incubated with cis- *and* trans-DDP *both at* $[DDP/DNA(N)]_{incubated} = 1.0$ *for short reaction times at 25 °C. The outer lanes contain control (C) SV40 DNA at 0 min (left) and 30 min (right). Lane 2 and even-numbered lanes contain* trans-DDP *modified DNA, while lane 3 and odd-numbered lanes contain similarly* cis-DDP *modified DNA for reaction times of 0, 3, 7, 12, 20, and 30 min. (Reproduced with permission from Ref. 15. Copyright 1982, Academic Press.)*

influence on unwinding the phosphodiester backbone and also in
producing locally denatured regions which would enhance the
effective unwinding process. Since the trans-DDP is expected to
exhibit primarily monodentate or monofunctional binding, it would
not be as effective in altering the DNA structure.

Cis-DDP Binding to DNA Stimulates Greater Levels of S1 Nuclease Digestion Than Does Trans-DDP (31)

A number of endonucleases exhibit a specificity for
digesting single-stranded regions in DNA (32). The utility of
these nucleases, including S1 nuclease from Aspergillus oryzae
(33), stems from their capability to recognize and excise modifications of DNA which induce local single-stranded segments.
Although single base pair mismatches are not recognized (34,35),
perturbations in structure produced by pyrimidine dimers (36,37),
carcinogens (38,39), cis-DDP (40), other drugs (41,42) or the
inherent torsional strain in supercoiled DNAs (44) stimulate S1
digestion.

Figure 6 compares the effect of cis- and trans-DDP modified
calf thymus DNA in stimulating S1 nuclease digestion (31). These
data, together with results with other DNAs at lower r_b values,
consistently show that cis-DDP binding produces a greater level
of DNA digestion than does trans-DDP at the same r_b values.
This is consistent with the proposal that cis-DDP intrastrand
crosslinks to guanines will "pinch" the DNA strand and result in
disruption of the complementary base pairing interaction. This
locally denatured region is then recognized and cut by S1
nuclease. Trans-DDP modification of DNA produces less recogni-
zable modifications to DNA structure, with the percent acid
soluble DNA produced being 3-5 times less than that for comparable levels of bound cis-DDP. Likewise, the data at r_b levels
greater than 0.05 indicate that the S1 digestion levels produced
on cis-DDP modified DNA are not obtained on trans-DDP modified
DNA until the r_b values are twice as great.

Both probes used to monitor structural changes in DDP-
modified DNA - (1) the mobility of c^3s DNA in gel electrophoresis
and (2) S1 nuclease sensitivity - clearly and consistently indicate differences in the mode of binding for the cis- and
trans-DDP isomers.

Relative Distribution of Cis- and Trans-DDP Binding in the SV40 Genome. (16)

Examination of SV40 DNA, which is 58% (A+T), reveals that
the most (G+C) rich region in the genome, which is locally
greater than 55% (G+C), is within the region responsible for the
regulation of gene expression (0.66 - 0.74 on the physical map)
(20,21). Since DDP exhibits a binding preference for (G+C) rich
regions and cis-DDP disrupts viral replication and the production
of selected proteins, it was of interest to determine the rela-

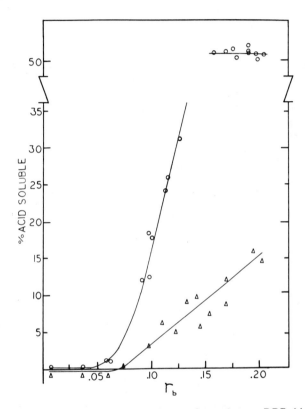

Figure 6. S1 nuclease digestion of cis-DDP *(○) and* trans-DDP *(△) modified calf thymus DNA as a function of* r_b. *(Reproduced with permission from Ref. 16. Copyright 1982, Academic Press.)*

Digestions were carried out on DNA samples that were reacted with various levels of DDP samples for 10 h at 37 °C, spin dialyzed, and then digested for 35 min at 37 °C with 90 u/mL of S1 nuclease. The assay procedure of Vogt (64) was used with the percent acid solubility determined by the A_{260} *reading and assuming a 41% hyperchromicity (31).*

tive distribution of bound DDP within or about specific locations
in the SV40 genome by monitoring the relative cleavage inhibition
of site specific restriction endonucleases, (R.E.). The analysis
assumes that DDP binding within or immediately adjacent to the
recognition site will modulate the sequence specific protein-DNA
interaction and thereby inhibit the subsequent cleavage of the
DNA.

The DNA is initially reacted with DDP, spot dialyzed and
then sufficient R.E. (Figure 3) is added to just completely
cleave an equivalent amount of unmodified DNA. Figure 7 shows
the electrophoretic pattern observed after reaction of the
modified DNA with Bgl 1, Bam HI, Hpa II, Kpn I and Eco RI,
respectively. Figure 1 identifies the location of the cleavage
site for each R.E. in SV40 DNA. The recognition sequences for
each R.E. plus a 10 base pair sequence on each side is shown in
Figure 8. A comparison of the band intensities in each lane of
the gel (Figure 7) shows that although the extents of inhibition
produced by DDP binding differ greatly for the five R.E.s, there
is little or no difference between the effect cis- and trans-DDP
binding to DNA exerts on any one R.E. Similar results were
obtained at incubated [DDP/DNA(N)] mole ratios of 0.2 and 0.05.
The relative band intensities indicate that the inhibition of
cleavage produced by either DDP isomer follows the order:

Bgl 1 ≳ Bam HI > Hpa II, Kpn I > Eco RI

Previous studies have led to predictions (7) and have shown
experimentally (7,8) that DDP binds preferentially to guanines
and therefore to (G+C) regions in DNA. Since support for this is
derived from both the determination of conditional formation
constants and kinetic measurements (7,44), it is expected that
this is the primary DNA modification responsible for the cleavage
inhibition. However, further studies by Stone et al with
poly(dG).poly(dC) and poly(dG-dC) showed there was a striking
base sequence effect on the binding reaction (9). In fact, it
was this unusually strong cis-DDP binding in poly(dG).poly(dC)
that stimulated the proposal that this isomer may form
intrastrand crosslinks to GpG units on the poly(dG) strand. This
mode of binding, of course, would be stereochemically impossible
for the trans-DDP to duplicate. In light of these arguments, and
after consideration of the nucleotide sequence within and adjacent to the R.E. recognition sequence, a number of additional
conclusions may be drawn with regard to the nature of DDP inhibition of endonuclease activity.

The observed order of cleavage inhibition for these R.E.s
does not parallel the % (G+C) content within the recognition
sequence as shown in Table I. The most obvious discrepancies are
with Hpa II and Bam HI. The Hpa II R.E. is only moderately inhibited although the recognition sequence is 100% (G+C), while Bam

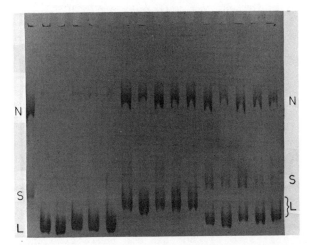

Figure 7. Cleavage of cis- *and* trans-*DDP modified SV40 DNA by restriction endonucleases that cut at a single unique site. (Reproduced with permission from Ref. 16. Copyright 1982, Academic Press.)*

Lane 1 shows the mobility of nicked (N) and supercoiled (S) forms of SV40 DNA. Lanes 2–6 contain SV40 DNA cleaved with Bam HI, Eco RI, Bgl 1, Hpa II, and Kpn I, respectively. These controls demonstrate complete cleavage to the linear (L) form. Lanes 7–11 contain SV40 DNA [9.0 × 10⁻⁵ M DNA(N)] that was reacted with cis-DDP (1.8 × 10⁻⁵ M) for 3 h at 25 °C, spot dialyzed, and then cleaved with the restriction enzyme. The order is the same as in the control series. Lanes 12–16 contain SV40 DNA reacted similarly with trans-DDP followed by cleavage with restriction enzymes in the same order as controls.

BAM HI	AGCTTCCTGGGGGATCCAGACATGATA TCGAAGGACCCCTAGGTCTGTACTAT
BGL I	TAGCTCAGAGGCCGAGGCGGCCTCGGCCTCT ATCGAGTCTCCGGCTCCGCCGGAGCCGGAGA
ECO RI	AGTGTGGCTAGAATTCCTTTGGCTAA TCACACCGATCTTAAGGAAACGGATT
HPA II	TGGTGCTGCGCCGGCTGTCACGGC ACCACGACGCGGCCGACAGTGCCG
KPN I	CGCCTCAGAAGGTACCTAACCAAGTT GCGGAGTCTTCCATGGATTGGTTCAA

Figure 8. Cleavage sites in SV40 DNA for restriction endonucleases.

The recognition sequence plus 10 base pairs on each side is shown for Bam HI, Bgl 1, Eco RI, Hpa II, and Kpn I. The base pairs essential in the recognition sequence are underlined with a solid line. Note that the central five-base-pair sequence for Bgl 1 underlined with a broken line is not an essential sequence (22). Sequences of two or more adjacent guanines are shown stippled. The vertical lines within the recognition sequence designate the cutting sites (16).

HI is greatly inhibited, yet with only a 67% (G+C) content in the recognition sequence. We have therefore considered these sequences plus 5-10 base pairs on either side as important in this sequence specific protein-DNA interaction. This seems reasonable in that, although the influence of DDP binding on DNA structure is not expected to be long range, its influence will most likely extend well beyond its immediate site of binding. Therefore, DDP binding to nucleotides immediately adjacent to the recognition sequence or cleavage sites may modulate the extent of cleavage. Focusing on these larger base pair segments, the cleavage inhibition produced by DDP binding to nucleotides parallels the number and the relative position of the guanines in the sequence. We find that adjacent guanines enhance the inhibition effect more so than non-adjacent guanines, with the inhibition being significantly greater if the number of adjacent guanines is more than two. For example, Bam HI, which is inhibited comparably to Bgl 1, has a sequence with fewer guanines (13 to 21), fewer adjacent guanine clusters (3 to 7), but has one nucleotide tract of four adjacent guanines, while the largest guanine tract occurring in the Bgl 1 site is two. This latter effect appears responsible for DDP binding producing a comparable inhibition of Bgl 1 and Bam HI cleavage, although the % (G+C) contents in the nucleotide sequences differ significantly. Base pairs in and about the recognition sequences which have one or more adjacent guanines are shown stippled in Figure 8. Our findings are consistent with those of Kelman and Buchbinder (45) and Ushay et al (46) to the extent that both previous reports find that cis-DDP binding to λ DNA and pBR322 DNA, respectively, inhibits Bam HI cleavage. In both studies, however, no comparison of the cleavage inhibition with trans-DDP was carried out.

TABLE I. Percentage of (G+C) Content in and Within 10 Base Pairs
          of the Restriction Endonuclease Recognition Sequence

Restriction Endonuclease	Location on Map	% (G+C) Content	
		Recognition Sequence	Recognition Sequence + 10 b.p.
Bgl 1	.660	91	71
Bam HI	.143	67	50
Hpa II	.726	100	74
Kpn I	.716	67	50
Eco RI	1.0/0	33	42

In addition, a similar examination with the R.E. Hind III (6 cleavage sites in SV40 DNA) shows differential cleavage inhibition at the six sites as a result of cis-and trans-DDP binding (16). This analysis adds further support that the inclusion of the 5-10 base pairs adjacent to the recognition sequence is necessary to explain the inhibition effect. Our finding that sequences of adjacent guanines in or immediately adjacent to the recognition-sequence enhance the inhibition effect agrees with Cohen et al (12) who found that cis-DDP binding on pSMI DNA produced preferential inhibition at only one of the four Pst I sites, presumably because the modified site was the only one with a (dG)₄(dC)₄ cluster adjacent to it. However, in contrast to our findings that both DDP isomers produce comparable inhibition on a restriction enzyme, for all six restriction enzymes studied, Cohen et al (12) report that the preferential inhibition at one of the four Pst I sites is unique to cis-DDP binding and is not observed with trans-DDP.

The studies presented in this work highlight the fact that different probes used to monitor DNA structure may exhibit very different sensitivities to the modification of interest. For example, both the electrophoretic mobility study with c^3s SV40 DNA and the S1 nuclease digestion on DNA clearly bring out differences in the cis- and trans-DDP modified DNA. Both these probes are sensitive to, and, in this case, reveal differences in the mode of binding of the two isomers. However, we find that for a particular restriction endonuclease, little or no differences are observed between the cleavage inhibition on the modified DNAs. The endonucleases used in this study, therefore, appear to be less sensitive to the mode of binding used and are influenced predominantly by the local physical coverage of DDP at or adjacent to the recognition sequence. We have found this same effect to occur with a more general nuclease, DNAase I, which digests both cis- and trans-modified DNA with equal ease (47).

Segments of the Regulatory Region of the SV40 Genome Are Hyperreactive Toward DDP Binding

The relative order of cleavage inhibition for the five single cut restriction endonucleases studied suggests the regulatory region, and specifically the sequences in and about the Bgl 1 and perhaps the Bam HI recognition sequences, are hyperreactive sites to DDP binding in the genome. Further studies, however, may reveal that these are but two of a number of such sites. These two sequences correspond to the site at or near the origin of replication and the general region at which DNA replication terminates, respectively (17,23,48). Beard et al. (49) have recently reported that the ultimate carcinogen, N-acetoxy-acetylaminofluorene (AAAF), which binds almost entirely to guanines in DNA, reacts preferentially with the control region in intracellular SV40 minichromosome. Our findings with DDP, taken

together with that for AAAF, would suggest that agents which
bind preferentially to guanines may exhibit a preference for
binding in the regulatory region in SV40 DNA and the minichromosome. It is of particular importance to consider of what relevance these findings on DNA are when extended to the minichromosome since this would be the actual cellular target of interest.
In this regard, a number of laboratories using electron
microscopy (50,51), digestions with nucleases (52-55), including
Bgl 1, have found that the region in or about the origin of
replication is topologically exposed, nucleosome free (56) and
encompasses sequences critical to gene expression and regulation
(17,19,57,58,59). This gapped region of about 400 bps extends
from about the Bgl 1 site to the Hpa II site and is apparent at
the top of Figure 9 which shows an electron micrograph of the
SV40 minichromosome. This structural characteristic of a fraction of the minichromosomes may enhance the reactivity of this
site to exogenous small molecules, with the expectation being
that this would be especially true for many molecules exhibiting
a preference for (G+C) rich regions.

Since it has been shown here that DDP binding inhibits a
particular class of sequence specific protein-DNA interactions
and that the SV40 DNA cleavage by Bgl 1 is most inhibited, it
might be expected that other site specific protein-DNA interactions in or about the origin of replication may be modulated by
DDP binding. Relevant to this point and possibly of some connection between the preferential binding affinity of DDP at the Bgl
1 recognition sequence and the reported influence of cis-DDP on
intracellular SV40 viral functions (25), it is intriguing to speculate how cis-DDP binding may influence the binding of T-antigen
to its specific binding sites at or near the Bgl 1 recognition
sequence (60,61,62). As noted above, the site specific binding
of T antigen to DNA is involved in both the autoregulation of T
antigen transcription and is required for the initiation of viral
DNA synthesis (17,18,19). Tjian (60) has shown that the T antigen related protein D2 binds specifically to three distinct and
closely spaced recognition sequences at and within 60-70 base
pairs of the Bgl 1 site. T-antigen binding site II, which is at
the Bgl 1 recognition sequence, is entirely contained within the
currently known boundaries of the origin of replication (23). In
addition, methylation studies on the D2 protein-DNA complex
revealed that a majority of the guanines, many of which occur in
clusters of two or three in the three binding sites, are shielded
from methylation and therefore thought to be involved in critically important contracts in the regulatory interaction. The
results of Shalloway (62), who used E. coli Exonuclease III to
probe the T-antigen binding site, support Tjian's conclusions,
but also reveal additional binding sites in the same general
region which include the 6 times reiterated sequence $G_{3-4}CG_2Pu_2$.
Collectively, these results emphasize the importance of this

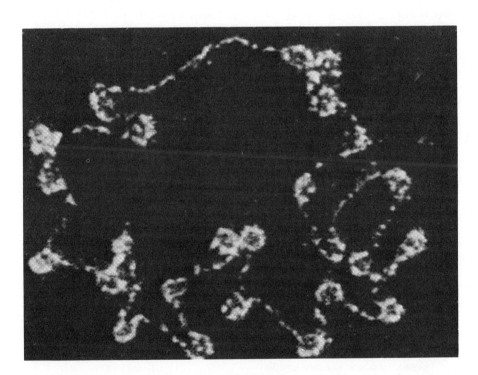

Figure 9.   Electron micrograph of an SV40 minichromosome that shows a stretch of the genome devoid of nucleosomes. This gap has been mapped from the Bgl 1 site to about 0.74 on the physical map. The nucleosomes appear as white circular clusters along the circular DNA. (Reproduced with permission from Ref. 50. Copyright 1980, Massachusetts Institute of Technology.)

(G+C) rich region of the genome and the importance and involvement of close, well-defined contacts of the guanines in DNA in regulatory interactions with T antigen. Therefore, any molecule which disrupts or weakens this sequence specific T-antigen-DNA interaction may be expected to have an influence on developmental functions of the virus. Although the detailed nature of cis-DDP and trans-DDP binding to this or other parts of the genome and the influence that the isomers may exert on SV40 viral gene expression is now speculative, there are a number of testable predictions which should help to understand the most salient features which relate DDP binding to the impairment of selected biological functions.

Conclusions

1. Cis-DDP unwinds SV40 DNA twice as effectively as trans-DDP (15).
2. Cis-DDP disrupts the structure of DNA to a greater degree than does trans-DDP as measured by the greater stimulation of S1 nuclease digestion on cis-DDP modified DNA (31).
3. These data indicate that of the modes of binding that the cis- and trans-DDP exhibit, the cis-DDP exhibits a mode of binding which is different than that for trans-DDP and is responsible for the more effective unwinding of the DNA backbone and for the greater disruption of DNA structure resulting in S1 nuclease sensitivity. A bidentate mode of binding by cis-DDP to form either (1) an intrastrand crosslink to adjacent guanines or possibly (2) an N-7, 0-6 chelate complex with guanine may explain our observations. Current evidence more strongly supports proposal (1).
4. The region of the Bgl 1 site on SV40 DNA is a hyper-reactive site for both cis- and trans-DDP binding (16). This is within the regulatory region of SV40 virus and may be one of the primary lesions directly responsible for the impairment of viral replication and transcription in SV40 infected African green monkey kidney cells.

[+]Legend of Symbols: DDP, $PtCl_2(NH_3)_2$; c^3s DNA, covalently, closed, circular supercoiled DNA; b.p., base pairs; DNA(N), DNA concentration expressed in molarity of nucleotides by using 1 O.D. = 50 μ g DNA/ml; r_b, mole ratio of DDP bound to DNA nucleotide; Pu, purine base; Υ , the number of supercoils in the DNA; α - the topological linking number for DNA.

Acknowledgments

We thank Mr. Bill Butcher for assistance with the photographic work and to Mathey Bishop Co. for the loan of cis-DDP and the National Cancer Institute for the gift of trans-DDP. This work was supported by the Ohio Division of the American Cancer Society, The Bowling Green State University Biomedical Research Support Grant, Alumni Association and Parents Club,

Faculty Research Committee and The American Cancer Society Support Grant number IN-130.

I would like this contribution dedicated to the memory of Professor R. Stuart Tobias, a distinguished scholar and good friend.

Literature Cited

1. Roberts, J.J. Antibiotics, Mechanism of Action of Antieukaryotic and Antiviral Compounds. Hahn, F.E., Ed., Springer-Verlag, Berlin, 1979, pg. 20-84.
2. Wallace, H.J.; Higby, D.J. Recent Results Cancer Res. 1974, 48, 167-170.
3. Roberts, J.J.; Thomson, A.J. Prog. Nucl. Acid Res. Mol. Biol. 1979, 22, 71-133.
4. Harder, H.C.; Rosenberg, B. Int. J. Cancer 1970, 6, 207-216.
5. Howle, J.A.; Thompson, H.E.; Stone, A.E., Gale, G.R. Proc. Soc. Exp. Biol. Med. 1971, 137, 820-825.
6. Howle, J.A., Gale, G.R. Biochem. Pharmacol. 1970, 19, 2757-2762.
7. Scovell, W.M.; O'Connor, T. J. Am. Chem. Soc. 1977, 99, 120-126.
8. Stone, P.J.; Kelman, A.D.; Sinex, F.M. Nature 1974, 251, 736-737.
9. Stone, P.J.; Kelman, A.D.; Sinex, F.M.; Bhargava, M.M.; Halvorson, H.O. J. Mol. Biol. 1976, 104, 793-801.
10. Roberts, J.J.; Pascoe, J.M. Nature 1972, 235, 282-284.
11. Deutsch, W.A.; Spiering, A.L., Newkome, G.R. Biochem. Biophys. Res. Commun. 1980, 97, 1220-1226.
12. Cohen, G.L.; Ledner, J.A.; Bauer, W.R.; Ushay, H.M.; Caravana, C.; Lippard, S.J. J. Am. Chem. Soc. 1980, 2487-2488.
13. Royer-Pokora, B.; Gordon, L.K.; Haseltine, W.A. Nucleic Acids Res. 1981, 9, 4595-4609.
14. Tullius, T.D.; Lippard, S.J. J. Am. Chem. Soc. 1981, 103, 4620-4622.
15. Scovell, W.M.; Kroos, L.R. Biochem. Biophys. Res. Commun. 1982, 104, 1597-1603.
16. Scovell, W.M.; Kroos, L.R., submitted for publication.
17. Lebowitz, P.; Weissman, S.M. Curr. Topics Microbiol. Immunol. 1979, 82, 44-172.
18. Das, G.C.; Niyogi, S.K. Prog. Nucleic Acid Res. Mol. Biol. 1981, 25, 187-241.
19. Tooze, J. DNA Tumor Viruses, Molecular Biology of Tumor Viruses, 2nd ed., Tooze, J., Ed., Cold Spring Harbor Laboratory, Cold Spring Harbor, N.Y., 1980.
20. Reddy, V.D.; Thunmaappaya, B.; Dhar, R.; Subramanian, K.N.; Zain, B.S.; Pan, J.; Ghosh, P.K.; Celma, M.L.; Weissman, S.M. Science 1978, 200, 494-502.
21. Fiers, W.; Contreras, R.; Haegeman, G.; Rogiers, R.; van de Voode, A.; Van Heuverswyn, H.; Van Herreweghe, J.; Volckaert, G.; Sebaert, M.Y. Nature 1978, 273, 113-120.

22. Van Heuverswyn, H.; Fiers, W. Gene 1980, 9, 195-203.
23. Gutai, M.W.; Nathans, D. J. Mol. Biol. 1978, 126, 259-274.
24. Tjian, R. Cell 1981, 26, 1-2.
25. Kutinova, L.; Vonka, V.; Zavadova, H.; Drobnik, J. Arch. ges Virusforsch 1972, 39, 196-202.
26. Waring, M. J. Mol. Biol. 1970, 54, 247-279.
27. Wakelin, L.P.G.; Waring, M. J. Mol. Pharmacol. 1974, 9, 544-561.
28. Beerman, T.A.; Lebowitz, J. J. Mol. Biol. 1973, 79, 451-470.
29. Depew, R.E.; Wang, J.C. Proc. Natl. Acad. Sci USA 1975, 72, 4275-4279.
30. Cohen, G.L.; Bauer, W.R.; Barton, J.K.; Lippard, S.J. Science 1979, 203, 1014-1016.
31. Scovell, W.M.; Capponi, V.J., submitted for publication.
32. Lehman, I.R. "The Enzymes', 3rd ed., Boyer, R., Ed., Academic Press, New York, 1981, Vol. 14, p. 193.
33. Wiegand, R.C.; Godson, N.; Radding, C.M. J. Biol. Chem. 1975, 8848-8855.
34. Silber, J.R.; Loeb, L.A. Biochim. Biophys. Acta 1981, 656, 256-264.
35. Dodgson, J.B.; Wells, R.D. Biochemistry 1977, 16, 2374-2379.
36. Shishido, K., Ando, T. Biochem. Biophys. Res. Commun. 1974, 59, 1380-1388.
37. Heflich, R.H.; Mahoney-Leo, E.; Maher, V.; McCormick, J.J. Photochem. Photobiol. 1979, 30, 247-250.
38. Fuch, R.P.P. Nature 1975, 257, 151-152.
39. Pulkrabek, P.; Leffler, S.; Grunberger, D.; Weinstein, I.B. Biochemistry 1979, 18, 5128-5134.
40. Mong, S.; Daskal, Y.; Prestayko, A.W.; Crooke, S.T. Cancer Res. 1981, 41, 4020-4026.
41. Sumner, W. II; Bennett, G.N. Nucleic Acids Res. 1981, 8, 2105-2119.
42. Nosikov, V.V.; Braga, E.A.; Karlishev, A.V.; Zhuze, A.L., Polyanovsky, O.L. Nucleic Acids Res. 1976, 3, 2293-2307.
43. Mechali, M.; Recondo, A.; Girard, M. Biochem. Biophys. Res. Commun. 1973, 54, 1306-1319.
44. Robins, A.B. Chem. Biol. Interactions 1973, 6, 35-45.
45. Kelman, A.D.; Buchbinder, M. Biochemie 1978, 60, 893-899.
46. Ushay, H.M.; Tullius, T.D.; Lippard, S.J. Biochemistry 1981, 20, 3744-3748.
47. Scovell, W.M.; Knezetic, J., unpublished findings.
48. Tack, L.C.; Wassarman, P.M.; DePamphilis, M.L. J. Biol. Chem. 1981, 256, 8821-2228.
49. Beard, P.; Kaneko, M.; Cerutti, P. Nature 1981, 291, 84-85.
50. Saragosti, S.; Moyne, G.; Yaniv, M. Cell, 1980, 20, 65-73.
51. Jakobovits, E.B.; Bratosin, S.; Aloni, Y. Nature 1980, 285, 263-265.
52. Varshavsky, A.J.; Sundin, O.; Bohn, M.J. Nucleic Acids Res. 1978, 5, 3469-3477.

53. Sundin, O.; Varshavsky, A.J. J. Mol. Biol. 1979, 132, 535-546.

54. Hartmann, J.P.; Scott, W.A. J. Virol. 1981, 37, 908-915.

55. Waldeck, W.; Fohring, B.; Chowdhuhy, K.; Gruss, P.; Sauer, G. Proc. Natl. Acad. Sci. USA 1978, 75, 5964-5968.

56. Varshavsky, A.J.; Sundin, O.; Bohn, M.J. Cell 1979, 16, 453-466.

57. Gruss, P.; Dhar, R.; Khoury, G. Proc. Natl. Acad. Sci. USA 1981, 78, 943-947.

58. Benoist, C.; Chambon, P. Nature 1981, 290, 304-310.

59. Mathis, D.J.; Chambon, P. Nature 1981, 290, 310-315.

60. Tjian, R. Cold Spring Harbor Symp. Quant. Biol. 1979, 43, 655-662.

61. McKay, R.D.G. J. Mol. Biol. 1981, 145, 471-488.

62. Shalloway, D.; Kleinberger, T.; Livingston, D.M. Cell 1980, 20, 411-412.

63. Subramanian, K.N.; Shenk, T. Nucleic Acids Res. 1978, 50, 3635-3652.

64. Vogt, V. Eur. J. Biochem. 1973, 33, 192-200.

RECEIVED October 4, 1982

PLATINUM BINDING TO DNA CONSTITUENTS

Platinum–Oligonucleotide Structures and Their Relevance to Platinum–DNA Interaction

JEAN-CLAUDE CHOTTARD, JEAN-PIERRE GIRAULT, and ERIC R.
GUITTET—Ecole Normale Supérieure, Laboratoire de Chimie, 75231 Cedex 05,
Paris, France

JEAN-YVES LALLEMAND—Laboratoire de RMN, CNRS, ICSN,
91190 Gif-sur-Yvette, France

GENEVIEVE CHOTTARD—Université Pierre et Marie Curie, Département de
Recherches Physiques, 75230 Cedex 05, Paris, France

The stoichiometric reactions of nine oxy and deoxy
guanine and/or cytosine containing dinucleotides with
cis - [Pt(NH$_3$)$_2$(H$_2$O)$_2$] (NO$_3$)$_2$ (10^{-5} - 5 × 10^{-4} M) in water
give monomeric platinum dinucleotide chelates in every case.
The complexes have been isolated by HPLC and characterized
by ^{1}H NMR and CD analyses. GpG, d - GpG and d - pGpG
give a single N7 - N7 anti-anti complex. CpC and d - pCpC
give a single N3 - N3 syn - anti complex. CpG and d - pCpG
give a mixture of N3 - N7 C anti - G anti and C syn - G anti
isomers in equilibrium. GpC and d - pGpC give two couples
of N7 - N3 isomers: G syn - C anti, G syn - C syn (in equilibrium) and G anti - C anti, G anti - C syn . The results
obtained point to a particular chelating aptitude of the
anti - anti GG sequence. Accordingly, the stoichiometric
reaction of the hexanucleotide d - TpGpGpCpCpA with the
platinum complex gives quantitatively the GN7 - GN7 chelate.
These results are in favor of the hypothesis of platinum
intrastrand cross-linking of adjacent guanines in DNA.

The mechanism of the cytotoxic action of the cis - diammine -
dichloroplatinum (II) complex (cis - DDP) is still unknown but there
is much evidence indicating that DNA is the main target in a
variety of biological systems (1). Three hypotheses are being
considered that imply a bifunctional coordination of the cis -
Pt^{II}(NH$_3$)$_2$ moiety to DNA: interstrand cross-linking (2, 3, 4),
intrastrand cross-linking (5, 6) and N(7) - 0(6) chelation of a
guanine (7, 8). The last two binding modes could be a first step
followed by further cross-linking reactions (6,8). Intrastrand
cross-linking appears to be involved in the inactivating lesions
produced by cis - DDP in phage λ DNA (9). Data obtained from
platinum coordination to nucleotides (10, 11, 12) oligonucleotides
(13, 14, 15) and polynucleotides (5, 6) suggest that cross-linking
of two adjacent guanines could be a favored process. However,
platinum chelation by adjacent inosines seems to be a minor event

0097-6156/83/0209-0125$06.25/0

for the interaction of cis - DDP with poly-I and poly-I . poly-C
(16). It has been shown that cis - DDP , at low platinum/nucleotide
ratios, selectively inhibits the activity of several restriction
endo - and exo - nucleases when their cutting sites are adjacent to
$(dG)_n - (dC)_n$ sequences with $n \geqslant 2$. This demonstrates the
sequence specificity of the binding of cis - DDP to DNA (17, 18,
19). GAG and GCG sequences also appear to be selectively
involved in base - pair substitution mutagenesis and this suggests
the possibility of platinum chelation by two guanines separated by
a third base (20).

The aim of our work was to investigate, from a chemical point
of view, the possibility of intrastrand cross-linking of two
adjacent bases by the cis - $Pt^{II}(NH_3)_2$ moiety. The simplest models
to test this chelation are the dinucleotides. It is known that
platinum binding to DNA increases with the %(G + C) content (21,22)
and we have therefore investigated the following dinucleotides :
GpG, d - GpG, d - pGpG (14, 23); CpG, d - pCpG ; GpC, d - pGpC and
CpC, d - pCpC. Preliminary results have also been obtained with the
hexanucleotide d - TpGpGpCpCpA .

Experimental

The dinucleotides were commercial (either ammonium salt or
free acid), the hexanucleotide was synthesized by Drs. J. Igolen
and T. Huynh-Dinh (Unité de Chimie Organique, Institut Pasteur,
Paris).

The stoichiometric reactions, 1:1 cis -[$Pt(NH_3)_2(H_2O)_2$] $(NO_3)_2$/
oligonucleotide were run at 10^{-5}M to 5×10^{-4}M concentration
(~ 2 mg of oligonucleotide) at pH ~ 5.5 and 37°C, in doubly
distilled water. In these conditions the diaquo and monoaquomono-
hydroxy species are predominant ($pK_1 = 5.51$, $pK_2 = 7.37$) and there
is no significant dimerisation of the latter (24). In each case
comparative reactions have been run with cis -[$Pt(NH_3)_2Cl_2$] in the
same conditions. The reactions were monitored by UV and HPLC
and the reaction products were analysed by Sephadex chromatography
(14), high pressure gel permeation chromatography and HPLC on a
Waters C 18 μ-Bondapak (reverse phase) column (14, 23).

The ^1H NMR spectra were recorded on a Cameca TSN 250
(250 MHz, Nicolet 1180 computer) or on a WM 400 Bruker (400 MHz,
Aspect 2000) spectrometer (14, 23). The concentrations of the
samples were 5×10^{-3} to $\sim 10^{-3}$M in D_2O . Chemical shifts are
referred to internal DSS (sodium 4,4 - dimethyl - 4 - silapentane -
1 - sulfonate) or TSP (sodium 3 - trimethylsilyl - 2, 2, 3, 3 d_4 -
1 - propionate). The CD spectra were recorded on a Jobin Yvon
Mark III. The $\Delta\varepsilon(\varepsilon_L - \varepsilon_R$, M^{-1} . cm^{-1}) are given per nucleotide
residue. The molar extinction coefficients of the complexes were
determined from the ratio of the optical densities of the oligonucleotide solution before and after incubation with the Pt(II)
complex, assuming that no concentration change had occurred. When a
mixture of complexes is formed, only a mean extinction coefficient

is obtained by this procedure; this mean   value has been used for the different isomers separated by   HPLC .

Analysis of the Reactions

The reactions run either with cis - [Pt(NH$_3$)$_2$(H$_2$O)$_2$](NO$_3$)$_2$ or cis - [Pt(NH$_3$)$_2$Cl$_2$] gave the same complexes or mixtures of complexes. Those with the dichloro complex were slower, e.g. the second order rate constant for the disappearance of GpC is about ten times smaller for the dichloro ($\sim$ 1 x 10^3 h^{-1} M^{-1}) than for the diaquo reaction.

UV and HPLC monitoring of the reactions run with the diaquo complex show that the presence of a free   5' - phosphate increases the rate of disappearance of the dinucleotide (23). In some cases this acceleration allowed us to detect the formation of an intermediate by HPLC , that is more slowly converted to the final complex(es). Such intermediates can also be seen for reactions run at higher concentration (10^{-2}M) but together with the formation of new products (further investigations are in progress). For all the dinucleotides studied: GpG, d - GpG, d - pGpG, CpG, d - pCpG, GpC, d - pGpC, CpC, d - pCpC , there were no unreacted starting material at the end of the stoichiometric reactions with cis - [Pt(NH$_3$)$_2$(H$_2$O)$_2$](NO$_3$)$_2$. We still have to collect precise comparative kinetic data for the different cases, however we can say that the diguanosine phosphates give the fastest overall reactions, whereas the dicytosine phosphates give the slowest. For example, for CpC   2.5 x 10^{-4}M, the final platinum chelate appears after 6 hours and the reaction is complete after about one week, while for CpG 1.5 x 10^{-4}M the formation of the chelates is over after 17 hours.

HPLC analysis of the products respectively exhibits one peak for the GG dinucleotides, two peaks for the CG dinucleotides, three peaks for the GC dinucleotides and one peak for the CC dinucleotides. In each case these peaks represent at least 95% of the overall product. Sephadex and gel permeation chromatographies show that the complexes formed are monomeric. In the CG cases the two complexes equilibrate after HPLC separation, as do the two complexes corresponding to peaks 1 and 3 (elution order) in the GC cases.

Assignment of the Platinum Coordination Sites

The possible coordination sites of the studied dinucleotides are guanine N7(G - N7), guanine N1 and cytosine N3 (C - N3) (25). In our conditions (stoichiometry of the reaction and   pH) G - N1 coordination is very unlikely (11). For several   5' - GMP mono or bis complexes, N7 coordination induces a characteristic 0.4 - 0.7 ppm downfield shift of the H8 in α position (26, 27, 11). It is very likely that, in solution the cis - bis (nucleotide) Pt^{II} complexes have the two purines in a head-to-tail arrangement

(12, 28). Platinum coordination to C - N3 of Cyd and 5' - CMP
gives smaller downfield shifts of the H6 and H5 signals,
respectively 0.11 - 0.28 and 0.12 - 0.26 ppm (27, 29). In most
cases, for the platinum - nucleotide complexes, one cannot observe,
at high magnetic fields, the expected ^{195}Pt - ^{1}H coupling constants
because of a dominant ^{195}Pt chemical shift anisotropy relaxation
(30). Platinum coordination is easily demonstrated by the disappearance of the free dinucleotide characteristic N7 and/or N3
titration curves observed for the variation of the H8 and H5
chemical shifts as a function of pH (5' - GMP - N7 pK_a = 2.4 ,
5' - CMP - N3 pK_a = 4.3). For the free dinucleotides, the downfield
shifts obtained upon acidification down to pD2 are ∿ 0.9 ppm for
G - H8 in GpG (23) GpC and CpG and respectively ∿ 0.35 ppm
for C - H5 and ∿ 0.25 ppm for C - H6 in GpC and CpG). For
all the platinum dinucleotide complexes containing a guanine, the
curves of the variation of the H8 chemical shifts versus pD
exhibit a titration of the NH1 (pK_a 8 - 8.7) that rules out a
platinum coordination to G - N1. Another consequence of G - N7
coordination is usually an acceleration of the H8 deuterium
exchange with D₂0 at basic pD (11). Such an acceleration occurs
for the GG complexes (23) but is not observed for several isomers
of the CG and GC complexes at 37°C, probably because of neighboring effects. For all the platinum - dinucleotide complexes
studied, the assignment of the coordination sites leads to the
conclusion that they are platinum chelates, N7 - N7 for the GG
series (14, 23), N3 - N7 for the CG series, N7 - N3 for the GC
series and N3 - N3 for the CC series. The stoichiometric
reaction of [Pt(dien)Br] Br with CpG and GpC gives only the
G - N7 monocoordinated complex in each case.

Assignments of the Base Configurations and Sugar Conformations

These assignments are made by ^{1}H NMR according to well
documented analyses of nucleotides (31) and oligonucleotides
(32, 33, 34). The identification of the 5' - sugar is based on the
^{31}P - ^{1}H coupling observed for its 3' - proton. The relative
rigidity of the platinum dinucleotide chelates and the fact that we
have isolated most of the different isomers, facilitate the assignment of the syn or anti configuration to the bases (syn and
anti respectively correspond to χ = 0 ± 90° and χ = 180 ± 90°
with χ = 0(4') C(1') N(9) C(4) for purines and 0(4')C(1')N(1)C(2)
for pyrimidines (31)) and of the conformation type to the sugar
rings.

GpG, d - GpG and d - pGpG Platinum Complexes. Only one complex
is obtained for each dinucleotide. The comparative ^{1}H NMR data are
collected in Table I . The anti - anti configuration has been
previously assigned to these three complexes (23) on the basis of
the following results: - a - The comparison of the 3' - and
5' - H8 deuterium exchange rates in D₂0 (pD 10) with those of the

Table I.   ¹H NMR data for the GpG[Pt], d-GpG[Pt] and d-PGPG[Pt] complexes a,b

	H		GG δ	GG J	GG[Pt] δ	GG[Pt] J	Δδ
GpG (pD 5.6) / GpG[Pt] (pD 5.5)	H8	Gp	7.97c	s	8.54	s	+ 0.55, + 0.65
		pG	7.90c	s	8.32	s	+ 0.35, + 0.4
	H1'	Gp	5.85	d 5	6.06	s	+ 0.2, + 0.3
		pG	5.76	d 3	5.90	d 7	+ 0.05, + 0.15
d-GpG (pD 6.1) / d-GpG[Pt] (pD 5.5)	H8	Gp	8.02c	s	8.28	s	+ 0.25, + 0.5
		pG	7.76c	s	8.56	s	+ 0.55, + 0.8
	H1'	Gp	6.16	t	6.22	–	+ 0.05, + 0.2
		pG	6.01	t			
d-pGpG / d-pGpG[Pt] (pD 6.6)	H8	pGp	8.02d		8.51•	s	+ 0.5
		pG			8.79	s	+ 0.75
	H1'	pGp	6.17d	t	6.19	d 6	0, + 0.15
		pG	6.02d		6.28	q 6;10	+ 0.1, + 0.25

a 250 MHz; samples ~10^{-3} M in D_2O; 17°C; chemical shifts (δ) in ppm from DSS; coupling constants (J) in Hz. b a brace is used for the δ values when the signals have not been assigned to each nucleoside. c signal broadening. d broad.

H8 of cis - bis(Guo) and cis - bis(5' - GMP) platinum complexes, and the comparison of the variation of the 3' - and 5' - H8 chemical shifts vs.pD, show that both H8 protons of d - pGpG [Pt] experience the proximity of the free 5' - phosphate. The 5' - G - H8 is more slowly exchanged and much more sensitive to the 5' - phosphate titration (35). - b - The absence of a significant increase of the T_1 relaxation time of the two H1' protons of GpG [Pt] after the complete deuterium exchange of the two H8 protons, excludes a guanine syn configuration (36).

The absence of one H1'- H2' coupling constant for the GpG [Pt] and d - pGpG [Pt] complexes (as well as for IpI [Pt] and ApA [Pt] (14)) has also been reported and taken as evidence for an N - type conformation (31) of one furanose ring, supposed to be the 5'- one from examination of the CPK models (23).

CpG and d - pCpG Platinum Complexes. In each case two isomers, 1 (∿15%) and 2 (∿85%) in the HPLC· elution order, are obtained that equilibrate after separation at room temperature. The 400 MHz ^{1}H NMR spectrum of their mixture is presented on Figure 1 for the CpG case. The comparative ^{1}H NMR data of the oxy and deoxy isomers are collected in Table II together with those of the G - N7 monocoordinated complex [Pt(dien)(CpG)] Br$_2$. Like in the GG series, there is an overall similarity between the CpG and the d - pCpG complexes.

We assign the C anti - G anti configuration to isomers 1 and the C syn - G anti configuration to the more abundant isomers 2 on the basis of the following results: - a - For the CpG [Pt]- 2 isomer there is a nuclear Overhauser enhancement of about 10% between the C - H6 and C - H1' protons. The T_1 relaxation time of these protons is 0.2 s at 17°C and 250 MHz, while that of the C - H6 and C - H1' of the CpG [Pt] - 1 isomer is 0.6 s. - b - For CpG [Pt] - 2 the C - H1' experiences a 0.4 ppm upfield shift, compared to its chemical shift in CpG , that is accompanied by a 0.8 ppm downfield shift of the corresponding H3' . Such shifts are not observed for CpG [Pt] - 1 . These data respectively support C anti and C syn configurations for the 1 and 2 isomers (38 - 41). - c - For the d - pCpG [Pt] - 2 isomer, upfield and downfield shifts of C - H1' and C - H3' are also observed. - d - For the two d - pCpG [Pt] complexes only the C - H6 chemical shift of the 1 isomer is sensitive to the titration of the free 5'- phosphate (Δδ + 0.2 ppm with pH increase) (35). - e - For both isomers, in the oxy series, there is no NOE between G - H8 and G - H1' . The T_1 relaxation times, at 17°C and 250 MHz, for isomers 1 and 2 are respectively 0.6 and 0.5 s for G - H8 and 0.6 s for both G - H1'. This is evidence for a G - anti configuration in both 1 and 2 isomers. Examination of CPK models suggests that the smaller downfield shifts of G - H8 in the oxy and deoxy isomers 1 , compared to those in isomers 2 , could be related to the ring current effect of the adjacent anti cytosine.

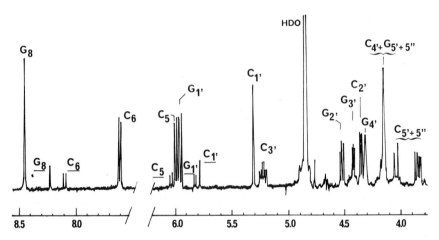

Figure 1. *^{1}H-NMR spectrum (400 MHz) of the mixture of the CpG[Pt]-1 and -2 isomers (15:85). Isomer 1 data are underlined. Conditions: 10^{-3} M in D_2O at 15 °C. Chemical shifts are in ppm from TSP.*

Table II. ^{1}H NMR data for the CpG[Pt] and d-pCpG[Pt] complexes[a,b]

	CG		CG[Pt] - 1[c]			CG[Pt] - 2[c]		
	δ	J	δ	J	Δδ	δ	J	Δδ
H8	8.02	s	8.22	s	+ 0.2	8.44	s	+ 0.4
H6	7.76	d 7.9	8.10	d 7.7	+ 0.35	7.62	d 7.7	- 0.15
H5	5.87	d 7.9	6.03	d 7.7	+ 0.15	5.99	d 7.7	+ 0.1
C - H1'	5.73	d 3.2	5.78[e]	s	+ 0.05	5.32	s	- 0.4
G - H1'	5.90	d 4.3	5.83[e]	d 6	- 0.05	5.96	d 7.7	+ 0.05
C - H3'	4.44	m (3'4':6.7)				5.23	m (3'4':9.8)	+ 0.8
G - H3'	4.51	m (3'4':5.4)				4.43	m (3'4':2.5)	- 0.1

CpG[d]
CpG[Pt] (pD 7.4)

	d-pCpG (pD 5.5)				Δδ	d-pCpG[Pt] (pD 6.5)		Δδ
H8	8.1 [f]		8.19	s	+ 0.1	8.42	s	+ 0.3
H6	7.83	d 7	8.13	d 7.5	+ 0.3	7.52	d 7.5	− 0.3
H5	~ 6		6.01	d 7.5		5.91	d 7.5	
C – H1'	6.13	t [f]	{6.06	m	}	5.65	q 7;3.5	− 0.5
G – H1'	6.26	t [f]	{6.09	m	} − 0.05, − 0.2	6.29	q 10; 5	0
C – H3'						5.25	m	> + 0.3

[a] 400 MHz ; samples ~ 10^{-3} M in D_2O; 15°C ; chemical shifts (δ) in ppm from TSP ; coupling contants (J) in Hz.
[b] a brace is used for the δ values when the signals have not been assigned to each nucleoside.
[c] For $[Pt(dien)(CpG)]^{2+}$ at pD 7.5, δ(J) $\Delta\delta$: H8, 8.51(s) + 0.5; H6, 7.83(d 8) + 0.05; H5, ~ 5.9(d) 0 ; C – H1'/G – H1', 5.9/5.96 (d 4/d 4) 0,+ 0.15/0.05,+ 0.2 .
[d] from ref. 43.
[e] assigned on the basis of the absence of $J_{1',2'}$ coupling that has been found characteristic of the 5'- ribose in all the studied dinucleotide complexes (Tables I and III).
[f] broad.

For the $\underset{\sim}{1}$ and $\underset{\sim}{2}$ isomers of the oxy complex, the absence of C - H1'H2' coupling shows that the 5'-ribose adopts an N - type conformation (C3'- endo) while the 3'-ribose has a predominantly S - type conformation (42). For the deoxy isomers the $(J_1^{'} {}_2^{'} + J_1^{'} {}_2^{''})$ values show that the 5' - and 3'- sugar conformations are respectively predominantly of the N - and S - type (42).

GpC and d - pGpC Platinum Complexes.   In each case a mixture of isomers is obtained which can be separated into three fractions by HPLC (numbered 1, 2, 3 in the elution order). Fractions 1 and 3 contain only one complex each, respectively $\underset{\sim}{1}$ and $\underset{\sim}{3}$. These complexes equilibrate after HPLC separation. This equilibration is slow enough to allow independent spectroscopic investigations of isomers $\underset{\sim}{1}$ and $\underset{\sim}{3}$ after collection at low temperature. Fraction $\underset{\sim}{2}$ contains two isomers $\underset{\sim}{2a}$ and $\underset{\sim}{2b}$. For GpC , the GpC [Pt] - $\underset{\sim}{2a}$ isomer represents about 95% of fraction 2 (^{1}H NMR), and the three main complexes GpC [Pt] - $\underset{\sim}{1}$, - $\underset{\sim}{3}$ and - $\underset{\sim}{2a}$ are about in 1:1:1 ratios. For d - pGpC the four isomers d - pGpC [Pt] - $\underset{\sim}{1}$, - $\underset{\sim}{3}$, - $\underset{\sim}{2a}$ and - $\underset{\sim}{2b}$ are in ca. 40:10:25:25 ratios. Their comparative ^{1}H NMR data are collected in Table III, together with those of the G - N7 monocoordinated complex [Pt(dien)(GpC)] Br$_2$. Like in the GG and CG series, there is an overall similarity between the GpC and the d - pGpC complexes in spite of different proportions of the isomers.

We assign the G syn - C anti and G syn - C syn configurations to isomers $\underset{\sim}{1}$ and $\underset{\sim}{3}$ on the basis of the following results: - a - For the cytosine of GpC [Pt] - $\underset{\sim}{3}$, one observes a positive NOE (> 10%) between C - H6 and C - H1', a 0.6 ppm upfield shift of C - H1' , and a 0.75 ppm downfield shift of C - H2' . These features are not observed for GpC [Pt] - $\underset{\sim}{1}$ and are characteristic of a C syn configuration for the $\underset{\sim}{3}$ isomer. - b - Similar chemical shift data are obtained for the cytosines in the corresponding complexes of the deoxy series. Moreover, while both H5 and H6 cytosine protons of d - pGpC [Pt] - $\underset{\sim}{3}$ are insensitive to the 5'- phosphate titration, the C - H5 of the $\underset{\sim}{1}$ isomer exhibits a small sensitivity in agreement with its C anti configuration. - c - For GpC [Pt] - $\underset{\sim}{1}$ a positive NOE is observed between G - H8 and G - H1' that supports a G syn configuration. A small NOE for the $\underset{\sim}{3}$ isomer requires further confirmation. Moreover none of the H8 of d - pGpC [Pt] - $\underset{\sim}{1}$ and $\underset{\sim}{3}$ is directly sensitive to the 5'- phosphate titration, supporting a G syn configuration for both isomers.

For the couple of isomers of fraction 2 , we assign the G anti - C anti configuration to isomer $\underset{\sim}{2a}$ and the G anti - C syn configuration to isomer $\underset{\sim}{2b}$ on the basis of the following data : - a - For GpC [Pt] - $\underset{\sim}{2a}$, there is no NOE between G - H8 and G - H1' and between C - H6 and C - H1' . This suggests a G anti configuration and, together with the C - H1', - H2' and - H3' chemical shifts, a C anti configuration. The latter should contribute to the large downfield shift of C - H5 because in the

complex this proton does not experience anymore the influence of
the guanine ring current. A similar shift is observed for the
C – H5 of d – pGpC [Pt]   – 2a , enhanced by the proximity of the
5'- phosphate. In the deoxy series, the 2a/2b assignment is based
on the similarity between the ¹H NMR data of the oxy and deoxy
– 2a complexes. – b – For d – pGpC [Pt] – 2a and – 2b the
G – H8 protons are sensitive to the 5' – phosphate titration
(Δδ ∿ 0.2 – 0.3 ppm) and this supports an anti configuration of the
guanines. Moreover the C – H5 of 2a is the only other proton to
be sensitive to this titration (Δδ ∿ 0.15 ppm) and this confirms
the C anti configuration of this isomer. The CPK models show
that among all the possible configurations of d – pGpC [Pt] ,
G anti – C anti is the only one that can bring the C – H5 in the
vicinity of the free 5' – phosphate. – c – The complete configuration assignment to the 2b isomers is more difficult because of
the few data available for the oxy complex and because of signal
overlapping between the sugar protons of the non separable 2a and
2b deoxy isomers. For d – pGpC[Pt] – 2b , the upfield shift of
C – H6 is in favor of a C syn configuration, but is not accompanied
by the expected upfield shift of C – H1', however one sees a
strongly deshielded H3' (5.07 ppm). We assign the G anti – C syn
configuration to the GpC [Pt] – and d – pGpC [Pt] – 2b isomers,
because of the previous assignments to the 1 , 3 and 2a isomers.

In the GpC [Pt] – 1 , – 3 and – 2a isomers, the 5'-riboses
adopt an N – type conformation (C3' – endo) characteristic of the
platinum chelation. To the 3' – riboses corresponds an equilibrium
between type S – and type N – conformers (42). The 3' – riboses can
be considered as ∿ 40% ²E for 1 and 3 , and ∿ 60% ²E for
2a in the simplified ²E ⇌ ³E description (32). It is noteworthy that even the d – pGpC [Pt] – 1 and – 3 isomers present
an N – type conformation of the 5' – sugar ($J_{1', 2'} + J_{1', 2''} = 7$ Hz) which
is usually less favored in the deoxy series (41, 42).

CpC and d – pCpC Platinum Complexes. Only one complex is
obtained from each dinucleotide. Their comparative ¹H NMR data
are collected in Table IV. Each complex contains both a syn and an
anti cytosine, the former being characterized by the upfield shifts
of the related H1' and H6 . From the sugar protons assignment,
based on the 5' – cytosine – H3' coupling with the bridging phosphorus atom, the upfield shifted H1' is a 5' – C – H1' . Therefore
the syn cytosine is identified as Cp in CpC [Pt] and pCp in
d – pCpC [Pt] . For the oxy complex there is no NOE between
pC – H1' and – H6 , however the effect between the corresponding
Cp protons is not significant enough to confirm the syn configuration of the 5' – cytosine. For the d – pCpC [Pt] complex only the
3' – cytosine – H6 and – H5 protons are sensitive to the
5' – phosphate titration (Δδ respectively + 0.17 and 0.08) in
agreement with a pC – anti configuration. From these data we
tentatively assign the 5' – C syn – 3' – C anti configuration to
both CpC [Pt] and d – pCpC [Pt] complexes .

Table III. ¹H NMR data of the GpC[Pt] and d-pGpC[Pt] complexes[a,b]

	GC δ	GC J	GC[Pt]-1[c] δ	J	Δδ	GC[Pt]-3[c] δ	J	Δδ	GC[Pt]-2a[c] δ	J	Δδ	GC[Pt]-2b[c] δ	J	Δδ
GpC (pD 7.4) / GpC[Pt] (pD 6.4)[d]														
H8	8.03	s	8.05	s	0	8.13	s	+0.1	8.75	s	+0.7	8.37	s	+0.35
H6	7.79	d 7.7	7.76	d 8	−0.05	7.66	d 7.8	−0.15	7.67	d 8	−0.1	7.37	d	−0.4
H5	5.65	d 7.7	6.2	d 8	+0.55	6.0	d 7.8	+0.35	6.52	d 8	+0.85			
G – H1'	5.85	d 2.6	6.05	s	+0.2	6.0	s	+0.15	6.13	s	+0.3			
C – H1'	5.88	d 2.2	5.88	d 3.7	0	5.25	d 4	−0.6	5.98	d 6	+0.1			
G – H3'	4.61	m (3'4':6.8)	~4.3			4.78	m (3'4':9)	+0.15	4.71	m (3'4':9.3)	+0.1			
C – H3'	4.28	m (3'4':7.5)	4.49	t (3'4':5.2)	+0.2	4.6	t (3'4':6)	+0.3	~4.4					
C – H2'	4.19	q (2'3':5.2)	4.61	q (2'3':5.2)	+0.4	4.95	q (2'3':6)	+0.75						
d – pGpC (pD 6.8) / d-pGpC[Pt] (pD 6.4)														
H8	8.11[e]		7.82	s	−0.3	8.05	s	−0.05	8.92	s	+0.9	8.53	s	+0.4
H6	7.76	d 8	7.77	d 8	0	7.57	d 8	−0.2	7.73	d 8	0	7.4[e]	d	−0.35
H5	5.81	d 8	6.33	d 8	+0.5	5.90	d 8	+0.1	6.98	d 8	+1.2	6.39[e]		+0.6
G – H1'	6.22		6.31[f]	d 7	+0.1	6.27[f]	d 7	+0.05	6.31			6.31		
C – H1'	6.27		6.37[f]	q 8;4	+0.1	5.72[f]	q 8;5	−0.55	6.36			6.36		

[a] 400 MHz ; samples ~ 10⁻³ M in D₂O ; 15°C ; chemical shifts (δ) in ppm from TSP ; coupling constants (J) in Hz. [b] a brace is used for the δ values when the signals have not been assigned to each nucleoside. [c] for [Pt(dien)(GpC)]²⁺ at pD 6.4, δ(J) Δδ: H8, 8.42 (s) + 0.4 ; H6, 7.87 (d 8) + 0.1 ; H5, 5.9 (d 8) + 0.35 ; G – H1'/C – H1' , 5.9 . [d] from ref. 43 . [e] broad. [f] assigned by analogy with the oxy isomers.

Table IV. ^{1}H NMR data for the CpC[Pt] and d–pCpC[Pt] complexes[a,b]

	H		CC		CC[Pt]		
			δ	J	δ	J	Δδ
CpC[c] (pD 7.4)	H6	Cp	7.90	d 7.7	7.55	d 7.5	− 0.35
	H6	pC	7.94	d 7.7	8.01	d 7.5	+ 0.05
CpC[Pt] (pD 7.4)	H5	Cp	5.95	d 7.7	5.95	d 7.5	0
	H5	pC	5.96	d 7.7	6.0	d 7.5	+ 0.05
	H1′	Cp	5.78	d 3	5.53	s	− 0.25
	H1′	pC	5.88	d 2.9	6.24	d 2	+ 0.35
	H6	pCp	7.97 ⎫	d 8	7.66	d 8	− 0.3
	H6	pC	8.01 ⎬	d 8	8.04	d 8	∼ 0
d – pCpC (pD 5.8)	H5	pCp	6.27 ⎬	m	5.97	d 8	− 0.15,− 0.3
	H5	pC			6.05	d 8	− 0.1 ,− 0.2
d – pCpC[Pt] (pD 5.6)	H1′	pCp	6.13[d] ⎭		5.89	q 7;3.2	− 0.25,− 0.4
	H1′	pC			6.58	q 7.8;4.9	+ 0.3 ,+ 0.45

^{a}400 MHz ; samples ∼ 10^{-3} M in D_2O ; 15°C ; chemical shifts (δ) in ppm from TSP ; coupling constants (J) in Hz. ^{b} a brace is used in the δ columns when the signals have not been assigned to each nucleoside. ^{c}from ref. 44. ^{d}broad.

In CpC [Pt] both the 5'- and 3'- riboses adopt an N-type
conformation. For the deoxy complex the N-type predominates for
the 5'- sugar and the S-type for the 3'- sugar.

CD analyses of the Dinucleotide Complexes

The CD spectra of the three diguanosine phosphate complexes
have been reported recently (23) and present a common characteristic feature. At neutral and acidic pHs there is a broad positive band in the 275-290 nm region instead of the negative band
that is always present for the free and protonated dinucleotides.
This change appears characteristic of the stacking of the anti
guanines within the N7-N7 chelates. The observed spectra are
different from those reported for solutions of GpG plus Zn^{2+}
and Cu^{2+} (45) and from those of the cis-bis(nucleotide)complexes,
[Pt(tn)(5'-GMP)$_2$]$^{2-}$ and [Pt(tn)(5'-dGMP)$_2$]$^{2-}$ (46), which
possess a head-to-tail arrangement of the purines (12,28). For the
CG- and GC-platinum complexes, the CD spectra of the different
syn anti isomers are reported on Figure 2 , together with those of
the corresponding free dinucleotides. The spectra of the dinucleotides all show a positive composite band with a maximum around
270-280 nm and a negative composite band with a minimum around
230 nm. Upon platinum chelation an enhancement of the CD spectra
is noticeable for the CG complexes whereas it is accompanied by a
striking signal inversion for the GC complexes. The separated syn
and anti isomers do show distinct CD spectra and these characteristic spectra give an excellent confirmation of the correspondance
between the different oxy and deoxy isomers, for the CG and GC
series, revealed by their ^{1}H NMR spectra. The CD spectra of the
CC-complexes are shown on Figure 3. Platinum chelation leads to a
red shift and an enhancement of the CD spectra.

Preliminary Results concerning d-TpGpGpCpCpA (d-TGGCCA)

The stoichiometric reaction between d-TGGCCA and
cis-[Pt(NH$_3$)$_2$(H$_2$O)$_2$](NO$_3$)$_2$(5 × 10^{-5}M) in H$_2$O , at pH 5.3 and
37°C, gives only one complex as revealed by HPLC and by the
^{1}H NMR spectrum of the crude reaction product (Figure 4). The
^{1}H NMR spectra of the low field base protons of the hexanucleotide,
at 70°C and pD 5.5 , and of its platinum complex, at 67°C and
pD 5.4 , are presented on Figure 4 (at lower temperatures one
observes signal broadening). The 7.94 and 7.85 ppm signals of
d-TGGCCA are assigned to the guanine H8 resonances, since these
are known to occur at higher fields than those of adenine (47).
The 8.40 ppm resonance is assigned to the adenine-H8 , in agreement with that of a 3'- terminal adenine (presence of a 5'- phosphate bridge) (47). The other straightforward assignments are
reported on Figure 4 . Platinum coordination leads to downfield
shifts of the thymine-H6 , of one cytosine-H6 and of the two
guanine-H8 protons. Acidification of the platinum complex, from

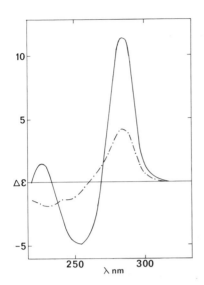

Figure 2a. Circular dichroism spectra of CpG[Pt] (—, ca. 10⁻⁴ M, pH 6.4) and CpG (– • –, ca. 10⁻⁴ M, pH 6.3) in NaCl (0.05 M).

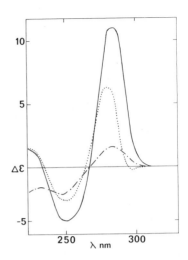

Figure 2b. Circular dichroism spectra of CG–platinum complexes (ca. 10⁻⁴ M) in NaCl (0.05 M). Key: • • •, d(pCpG)-[Pt]-1 at pH 5.6; —, d(pCpG)[Pt]-2 at pH 6.5; and – • –, d(pCpG)[Pt] at pH 6.9.

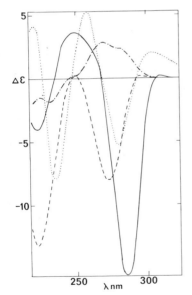

Figure 2c. Circular dichroism spectra of GC–platinum complexes (ca. 10⁻⁴ M) in NaCl (0.05 M). Key: – –, GpC[Pt]-1 at pH 5.5; • • •, GpC[Pt]-2a at pH 6.1; —, GpC[Pt]-3 at pH 6.7; and – • –, GpC at pH 6.8.

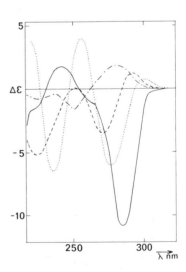

Figure 2d. Circular dichroism spectra of GC–platinum complexes (ca. 10⁻⁴ M) in NaCl (0.05 M). Key: – –, d(pGpC)-[Pt]-1 at pH 4.8; • • •, d(pGpC)[Pt]-2a + 2b) at pH 6.8; —, d(pGpC)[Pt]-3 at pH 6.2; and – • –, d(pGpC) at pH 6.6.

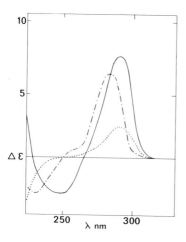

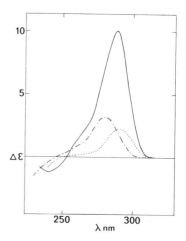

Figure 3a. Circular dichroism spectra of CC–platinum complexes (10^{-4} M) in NaCl (0.05 M). Key: —, CpC[Pt] at pH 6; – • –, CpC at pH 6.2; and • • •, CpC at pH 1.6.

Figure 3b. Circular dichroism spectra of CC–platinum complexes (10^{-4} M) in NaCl (0.05 M). Key: —, d(pCpC)[Pt] at pH 5; – • –, d(pCpC) at pH 6; and • • •, d(pCpC) at pH 1.5.

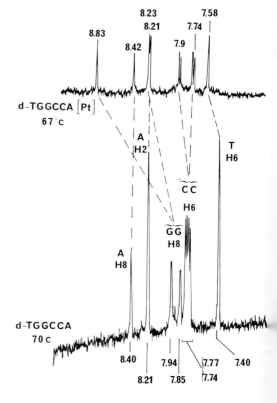

Figure 4. ^{1}H-NMR spectra (400 MHz) of the low-field base protons of d(TGGCCA) and crude d(TGGCCA)[Pt]. Conditions of d(TGGCCA: 2×10^{-3} M in D_2O, pD 5.5, 70 °C. Conditions of d(TGGCCA) [Pt]: 2×10^{-3} M in D_2O, 1 M KCl, pD 5.4, 67 °C. Chemical shifts in ppm from TSP. The purine H8 protons of d-(TGGCCA) have been partially exchanged for deuterium by previous heating of the D_2O solution.

pD 7.6 to pD 3 , at 17°C, first reveals the protonation of the
two cytosines (C – H6 doublets $\Delta\delta$ + 0.3 and + 0.4 ppm) followed
by the downfield shift of one of the 8.21-8.23 resonances. In this
pH range, the latter shift ($\Delta\delta$ + 0.36 ppm) can only be assigned to
the H2 proton of the unbound adenine. As thymine cannot be a
ligand in our conditions, these data establish G – N7 coordination.
The influence of this coordination on the T – H6 and one of the
C – H6 protons suggests a GG – chelation. The G – H8 downfield
shifts are in agreement with such a chelation when compared with
those of the diguanosine phosphate complexes.

Discussion

Our results show that, within oxy or deoxy dinucleotides,
adjacent guanines, cytosines or guanine and cytosine always stoi-
chiometrically chelate the cis – $Pt^{II}(NH_3)_2$ moiety upon reaction
with cis – $[Pt(NH_3)_2(H_2O)_2]$ $(NO_3)_2$ or cis – $[Pt(NH_3)_2Cl_2]$. GpG,
d – GpG and d – pGpG give a single N7 – N7 anti – anti complex.
CpC and d – pCpC give a single N3 – N3 syn – anti complex. CpG
and d – pCpG give a mixture of N3 – N7 C anti – G anti (1) and
C syn – G anti (2) isomers. GpC and d – pGpC give a mixture of
two N7 – N3 couples of isomers G syn – C anti (1), G syn – C syn
(3) and G anti – C anti (2a) , G anti – C syn (2b). Precise
comparative kinetic data have to be recorded but the formation of
the platinum chelates is the fastest with the diguanosine phosphates
and the slowest with the dicytosine phosphates.

When CpG or GpC are reacted with [Pt(dien)Br] Br only
the G – N7 monocoordinated complexes are formed and no other
complex could be detected by HPLC monitoring of the reaction.
This is in agreement with the known binding kinetic selectivity in
favor of guanine – N7 (48). For the couples of CG or GC equi-
librating complexes, the isomerisation only affects the cytosine
configuration. Examination of the CPK models suggests that this
isomerisation requires a dissociation of the cytosine – N3 – Pt bond.
We have not yet been able to trap the "open" intermediate. However
a dissociation – recombination process affecting only the cytosine –
platinum bond might be related to the larger stability constants
recently reported for $Pd^{II}(dien)$ binding to G – N7 than to
C – N3 (49).

For all the dinucleotides studied, independently of the nature
of the bases, platinum chelation induces an N – type conformation
for the 5'- sugar, while the 3'-sugar adopts a predominantly S – type
conformation (42, 32). A more detailed analysis of the sugar
conformations is undertaken.

There is a striking difference between the CD spectra of the
CG – and GC – complexes. While upon platinum chelation, the
overall features of the CD are retained in the CG series, a
signal inversion occurs in the GC series. Moreover this inversion
is present for the different isomers which have been isolated
(1, 3, 2a for GpC [Pt] , 1, 3, 2a + 2b for d – pGpC [Pt]) so

that we can rule out that it is characteristic of a guanine with a
syn configuration (Isomers 1 and 3 have a G syn-, isomers 2a
and 2b a G anti- configuration). This similarity shows also
that within a series a change of configuration from anti to syn
around one glycosidic bond does not invert the CD . Accordingly
the CD of the GpC [Pt] - 1 syn-anti isomer is not significantly different from that of the GpC [Pt] - 3 syn-syn isomer.
By close inspection of the whole series of spectra of the platinum
complexes, it appears that for the oxy and deoxy series the CD
of the GC [Pt] - 3 syn-syn isomer is almost the mirror image of
that of the CG [Pt] - 2 syn-anti isomer. The use of CPK models
shows that in the case of CpG , the C syn-G anti chelation of
the platinum can be done with a slight modification of the sugar-
phosphate backbone conformation, whereas for GpC the G syn-
C syn chelation implies an important perturbation leading to a
zigzag conformation of the backbone (50, 51). For the CG series,
the CPK models also point to a backbone perturbation for the
C anti-G anti chelation of platinum. However the CD of the
d-pCpG [Pt] - 1 isomer is of the regular type with a positive
maximum at 279 nm. So that it appears that a change of the sugar
phosphate backbone conformation does not necessarily invert the
CD . We tentatively conclude i that the sequence is primarily
responsible for the CD inversion observed in the GC [Pt] series
ii that the zigzag helical structure leads to a reinforcement of
the negative long wavelength CD band characteristic of the
GC [Pt] series. Our conclusions are in agreement with the results
showing that the CD of synthetic double stranded RNAs is
primarily sequence dependent (52), if we consider the conformational restrictions brought by platinum chelation. They agree also
with calculations on poly-I showing that a long wavelength negative
CD band is not necessarily related to a particular helix sense (53).
   When compared to the reactions of the other dinucleotides
studied the faster coordination of the diguanosine phosphates, to
give a single N7-N7 anti-anti platinum complex, points to a
particular chelating aptitude of the anti-anti GG sequence. A
preferred GG chelation has recently been reported for d-CCGG
(15) and our preliminary results with d-TGGCCA clearly demonstrate the sequence specificity of platinum binding. These results
are in agreement with those obtained from the restriction enzyme
studies of platinated DNAs (17, 18, 19) and support the hypothesis
of platinum intrastrand cross-linking of adjacent guanines.

Acknowledgments

   We are deeply indebted to Drs. J. Igolen and T. Huynh-Dinh
for the synthesis of d-TGGCCA . We thank Miss V. Michon for NMR
technical assistance, Miss N. Claquin for typing of the manuscript
and Engelhardt industries, France, for a loan of platinum.

Abbreviations used

In dinucleoside monophosphates and oligonucleotides, A, C, G, T respectively represent adenosine, cytidine, guanosine and thymidine. p to the left of a nucleoside symbol indicates a 5'- phosphate and to the right, it indicates a 3'- phosphate. In GpG the 5'- H8 is the H8 proton of the 5'- guanine (Gp). The dinucleoside monophosphates GpG, d - GpG, etc... will be occasionally referred to as dinucleotides. Guo = guanosine, Cyd = cytidine, 5'- GMP = 5'- guanosine monophosphate, 5'- CMP = 5'- cytosine monophosphate. HPLC = high - pressure liquid chromatography; NMR = nuclear magnetic resonance, s = singlet, d = doublet, t = triplet, q = quartet, m = multiplet, NOE = nuclear Overhauser effect, CD = circular dichroism. tn = trimethylene diamine, dien = diethylenetriamine. CPK models = Corey - Pauling - Koltun atomic models.

Literature Cited

1. Roberts, J.J.; Thomson, A.J. Prog. Nucleic Acis Res. Mol. Biol. 1979, 22, 71-133, *and references cited therein.*
2. Pascoe, J.M.; Roberts, J.J. Biochem. Pharmacol. 1974, 23, 1345-57.
3. Roberts, J.J.; Friedlos, F. Biochim. Biophys. Acta 1981, 655, 146-51.
4. Pera, M.F.; Rawlings, C.J.; Shackleton, J.: Roberts, J.J. Biochim. Biophys. Acta 1981, 655, 152-66.
5. Stone, P.J.; Kelman, A.D.; Sinex, F.M. J. Mol. Biol. 1976, 104, 793-801.
6. Kelman, A.D.; Peresie, H.J. Cancer Treat Rep. 1979, 63, 1445-52, *and references cited therein.*
7. Macquet, J.P.; Theophanides, T. Biopolymers 1975, 14, 781-99.
8. Macquet, J.P.; Butour, J.L. Biochimie 1978, 60, 901-14.
9. Filipski, J.; Kohn, K.W.; Bonner, W.M. Chem.- Biol. Interactions 1980, 32, 321-30.
10. Goodgame, D.M.L.; Jeeves, I.; Phillips, F.L.; Skapski, A.C. Biochim. Biophys. Acta 1975, 378, 153-7.
11. Chu, G.Y.H.; Mansy, S.; Duncan, R.E.; Tobias, R.S. J. Am. Chem. Soc. 1978, 100, 593-606.
12. Marzilli, L.G.; Chalilpoyil, P.; Chiang, C.C.; Kistenmacher, T.J. J. Am. Chem. Soc. 1980, 102, 2480-2, *and references cited therein.*
13. Chottard, J.-C.; Girault, J.-P.; Chottard, G.; Lallemand, J.-Y.; Mansuy, D. Nouv. J. Chim. 1978, 2, 551-3.
14. Chottard, J.-C.; Girault, J.-P.; Chottard, G.; Lallemand, J.-Y.; Mansuy, D. J. Am. Chem. Soc. 1980, 102, 5565-72.
15. Marcelis, A.T.M.; Canters, G.W.; Reedijk, J. Recl. Trav. Chim. Pays-Bas 1981, 100, 391-2.
16. Fazakerley, G.V.; Hermann, D.; Guschlbauer, W. Biopolymers 1980, 19, 1299-1310.

17. Cohen, G.L.; Ledner, J.A.; Bauer, W.R.; Ushay, H.M.; Caravana, C.; Lippard, S.J. J. Am. Chem. Soc. 1980, 102, 2487-8.
18. Ushay, H.M.; Tullius, T.D.; Lippard, S.J. Biochemistry 1981, 20, 3744-8.
19. Tullius, T.D.; Lippard, S.J. J. Am. Chem. Soc. 1981, 103, 4620-2.
20. Brouwer, J.; Van de Putte, P.; Fichtinger-Schepman, A.M.J.; Reedijk, J. Proc. Natl. Acad. Sci. USA 1981, 78, 7010-4.
21. Macquet, J.P.; Butour, J.L. Eur. J. Biochem. 1978, 83, 375-87.
22. Srivastava, R.C.; Froehlich, J.; Eichhorn, G.L. Biochimie 1978, 60, 879-91.
23. Girault, J.-P.; Chottard, G.; Lallemand, J.-Y.; Chottard, J.-C. Biochemistry 1982, 21, 1352-6.
24. Rosenberg, B. Biochimie 1978, 60, 859-67.
25. Barton, J.K.; Lippard, S.J. "Nucleic Acid - Metal Interactions"; Spiro, T.G., Ed.; Wiley: New York 1980; Chapter 2.
26. Kong, P.C.; Theophanides, T. Inorg. Chem. 1974, 13, 1167-70.
27. Kong, P.C.; Theophanides, T. Bioinorg. Chem. 1975, 5, 51-8.
28. Cramer, R.E.; Dahlstrom, P.L. J. Am. Chem. Soc. 1979, 101, 3679-81.
29. Kong, P.C.; Theophanides, T. Inorg. Chem. 1974, 13, 1981-5.
30. Lallemand, J.-Y.; Soulié, J.; Chottard, J.-C. J.C.S. Chem. Comm. 1980, 436-8.
31. Davies, D.B. "Progress in Nuclear Magnetic Resonance Spectroscopy"; Emsley, J.W., Feeney, J., Sutcliffe, L.H., Eds.; Pergamon Press: Oxford, 1978, 12, Part 3, 135-225.
32. Dhingra, M.M.; Sarma, R.H. "Stereodynamics of Molecular Systems"; Sarma, R.H., Ed.; Pergamon Press: New York, 1979, 3-38.
33. Patel, D.J. Biochemistry, 1975, 14, 3984-9.
34. Patel, D.J.; Tonelli, A.E. Biochemistry, 1975, 14, 3990-6.
35. Schweizer, M.P.; Broom, A.D.; Ts'o, P.O.P.; Hollis, D.P. J. Am. Chem. Soc. 1968, 90, 1042-55.
36. Neumann, J.M.; Guschlbauer, W.; Tran-Dinh, S. Eur. J. Biochem. 1979, 100, 141-8.
37. Guéron, M.; Chachaty, C.; Tran-Dinh, S. Ann. N.Y. Acad. Sci. 1973, 222, 307-23.
38. Niemczura, W.P.; Hruska, F.E.; Sadana, K.L.; Loewen, P.C. Biopolymers 1981, 20, 1671-90.
39. Plochocka, D.; Rabczenko, A.; Davies, D.B. J.C.S. Perkin II 1981, 82-9.
40. Giessner-Prettre, C.; Pullman, B. J. Theor. Biol. 1977, 65, 171-88.
41. George, A.L.; Hruska, F.E.; Ogilvie, K.K.; Holy, A. Canad. J. Chem. 1978, 56, 1170-6.
42. Altona, C.; Sundaralingam, M. J. Am. Chem. Soc. 1973, 95, 2333-44.
43. Ezra, F.S.; Lee, C.H.; Kondo, N.S.; Danyluk, S.S.; Sarma, R.H. Biochemistry 1977, 16, 1977-87.

44. Lee, C.H.; Ezra, F.S.; Kondo, N.S.; Sarma, R.H.; Danyluk, S.S. Biochemistry 1976, 15, 3627–38.
45. Zimmer, C.; Luck, G.; Holy, A. Nucl. Ac. Res. 1976, 3, 2757–70.
46. Marzilli, L.G.; Chalilpoyil, P. J. Am. Chem. Soc. 1980, 102, 873–5.
47. Patel, D.J. Biochemistry 1975, 14, 3984–96 *and references cited therein.*
48. Mansy, S.; Chu, G.Y.H.; Duncan, R.E.; Tobias, R.S. J. Am. Chem. Soc. 1978, 100, 607–16.
49. Scheller, K.H.; Scheller-Krattiger, V.; Martin, R.B. J. Am. Chem. Soc. 1981, 103, 6833–39.
50. Wang, A.H.J.; Quigley, G.J.; Kolpak, F.J.; Crawford, J.L.; Van Boom, J.H.; Van der Marel, G.; Rich, A. Nature 1979, 282, 680–6.
51. Crawford, J.L.; Kolpak, F.J.; Wang, A.H.J.; Quigley, G.J.; Van Boom, J.H.; Van der Marel, G.; Rich, A. Proc. Natl. Acad. Sci. USA 1980, 77, 4016–20.
52. Gray, D.M.; Liu, J.J.; Ratliff, R.L.; Allen, F.S. Biopolymers 1981, 20, 1337–82.
53. Cech, C.L.; Tinoco, I. Nucl. Ac. Res. 1976, 3, 399–404.

RECEIVED October 4, 1982

Platinum(II) Complex Formation with Uracil and Thymine

BERNHARD LIPPERT

Technische Universität München, Anorganisch-Chemisches Institut,
Lichtenbergstrasse 4, 8046 Garching, Federal Republic of Germany

Replacement of an amide proton in pyrimidine-2,4-
diones by less electron-attracting Pt(II) electrophile causes an increase in electron density at
the exocyclic oxygens, and allows easy formation
of N,O-bridged complexes with additional metal
ions, or proton binding at the oxygen(s). With
cis-Pt(NH$_3$)$_2$L$_2$ (L= monoanion of 1-methyluracil or
1-methylthymine) a number of dimeric and heteronuclear complexes of Pt,M, Pt$_2$,M, and Pt$_4$,M stoichiometries have been isolated and studied using
crystallographic and spectroscopic methods.
With unsubstituted uracil and thymine the situation is complicated due to the existence of two
tautomers of the monoanions. Pt binding occurs
through the N donors and via exocyclic oxygens.
In aqueous solution a slow mutual interconversion
of the various complexes takes place.

The interest in the interaction between metal ions and
nucleic acids in general (1,2) and the finding on the antitumor
activity of complexes formed between aquated cis-Pt(NH$_3$)$_2$Cl$_2$
and pyrimidine-2,4-dione ligands such as uracil and thymine
in particular (3,4) have led to a considerable activity in this
area of bioinorganic chemistry. With these ligands representing
typical multisite ligands, frequently no straightforward interpretation of spectroscopic results is possible. As will subsequently be shown, the combination of different spectroscopic
techniques and the use of X-ray crystallography permits a
reasonable, although still incomplete, understanding of the coordinating behavior of cis-Pt(NH$_3$)$_2$(II), enPt(II), and
Pt(NH$_3$)$_3$(II) with these ligands.

Pt(II) Complexes of Unsubstituted Uracil and Thymine

The tautomerism of the monoanions of unsubstituted uracil with its N1 and N3 deprotonated forms is well established (5-9) (Figure 1). With thymine, the crystal structure of the N1 deprotonated tautomer has been performed (10), and IR and Raman spectroscopic evidence has been presented for the existence of the second tautomer in the solid state as well (11). The high degree of charge delocalization in both tautomers, deduced from theoretical calculations (12), suggests that metal binding could conceivably take place at a number of sites and combinations of these, leading to a variety of products. The situation is further complicated by the fact that once a metal is attached to the heterocyclic ring, the complex may be involved in acid-base equilibria, thus leading to dianionic or neutral ligands. With the metal binding site being an endocyclic nitrogen, any neutral ligand in a complex necessarily occurs in a rare tautomeric form (Figure 2). Moreover, binding of more than just one metal to a single uracil or thymine ligand is possible.

It may be a combination of these reasons why there appears to be some uncertainty concerning metal binding sites of these ligands in studies not supported by crystal structures (13-18). Although the existence of tautomer complexes of uracil and thymine had been taken into consideration (19), until recently, only in a single case, with uracil complexes of triammineplatinum(II), it has clearly been demonstrated by Kidani and Inagaki (20).

Among the limited number of crystallographically confirmed binding sites of metal ions with the monoanions of unsubstituted uracil (21,22,23) and thymine (21,24,25,26) one observes a striking predominance of N1 coordination.Only in one case, with Cd binding to uracil, N3 binding is documented (23).

Two more binding possibilities - via one of the exocyclic oxygens (27,28) or with replacement of the proton at C5 (29,30) will not be considered here, since they occur with the neutral ligands and do not involve the N1,N3 tautomer equilibrium of the monoanionic ligands, respectively.

Methods of Differentiation. Apart from X-ray crystallography that had been applied in a few cases with N1 platinated uracil and thymine compounds (21,25,26), spectroscopic methods were used to determine the sites of platinum coordination In sequence of their usefulness these were:

UV spectroscopy. It proved to be applicable in cases with isolated tautomer complexes of uracil (20) and thymine (31), but is of very limited usefulness in mixtures of various tautomer and/or bridged complexes.

IR spectroscopy.The double bond stretching region in all cases permits a differentiation of N1 and N3 tautomer complexes of the thymine (31) and uracil monoanion complexes. Typically, N1 coordination gives rise to an intense band around 1640 cm^{-1}

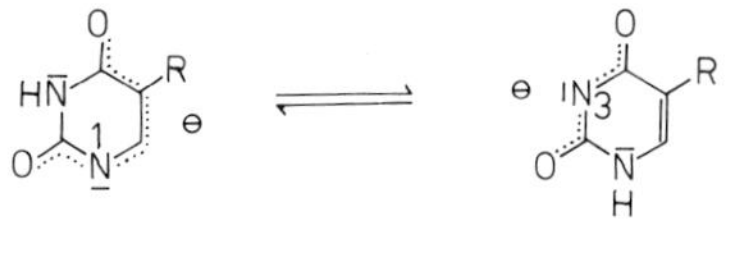

Figure 1. *Two tautomeric forms of uracil (R = H) and thymine (R = CH₃) monoanions.*

Figure 2. *Relevant acid–base equilibria of a N3 platinated uracil. Analogous equilibria exist for N1-platinated uracil as well (32).*

with shoulders both on the lower and higher frequency side, whereas N3 coordination is recognized by a characteristic band around 1550 cm^{-1} with a second one around 1650 cm^{-1}, which frequently is split. These differences result from the differences in charge distribution in both ligands and the inability of the metal electrophile to restore conditions as with the proton attached. The situation with the uracil tautomer complexes of cis-Pt(NH$_3$)$_2$(II), cis-Pt(NH$_3$)$_2$(HU)Cl·(H$_2$O)$_x$ (HU= monoanion of uracil; x= 1 for HU-N1; x= 2 for HU-N3) expectedly is rather similar to the situation with the triammineplatinum(II) complexes described by Kidani and Inagaki (20), with intense bands around 1660sh, 1635vs, 1575sh, 1420s (HU-N1), and 1670s, 1625s, 1540vs, 1415 (HU-N3). However, the two chloro complexes are obtained quite differently from the corresponding (NH$_3$)$_3$ compounds (32,33). On the other hand, with mixtures of tautomer complexes or mixed tautomer complexes such as cis-Pt(NH$_3$)$_2$ (TH-N1)(TH-N3) (TH= thymine monoanion) these characteristic bands are superimposed, and the interpretation of the infrared spectra is less straightforward (31).

Raman spectroscopy. The fundamentals of planar heterocyclic rings having C$_s$ molecular symmetry are distributed into in-plane (A') and out-of-plane (A") vibrations. Both symmetry species are IR and Raman active, but only in-plane vibrations usually are intense in the Raman. As has been shown, these modes are quite suitable for a differentiation of tautomers (9,11), tautomer complexes (34) or even mixtures of these (32). With pyrimidine derivatives, the most intense Raman bands usually are those of ring-stretching (1200-1300 cm^{-1}) and ring-breathing (ca. 800 cm^{-1}) vibrations, with the latter being particularly sensitive to changes in metal coordination sites and to the charge of the ligand. Due to the high intensities of these Raman bands, in many cases mixtures of complexes with different metal binding sites can be analyzed and semi-quantitative estimations of their concentrations can be done (32).

^{1}H NMR spectroscopy. Despite the disadvantage of a slow time scale which, in contrast to vibrational spectroscopy does not permit a direct observation of individual tautomers (at least not of tautomers with amide, iminol structures), NMR spectroscopy proved to be a powerful technique for the investigation of kinetically inert metal complexes of tautomers. Its usefulness is based on the following arguments:
(a) Chemical shift. N1 and N3 platinated uracil exhibts markedly different shifts for its H6 and H5 resonances, for example ca. 7.7. and 5.7 ppm, respectively for the HU-N1 complexes (D$_2$O, pD 8- 1.5), but ca. 7.4 and 5.7 ppm for the HU-N3 complexes (D$_2$O, pD 7- 3) (32). Similarly, the corresponding thymine complexes have their H6 resonances in Me$_2$SO-d$_6$ around 7.3 ppm (TH-N1) and 7.0 ppm (TH-N3) (31). (b) A particularly useful property of Pt complexes is the nuclear spin of 1/2 of the ^{195}Pt isotope (natural abundance 33.8 %), which gives rise to satel-

lites of H resonances if coupling occurs. For example, TH–N1
complexes show satellites of the H6 resonance with $^3J= 36- 40$ Hz,
whereas no coupling is observed with N3 platinum binding (31).
The ^1H NMR spectra of the uracil tautomer complexes represent
textbook examples on the effect of bond separation between two
atoms having a nuclear spin on the magnitude of coupling with
$^3J= 38.8$ Hz, $^4J= 15-4.3$ Hz, and $^5J \approx 0$ Hz (Figure 3). Taking
these differences into consideration, it is possible to assign
binding sites on this basis. It should be noted, however, that
a number of factors, in particular chemical shift anisotropy
relaxation may prevent observation of $^{195}Pt-^1H$ coupling (35).
(c) Under acidic pH conditions uracil complexes with N1 platinum
binding readily undergo isotopic exchange at the C5 position in
D_2O, thus simplifying the ^1H NMR spectrum (triplet of relative
intensities 1:4:1 for H6, H5 resonance disappeared) (32). In
contrast, uracil complexes with N3 platinum binding do not show
this phenomenon in this pH range. Interestingly, N3 platinated
uridine does undergo isotopic exchange at C5, but under alkaline
conditions (36). (d) Another remarkable difference between N1
and N3 platinated uracil and thymine in their response to acid
treatment. While the Pt–N1 bond is very stable, the Pt–N3 bond
is readily cleaved on addition of acid and slight warming, and
the neutral ligand is expelled from the complex (31,32). This
mechanism can befollowed nicely with both NMR and Raman spectroscopy.

    Isolation of Tautomer Complexes.Until recently, there has
been little or no rationale behind the selective synthesis of
uracil and thymine tautomer complexes. With a better understanding of the factors that influence metal binding sites – e.g.
solvent, solubility, pH (with water being the solvent), reaction
time, and hydrogen bonding properties of adjacent ligands (31) –
it now is possible to predict with a higher degree of certainty
the formation of a certain tautomer complex. For example, in
DMF,cis-Pt(NH_3)$_2$(HU–N1)Cl is formed preferentially due to its
low solubility in this solvent, whereas under moderately acidic
conditions in water,cis-Pt(NH_3)$_2$(HU–N3)Cl·$2H_2O$ is formed and no
N1 product (33). Formation of the uracil tautomer complexes of
triammineplatinum(II) in water in a 1:1 ratio (20) appears to be
the exception rather than the rule, and should be attributed
mainly to the similar solubilities of both products, which
prevents early precipitation of one species.
    Preparative High Pressure Liquid Chromatography, HPLC,
proved to be a good technique for separating tautomer complexes.
For example, all three possible bis(thyminato) complexes of
cis-Pt(II), cis-Pt(NH_3)$_2$(TH–N1)$_2$, cis-Pt(NH_3)$_2$(TH–N1)(TH–N3),
and cis-Pt(NH_3)$_2$(TH–N3)$_2$ have been isolated (31).
    Linkage Isomerization. Complexes of cis-Pt(II) and
enPt(II) containing a single uracil (32) or thymine (31) ligand
and an aquo ligand, show a remarkable tendency to undergo con-

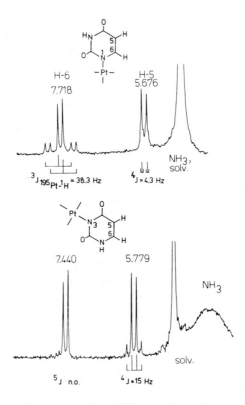

Figure 3. ¹H-NMR spectra of [(NH₃)₃Pt(HU–N1)]⁺ (0.15 M, D₂O, and pD 1–8)
and [(NH₃)₃Pt(HU–N3)]⁺ (0.1 M, D₂O, and pD 1) in the H5,H6 region. (Reproduced from Ref. 32. Copyright 1981, American Chemical Society.)

densation reactions with the pyrimidine ligand acting as a bridge. As a result, cleavage of the original platinum-ligand bond takes place, and formation of complexes with the metal linked to another donor atom. This phenomenon is also observed with coordinatively saturated complexes such as $\underline{cis}$-Pt(NH$_3$)$_2$L$_2$, enPtL$_2$ and Pt(NH$_3$)$_3$L$^+$ (L= TH or UH) in the presence of aquo-platinum(II) complexes and can be demonstrated particularly well with mixtures of the respective N1 and N3 complexes of Pt(NH$_3$)$_3$(HU)$^+$ and Pt(NH$_3$)$_3$(H$_2$O)$^{2+}$/ as shown in Figures 4 and 5: after a while the proton NMR spectra of both mixtures are virtually identical with at least three discernible species present. Signal A represents the HU-N1 complex, signal C the HU-N3 complex, and signal B a dimer which most likely is the N1,N3 bridged complex. In both spectra only H6 singlets (with ^{195}Pt satellites in the case of HU-N1) are observed due to isotopic exchange at C5. Since it only proceeds via the N1 complex, yet also is observed for the mixture of the HU-N3/Pt(H$_2$O) compounds, an additional argument in favour of the interconversion of binding sites is posed.

The very complicated Raman and, after partial decomposition ^{1}H NMR spectra (32) of "Platinum Pyrimidine Blues" (3,4) and "Patinum Pyrimidine Tans" (37) are not easy to interpret. Nevertheless two important conclusions can be drawn from NMR and Raman spectra: first, they consist of a mixture of complexes with different binding sites of platinum and differing oligomeric size. Second, in slightly to moderately acidic medium an interconversion of binding sites of the Pt electrophile occurs, as can be seen from the time dependence of the spectroskopic changes when the pH of the medium is altered (32).

Pt(II) Complexes of N1-Methylated Uracil and Thymine.

With the N1 position for metal binding blocked, the co-ordination properties of uracil and thymine are reduced (Figure 6). In the course of our systematic studies of possible reaction products between $\underline{cis}$-Pt(II) and model nucleobases, the 2:1 complexes of 1-MeT (monoanion of 1-methylthymine, 1-MeTH) and 1-MeU (monoanion of 1-methyluracil, 1-MeUH) have been prepared.

The crystal structure of $\underline{cis}$-Pt(NH$_3$)$_2$(1-MeU)$_2$·4H$_2$O has been determined (38). The molecule has approximately C$_2$ molecular symmetry with the two heterocyclic ligands arranged in head-tail fashion, similar to the respective complexes of 1-methylcytosine (39), various guanine derivatives (40) and also α-hydroxopyridine (41).

Platinum binding to N3 of the uracil and thymine ligands facilitates binding of additional metals or of a proton through the exocyclic oxygens, and is a consequence of an increase in electron density at these sites due to the replacement of the proton at N3 by Pt. Using this property for synthetic purposes,

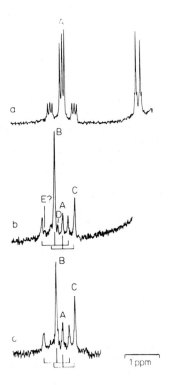

Figure 4. *¹H-NMR spectra of a mixture of $[(NH_3)_3Pt(HU–N1)]^+$ (0.1 M) and $[(NH_3)_3Pt(D_2O)]^{2+}$ (0.2 M) in D_2O in the H5,H6 region. Key to conditions: a, after 3 h at 40 °C and pD 2.6; b, after 43 h at 40 °C and pD 1.8; and c, after 10 d at 40 °C and pD 1.7. Because of isotopic exchange at C5, no H5 resonances are observed in b and c. (Reproduced from Ref. 32. Copyright 1981, American Chemical Society.)*

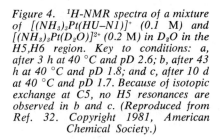

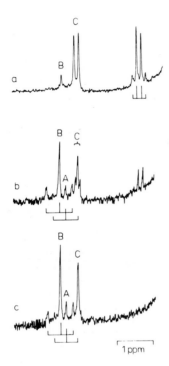

Figure 5.   ¹H-NMR spectra of a mixture of [(NH₃)₃Pt(HU–N3)]⁺ (0.1 M) and [(NH₃)₃Pt(D₂O)]²⁺ (0.2 M) in D₂O. Key to conditions: a, after 6 h at 40 °C and pD 2.3; b, after 4 d at 40 °C and pD 2.0; and c, after 7 d at 40 °C and pD 1.9. (Reproduced from Ref. 32. Copyright 1981, American Chemical Society.)

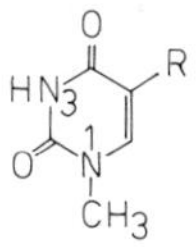

Figure 6.   The structure of 1-methyluracil (R = H) and 1-methylthymine (R = CH₃).

it is possible to obtain a range of interesting compounds from
the 2:1 complex of 1-MeU and 1-MeT, as is outlined in the scheme
shown in Figure 7.

Mono(1-MeT) and Mono(1-MeU)Complexes. Addition of acid to
a solution of cis-Pt(NH$_3$)$_2$L$_2$ (L= 1-MeT or 1-MeU) yields crystalline products of composition cis-[Pt(NH$_3$)$_2$L(LH)]X·(H$_2$O)$_n$ (42).
In these compounds one of the two ligands is present in its neutral form and, with N3 being the site of metal coordination,
consequently occurs in a rare iminol tautomeric structure. The
acidic proton has a pK$_a$ $\simeq$ 2 in the case of the 1-MeT compound.
As with the N3 platinated unsubstituted uracil and thymine, the
Pt-N3(LH) bond is easily cleaved on brief warming and results in
a selective removal of the LH ligand from the complex:

$$\text{cis-[Pt(NH}_3)_2\text{L(LH)]X} \xrightarrow{\Delta} \text{cis-Pt(NH}_3)_2\text{LX} + \text{LH}$$

Naturally, the LH ligand expelled from the complex originally
has the rare tautomeric structure. With water being the solvent,
the interconversion into the normal diketo tautomer is an in-
stantaneous one, but with an aprotic solvent it is feasible
that an iminol tautomer may have a measurable life-span. One
may further speculate that a metal catalyzed tautomerization of
thymine or uracil under biological conditions could take place
via such a mechanism (42).

With X= Cl$^-$, cis-Pt(NH$_3$)$_2$LCl is obtained in good yield.
cis-[Pt(NH$_3$)$_2$L(H$_2$O)]Y$_2$ prepared by reaction of the chloro complex with AgY (Y= NO$_3^-$, ClO$_4^-$), is a suitable starting material
for a number of products.

Condensation Products. In a condensation reaction, the
aquo complex dimerizes to give the respective head-tail Pt dimers with N3,O4 bridged uracil (thymine) among other products.
The obtained dimers are identical with those prepared in a
different way and studied by Lock, Rosenberg and coworkers (43,
44), as evident from elemental analysis, density measurements
and determination of the cell constants. With 1-MeT as ligand,
in addition we isolated an interesting second modification of
the head-tail dimer, which has a rather different crystal structure from the known one (43). This second modification crystallizes in stacks of dimers which are linked by strong hydrogen
bonds between the NH$_3$ groups and the non-coordinating exocyclic
oxygen of adjacent dimers, leading to inter-dimer separations of
about 3.9 Å (45).

Mixed Nucleobase Complexes. The preparation of possible
crosslinking products of cis-Pt(II) with the anionic 1-MeU or
1-MeT as one base, and neutral cytosine, guanine or adenine as
second nucleobase proceeds without formation of undesired side
products only if the anionic ligand is attached to Pt first. On
the other hand, reaction of cis-Pt(II) with uracil or thymine in
1:1 ratio results in formation of the complicated platinum blues

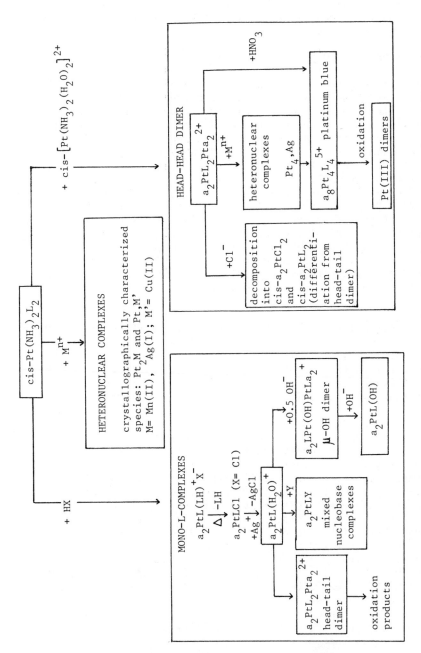

Figure 7.   Reaction scheme of compounds accessible via cis-Pt(NH₃)₂L₂ (L = 1-MeU or 1-MeT).

(3,4,37,46). The above outlined synthesis of 1:1 complexes of
1-MeU and 1-MeT enables formation of L containing mixed nucleobase complexes according to

$$cis-[Pt(NH_3)_2L(H_2O)]^+ + Y \longrightarrow cis-[Pt(NH_3)_2LY]^+$$

With L= 1-MeT, the complexes with Y= 1-methylcytosine, 9-ethyl-
guanine and 9-methyladenine have been prepared and studied (47),
and similar complexes with L= 1-MeU are presently being studied
(48). In another step the remaining L ligand can be removed from
the compound via acid treatment and a new nucleobase Z introduced, thus giving eventually $cis-Pt(NH_3)_2YZ$ complexes. As an
example of such nucleobase complexes, the ^1H NMR spectrum of
$cis-[Pt(NH_3)_2(1-MeT)(9-EtG)]ClO_4$ in Me_2SO-d_6 is shown in Figure
8. ^{195}Pt coupling of the H8 resonance of the guanine ligand
(^3J 23.3 Hz) indicates N7 platinum binding, and the chemical
shifts of H8 and NH_2 resonances are also consistent with related
complexes with N7 platination of 9-ethylguanine (49).

Reaction with Base. Titration of $cis-[Pt(NH_3)_2L(H_2O)]^+$
with one equivalent of base gives $cis-Pt(NH_3)_2L(OH)$. Titration
with 0.5 equivalents yields a dimeric complex of composition
$[(NH_3)_2PtL(OH)LPt(NH_3)_2]^+$ with a bridging OH group and terminal
L ligands:

$$2\ cis-[Pt(NH_3)_2L(H_2O)]^+ + OH^- \rightarrow [(NH_3)_2PtL(OH)LPt(NH_3)_2]^+ + H_2O$$

In an analogous way a μ-OH dimer with L= 1-methylcytosine has
been obtained (charge of the complex +3). From the pK_a of the
aquo ligand in $cis-[Pt(NH_3)_2L(H_2O)]^+$ (ca 6- 6.5) it is evident
that the dimer can exist at neutral pH, and ^1H NMR spectroscopy
confirms that it is the major component in water of pH 7. Formation of this dimer with a single hydroxo bridge leads to an
attractive hypothesis of how adjacent bases in DNA might be
linked by a cis-Pt(OH)Pt moiety either in an inter- or intrastrand fashion. In contrast, a trans-Pt(OH)Pt unit could
accomplish interstrand crosslinking only (Figure 9). It had
previously been argued against the existence of closely adjacent Pt centers in DNA treated with cis-Pt(II) on the basis
of an Extended X-Ray Absorption Fine Structure Spectroscopy
study (EXAFS) (50). However, only Pt-Pt distances shorter than
3.2 Å could be ruled out whereas in the present situation, from
comparison with cyclic hydroxo bridged complexes of composition
$cis-[(NH_3)_2Pt(OH)]_n^{n+}$ (n= 2, 3) (51), Pt-Pt separations of about
3.5 Å might be expected. It is evident that a Pt dimer with a
single OH bridge can accomodate binding of adjacent bases much
better than a monomer can and that this way of crosslinking is
by no means restricted to the pyrimidine beases. The rather un-
expected existence of hydroxo complexes of cis-Pt(II), not only
in the solid state but also over a wide pH range in solution
(52,53), certainly makes the idea of this type of crosslinking
feasible.

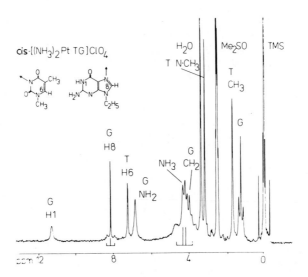

Figure 8. *¹H-NMR spectrum of* cis-*[(NH₃)₂(1-MeT)(9-EtG)]ClO₄ in Me₂SO-d₆.*

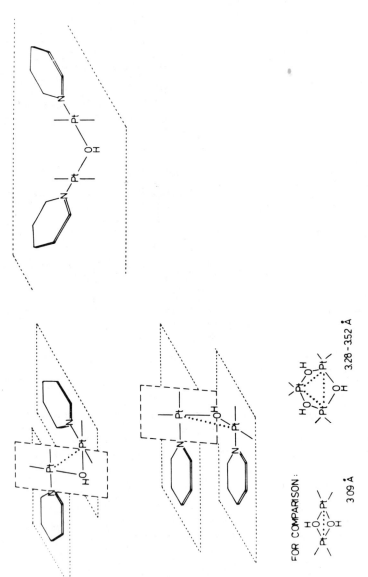

Figure 9. *Possible arrangements of two nucleobases in a Pt–OH–Pt moiety. Key: cis-Pt(II), left; and trans-Pt(II), right.*

Heteronuclear Complexes. Like protonation of cis-Pt $(NH_3)_2L_2$, binding of heterometals or of a second Pt (vide infra) occurs readily. Guay and Beauchamp have reported similar findings with Ag (54) and CH_3Hg (55) coordinated to N3 of 1-MeT. Among the isolated heteronuclear complexes of cis-Pt$(NH_3)_2L_2$ two types of complexes have been established using X-ray crystallography: complexes of Pt,M and Pt_2,M stoichiometries.

For example, in cis-$[(NH_3)_2Pt(1-MeU)_2Cu(H_2O)_2]$ $SO_4 \cdot 4.5H_2O$ (38), Pt is coordinated by two NH_3 groups and two N3 donor atoms of the 1-MeU ligands, Cu(II) by two aquo ligands and two O4 donors of the heterocyclic rings. Both Pt and Cu have roughly square planar coordination spheres with the metals slightly out of these planes and directed towards each other, giving Pt-Cu separations of 2.765 Å. Formation of the head-head Pt,Cu dimer out of the head-tail cis-Pt$(NH_3)_2L_2$ compound indicates that rotation of one of the two ligands in the starting compounds has preceded formation of the heteronuclear Pt,Cu compound and may be considered a hint that O4 is more basic than O2. Nevertheless the possibility of N3,O2 bridging should not be excluded.

Two crystallographically confirmed examples of heteronuclear complexes of Pt_2,M stoichiometry exist, cis-$[(NH_3)_2$ $PtL_2ML_2Pt(NH_3)_2]^{n+2}X_n$ with M= Ag (56) and Mn (57) and L= 1-MeT as bridging ligand (Figures 10 and 11). In both cases the two Pt atoms have square planar coordination, bonded to two NH_3 groups and two N3 atoms of the 1-MeT ligands, and the heterometal M is coordinated by four oxygens of 1-MeT, most likely O4. (An unambiguous differentiation from O2 is not possible due to the crystallographic peculiarity of 1-MeT with its pseudotwofold axis through N3 and C6.) The main difference between the two compounds is in the coordination sphere of the heterometal: while Ag has a distorted tetrahedral coordination geometry, Mn has a square planar one. IR and Raman spectra of the compounds suggest that only in the Pt_2,Mn compound the Mn-O interaction has a marked covalent character, whereas the Ag-O interaction appears to be essentially ionic, since only in the case of the Pt_2, Mn compound the heterocyclic modes of the 1-MeT ligands are strongly perturbed compared with the bis (1-MeT)platinum complex. This conclusion is in agreement with the differences in M-O distances as well.

If one compares the distances between the respective coordinating and non-coordinating oxygens in the two compounds, e.g. Pt_2,Ag: O14-O24, 3.118 Å; O34-O44, 3.366 Å; O12-O22, 3.352 Å; O32-O42, 3.376 Å, one finds that they are rather similar. The same is true with the Pt_2Mn compound, although the distances are considerably shorter, as expected. If one thinks of binding of another heterometal M' to the available O2 atoms of Pt_2,ML_4 this implies, that the coordination sphere of M' must

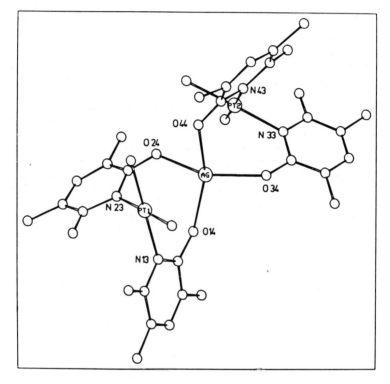

*Figure 10.   Molecular cation of [(NH₃)₂Pt(1-MeT)₂Ag(1-MeT)₂Pt(NH₃)₂]NO₃ •-
5H₂O. (Reproduced with permission from Ref. 56.)*

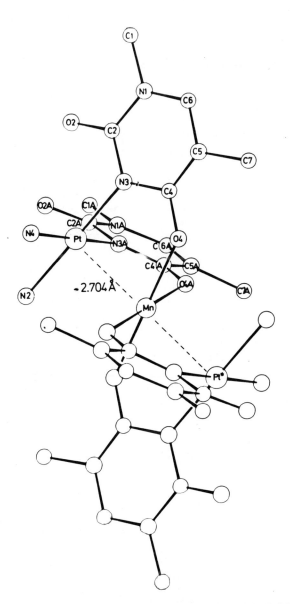

Figure 11.   Molecular cation of [(NH₃)₂Pt(1-MeT)₂Mn(1-MeT)₂Pt(NH₃)₂]Cl₂ •-
10H₂O. (Reproduced with permission from Ref. 57.)

be identical with that of the metal M. This is, for example, confirmed with the Pt_4,Ag complex described below, where the square
planar coordination geometry of the Pt bound to O4 forces Ag to
take the unusual square planar coordination as well.

Head-Head Platinum Dimer. Preparation and Reactivity.

Reaction of cis-Pt$(NH_3)_2L_2$ with one equivalent of the "diaquo"
species of Cisplatin gives in high yield the platinum dimer with
head-head arranged L ligands:

$$\text{cis-Pt}(NH_3)_2L_2 + \text{cis-}[Pt(NH_3)_2(H_2O)_2]^{2+}$$
$$\text{cis-}[Pt(NH_3)_2L_2Pt(NH_3)_2]^{2+}$$

With L= 1-MeT the structure of the head-head dimer has been
determined (58). Pt coordination occurs through N3 and (most
likely) O4. The compound bears some similarity with one half of
the α-pyridone dimer-of-dimers described by Hollis and Lippard
(41) which is the precursor of the tetrameric α-pyridone blue
described by Barton et al. (59), but the intermolecular Pt-Pt
separation in the 1-MeT compound (5.62 Å) is almost twice as
long as with the α-pyridone dimer-of-dimers (3.13 Å).

In an attempt to attach yet another metal to the
available second exocyclic oxygen of L, the 1-MeU head-head dimer
was reacted with Ag^+, and a compound of composition $[(NH_3)_8Pt_4$
$(1-MeU)_4Ag](NO_3)_5$ has been isolated (60). The pentanuclear
complex is composed of two head-head dimers, each with Pt bonded
to N3 and O4, and the two dimers are linked by Ag through the
available O2 atoms (Figure 13). Ag has square planar coordination
and is situated on the inversion centre of the cation, having
Ag-O distances of 2.34- 2.45 Å. Adjacent pentanuclear cations
are related by an inversion center, thus leading to stacks of Pt_4
units interrupted by Ag (Figure 14). The intermolecular distance
between neighboring Pt atoms is 3.25 Å only, and the Pt dimers
are oriented in a way identical with that of the Pt(II) dimer-of-
dimers of α-pyridone and that of the partially oxidized spezies.

The crystal structure of this Pt_4,Ag complex offers a
rationale as to how formation of a partially oxidized Pt complex
could conceivably take place. If one assumes that in a redox
reaction Ag^+ oxidizes a Pt_4 unit and is reduced to Ag^0, then the
oxidation state of Pt is increased from +2 to +2.25, as in the
α-pyridone blue. Indeed, slight warming of the Pt_4,Ag compound
in water gives a crystalline blue product of composition
$[(NH_3)_8Pt_4(1-MeU)_4](NO_3)_5 \cdot 5H_2O$ (60). Despite the lack of a
crystallographic confirmation due to insufficient crystal size,
all the other evidence - elemental analysis, reductive titration,
EPR spectrum - suggests that it is the analogue of the α-pyridone
blue. This assumption is further supported by an alternative
synthesis of the 1-methyluracil blue through HNO_3 oxidation of
the head-head dimer analogous to a method of Hollis and Lippard

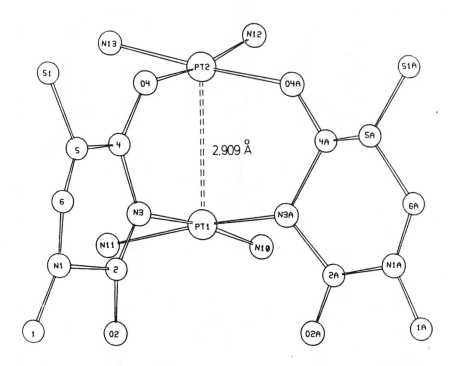

Figure 12.   Molecular cation of the head–head dimer cis-[(NH₃)₂Pt(1-MeT)₂Pt-(NH₃)₂](NO₃)₂. (Reproduced with permission from Ref. 58.)

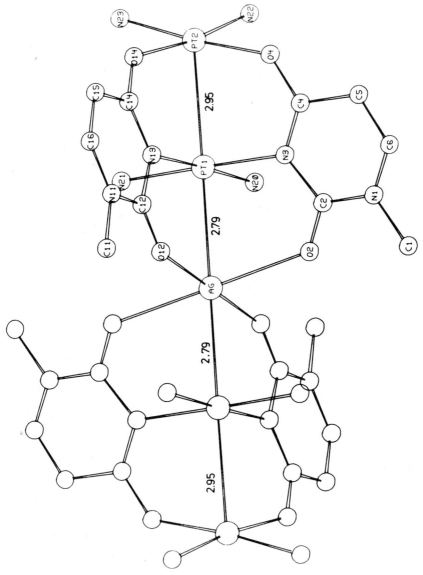

Figure 13.   Molecular cation of $[(NH_3)_8Pt_4(1\text{-}MeU)_4Ag]NO_3$. (Reproduced from Ref. 60. Copyright 1982, American Chemical Society.)

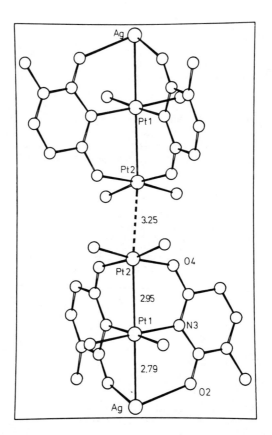

Figure 14.   Arrangement of adjacent cations of the Pt$_4$Ag compound. Only two halves of pentanuclear units are shown. (Reproduced from Ref. 60. Copyright 1982, American Chemical Society.)

to obtain the α-pyridone blue, and by the fact that the 1-MeU
blue, like the α-pyridone blue (61), can be further oxidized to
yellow-orange, diamagnetic, 1-MeU bridged complexes which most
likely are the analogues of the Pt(III) dimers obtained by
Hollis and Lippard (61).

Acknowledgments

        The work presented here has been made possible by the
joint efforts of Dr. Dietmar Neugebauer, Dr. Ulrich Schubert,
Jürgen Riede (crystal structures of 1-MeU and 1-MeT compounds),
Ruth Beyerle and Gabi Raudaschl (mixed nucleobase complexes),
Dr. Rudolf Pfab (complexes of unsubstituted thymine), Dr. Petr
Jandik (HPLC), Professor Colin J. L. Lock and Romolo Faggiani of
McMaster University, Hamilton, Canada (crystal structures of
complexes of unsubstituted uracil and thymine) and Dr. H. Howard-
Lock for corrections of the text. The generous financial support
by the Deutsche Forschungsgemeinschaft, DFG, and the Technische
Universität München is gratefully acknowledged.

Literature Cited

1. Marzilli, L. G.; Kistenmacher, T.J.; Eichhorn, G. L.
    Nucleic Acid-Metal Ion Interactions", Spiro, T. G., Ed.;
    John Wiley Sons:„New York, 1980; pp. 181-250.
2. Eichhorn, G. L. "Metal Ions in Biological Systems",
    Sigel, H., Ed., Marcel Dekker: New York, 1980; Vol. 10;
    pp. 1-21.
3. Davidson, J. P.; Faber, P. J.; Fischer, R. G.; Mansy, S.;
    Peresie, H. J.; Rosenberg, B.; Van Camp, L. Cancer
    Chemother. Rep., Part 1 1975, 59, 287.
4. Speer, R. J.; Ridgway, H.; Hall, L. M.; Stewart, D. P.;
    Howe, K. E.; Liebermann, D. Z.; Newman, A. D.; Hill, J. M.
    Ibid. 1975, 59, 629.
5. Wierzchowski, K. L.; Litonska, E.; Shugar, D. J. Am. Chem.
    Soc. 1974, 96, 6832.
6. Wittenberg, E. Chem. Ber. 1966, 99, 2391.
7. Nakanishi, K.; Suzuki, N.; Yamazaki, F. Bull. Chem. Soc. Jap.
    1961, 34, 53.
8. Shapiro, R.; Kang, S. Biochim. Biophys. Acta 1971, 231, 1.
9. Lippert, B. J. Raman Spectrosc. 1980, 9, 324.
10. Lock, C. J. L.; Pilon, R.; Lippert, B. Acta Crystallogr.,
    Sect. B. 1979, B 35, 2533.
11. Lippert, B. J. Raman Spectrosc. 1980, 9, 324.
12. Snyder, L. C.; Shulman, R. G.; Neuman, D. B. J. Chem. Phys.
    1975, 53, 199.
13. De Member, J. R.; Wallace, F. A. J. Am. Chem. Soc. 1975, 97,
    6240.
14. Tan, Y. L.; Beck, A. Biochim. Biophys. Acta 1973, 299, 500.
15. Weiss, R.; Venner, H. Hoppe-Seyler Z. Physiol. Chem. 1969,
    350, 396.

16. Srivastava, R. C.; Srivastava, M. N. J. Inorg. Nucl. Chem. 1978, 40, 1439.
17. Taqui Khan, M. M.; Krishnamoorthy, C. R. J. Inorg. Nucl. Chem. 1974, 36, 711.
18. Bhandari, A. M.; Solanki, A. K.; Wadhwa, S. J. Inorg. Nucl. Chem. 1981, 43, 2995.
19. Beck, W.; Kottmair, N. Chem. Ber. 1976, 109, 970.
2o. Inagaki, K.; Kidani, Y. Bioinorg. Chem. 1978, 9, 157.
21. Faggiani, R.; Lippert, B.; Lock, C. J. L. Inorg. Chem. 1980, 19, 295.
22. Lumme, P.; Mutikainen, I. Acta Crystallogr., Sect. B. 1980, B36, 2251.
23. Mutikainen, I.; Lumme, P. Acta Crystallogr., Sect. B. 1980, B36, 2237.
24. Kistenmacher, T. J.; Sorrell, T.; Marzilli, L. G. Inorg. Chem. 1975, 14, 2479.
25. Lippert, B.; Pfab, R.; Neugebauer, D. Inorg. Chim. Acta 1979, 37, L 495.
26. Faggiani, R.; Lippert, B; Lock, C. J. L.; Pfab, R. Inorg. Chem. 1981, 20, 2381.
27. Carrabine, J. A.; Sunderalingam, M. Biochemistry 1971, 10, 292.
28. Goodgame, M.; Johns, K. W. J. Chem. Soc., Dalton 1977, 17, 1680.
29. Dale, R. M. K.; Martin, E.; Livingston, D. C.; Ward, D. C. Biochemistry 1975, 14, 2447.
30. Mansy, S.; Tobias, R. S. Inorg. Chem. 1975, 14, 287.
31. Pfab, R.; Jandik, P.; Lippert, B. Inorg. Chim. Acta, in press.
32. Lippert, B. Inorg. Chem. 1981, 20, 4326.
33. Lippert, B.; unpublished results.
34. Lippert, B. Proc. Int. Conf. Raman Spectrosc. 7th 1980, 582.
35. Lallemand, J. Y.; Soulie, J.; Chottard, J. C. J. Chem. Soc., Chem. Commun. 1980, 436.
36. Lim, M. C.; Martin, R. B. J. Inorg. Nucl. Chem. 1976, 38, 1915.
37. Flynn, C. M.; Viswanathan, T. S.; Martin, R. B. J. Inorg. Nucl. Chem. 1977, 39, 437.
38. Neugebauer, D.; Lippert, B.; submitted.
39. (a) Orbell, J. D.; Marzilli, L. G.; Kistenmacher, T. J. J. Am. Chem. Soc. 1981, 101, 5126. (b) Faggiani, R.; Lippert, B.; Lock, C. J. L. Inorg. Chem., in press.
40. (a) Gellert, R. W.; Bau, R. J. Am. Chem. Soc. 1975, 97, 7379. (b) Cramer, R. E.; Dahlstrom, P. L.; Seu, M. J. T.; Norton, T.; Kashiwaga, M. Inorg. Chem. 1980, 19, 148. (c) Bau, R.; Gellert, R. W. Biochimie 1978, 60, 1040. (d) Marzilli, L. G.; Chalilpoyil, P.; Chiang, C. C.; Kistenmacher, T. J. J. Am. Chem. Soc. 1980, 102, 2480.
41. Hollis, L. S.; Lippard, S. J. J. Am. Chem. Soc. 1981, 103, 1230.

42. Lippert, B. Inorg. Chim. Acta 1981, 55, 5.
43. Lock, C. J. L.; Peresie, H. J.; Rosenberg, B.; Turner, G.
    J. Am. Chem. Soc. 1978, 100, 3371.
44. Faggiani, R.; Lock, C. J. L.; Pollock, R. J.; Rosenberg, B.;
    Turner, G. Inorg. Chem. 1981, 20, 804.
45. Neugebauer, D.; Lippert, B.; submitted.
46. Lippert, B. J. Clin. Hematol. Oncol. 1977, 7, 26.
47. Beyerle, R.; Lippert, B. Inorg. Chim. Acta 1982, 66, 141.
48. Raudaschl, G.; Lippert, B.; unpublished results.
49. Lippert, B. J. Am. Chem. Soc. 1981, 103, 5691.
50. Teo, B.-K.; Eisenberger, P.; Reed, J.; Barton, J. K.;
    Lippard, S. J. J. Am. Chem. Soc. 1978, 100, 3225.
51. Lippert, B.; Lock, C. J. L.; Rosenberg, B.; Zvagulis, M.
    Inorg. Chem. 1978, 17, 2971 and references.
52. Rosenberg, B. Biochimie 1978, 60, 859.
53. Boreham, C. J.; Broomhead, J. A.; Fairlie, D. P.
    Aust. J. Chem. 1981, 34, 659.
54. Guay, F.; Beauchamp, A. L. J. Am. Chem. Soc. 1979, 101, 6260.
55. Guay, F.; Beauchamp, A. L. Inorg. Chim. Acta 1982, 66, 57.
56. Lippert, B.; Neugebauer, D. Inorg. Chim. Acta. 1980. 46. 171.
57. Lippert, B.; Schubert, U. Ibid. 1981, 56, 15.
58. Lippert, B.; Neugebauer, D.; Schubert, U. Ibid. 1980, 46,L11.
59. (a) Barton, J.K.; Rabinowitz, H. N.; Szalda, D. J.;
    Lippard, S. J. J. Am. Chem. Soc. 1977, 99, 2827.
    (b) Barton, J. K.; Szalda, D. J.; Rabinowitz, H. N.;
    Waszczak, J. V.; Lippard, S. J. Ibid. 1979, 101, 1434.
60. Lippert, B.; Neugebauer, D. Inorg. Chem. 1982, 21, 451.
61. (a) Hollis, L. S.; Lippard, S. J. J. Am. Chem. Soc.
    1981, 103, 6761.
    (b) Hollis, L. S.; Lippard, S. J.; personal communication.

RECEIVED October 4, 1982

^{195}Pt- and ^{15}N-NMR Studies of Antitumor Complexes

ISMAIL M. ISMAIL and PETER J. SADLER

Birkbeck College, Department of Chemistry, University of London, Malet Street, London WC1E 7HX England

^{195}Pt and ^{15}N NMR studies at 4.7 and 9.4 T are used to characterise new Pt(II) and Pt(IV) anti-tumour drugs, to study the interaction of inosine (I) and 5^1-adenosine monophosphate (AMP) with cisplatin, and release of amines induced by binding to methionine sulphur of peptides and proteins. Drug characterisation is aided by the predictability of ^{195}Pt shifts and ^{195}Pt – ^{15}N coupling constants. Broadening through scalar coupling to ^{14}N can sometimes be overcome by raising the temperature. Contributions to ^{195}Pt relaxation from chemical shift anisotropy, not only make it difficult to observe signals from Pt bound to macromolecules, but can also lead to broadening of ^{195}Pt satellites of ^{1}H, ^{13}C, and ^{15}N resonances. N7–O6 chelation was not detected for I bound to cis-Pt(^{15}NH$_3$)Cl$_2$ at acidic pH levels, but may occur for the diaquo complex. Several previously undetected I and AMP species are reported. Finally, facile release of both NH$_3$ and a chelated diamine (ethylenediamine) was observed on reaction with N-Ac-Met, Gly-Met and RNase A in solution near neutral pH and it is suggested that such reactions may play an important part in the mechanism of action of Pt anti-tumour drugs.

0097-6156/83/0209-0171$06.00/0

In this paper we study three problems:
(i) the characterisation of Pt(II) and Pt(IV) anti-tumour drugs in solution by [195]Pt NMR,
(ii) the interaction of two nucleic acid bases inosine (I) and adenosine 5^1-monophosphate (AMP) with ^{15}N-labelled cis-Pt(NH$_3$)$_2$Cl$_2$ and cis-Pt(NH$_3$)$_2$(H$_2$O)$_2{}^{2+}$ by ^{15}N and [195]Pt NMR, and
(iii) the release of amines from cis-Pt(NH$_3$)Cl$_2$ and Pt(en)Cl$_2$ on binding to methionine-containing peptides and proteins, using primarily ^{15}N NMR.

Multinuclear NMR is potentially a very powerful technique for defining fully the coordination sphere of platinum anti-tumour drugs in solution and upon interaction with biomolecules. The properties of some useful nuclei are listed in Table I. In our studies we seek information about the oxidation state of platinum usually Pt(II) or Pt(IV),

Table I

Properties of some NMR nuclei useful in the study of
Pt anti-tumour drugs

Isotope	I	Abund.(%)	Freq.(MHz)	n.O.e.	Recept.
[1]H	1/2	99.98	200	–	1.0
[13]C	1/2	1.11	50.29	+3.0	1.8×10^{-4}
[15]N	1/2	0.37	20.27	-3.9	3.9×10^{-6}
[35]Cl	3/2	75.53	39.19	–	3.6×10^{-3}
[195]Pt	1/2	33.8	42.82	+3.3	3.4×10^{-3}

the number and types of coordinated ligands, their stereochemical arrangements, and dynamic processes including the rates of ligand substitution. Pt-induced ligand activations (e.g. lowered pK$_a$'s) are sometimes also detectable. All of these features appear to contribute to the biological activity of platinum complexes as exemplified by the following: cis but not trans Pt(II) diamine complexes are active anti-tumour drugs (1), PtCl$_4{}^{2-}$ and PtCl$_6{}^{2-}$ are potent allergens (2), whereas Pt(en)$_3{}^{4+}$ is a neurotoxin (3).

^{1}H NMR has the advantage of high sensitivity, and Pt binding can often be detected via spin-spin couplings to ligand nuclei up to 4 bonds away from Pt. These couplings can provide stereochemical information (4). However, [195]Pt satellites of ^{1}H, ^{13}C and ^{15}N resonances can be very broad and difficult to assign at high fields (5,6) where sensitivity is greatest for work on biomolecules. [35]Cl NMR is useful for studying Cl[-] release (7), but signals for Pt-bound chloride are too broad to observe.

We were attracted to [195]Pt NMR by its large, predictable chemical shift range of ca. 15,000 ppm.(8). [195]Pt - [15]N one-bond coupling constants are particularly sensitive to the nature of the _trans_ ligand (9,10,11,12). Sometimes [195]Pt coupling to quadrupolar ^{14}N is resolvable but, in general, we have resorted to enrichment of Pt diamines with [15]N. This has the advantage of making direct observation of ^{15}N NMR signals possible. Most of the work described here has only become possible in the last few years with the routine availability of high field (4.7 - 9.4 T) Fourier transform spectrometers with large sample tubes (10 - 15 mm diameter).

Experimental

[195]Pt and ^{15}N NMR spectra were recorded on Varian XL 200 (4.7 T), Bruker WM200 (4.7 T) or Bruker WH400 (9.4 T) spectrometers in 10 or 15 mm diameter tubes. H_2O was used as solvent, with 5-10% D_2O added or D_2O in a concentric tube for lock. This avoided significant deuteration of amine ligands. References were 1 M Na_2PtCl_6 in D_2O for [195]Pt, and 2.4 M [15]NH_4Cl in 1 M HCl for [15]N. Most ^{15}N spectra were obtained from overnight accumulations using 30°-60° pulses, 3.6s pulse repetition rates and a data point resolution of 0.6 Hz/point. In view of possible negative n.o.e.'s several spectra were checked against a phase reference. The high frequency - positive shift sign convention is used.

[195]Pt Chemical Shift Range

Most Pt complexes have low-lying excited electronic states, and [195]Pt NMR shifts are dominated by the paramagnetic term in Ramsey's equation (8). The Pt(IV) halides alone span some 12,500 ppm (8):

	PtF_6^{2-}	$PtCl_6^{2-}$	$PtBr_6^{2-}$	PtI_6^{2-}
δ/ppm	7326	0	-1870	-5121

The calculated shift of Pt(0) is -10,427 ppm (8), and removal of electrons to give Pt(II) leads to deshielding and high-frequency shifts. Pt(IV) resonances tend to be furthest to high frequency (low field), but there is considerable overlap.

Ligand exchange reactions of Pt(II) and (even more so) Pt(IV) are usually slow enough on the NMR timescale for separate resonances to be observable for each distinct Pt complex in solution. Interesting exceptions are Pt(II) aquo-hydroxo complexes which titrate as a single, averaged resonance (13), and exchange of amine with trans-Pt(ethene)(amine)Cl$_2$ which is rapid in CDCl$_3$(14). The latter may be relevant to the behavior of anti-tumour drugs in membranes.

Substitution shifts usually show regular, incremental patterns (15). For substitution of Br$^-$ into PtCl$_4{}^{2-}$ and PtCl$_6{}^{2-}$, the shift increments ($\Delta\delta$) vary with substitution step, n, according to (16):

$$-\Delta\delta(II) = 203 + 23.5n \text{ ppm}$$
$$-\Delta\delta(IV) = 275 + 11.7n \text{ ppm}$$

Even cis-trans and mer-fac isomers are usually well-separated in the spectrum: 10 ppm for the isomers of PtCl$_2$Br$_2{}^{2-}$, 208 ppm for Pt(NH$_3$)$_2$(H$_2$O)$_2{}^{2+}$, and 310 ppm for Pt(NO$_2$)$_4$Cl$_2{}^{2-}$ (12). Substitution shifts are smallest for substitutions trans to ligands with high trans influences. Thus, in Pt(IV) nitrite complexes, a Br$^-$ for Cl$^-$ substitution is ca. 50 ppm larger when trans to Cl$^-$ compared to trans to NO$_2{}^-$ (12). The term "trans influence" is used to denote the dependence of NMR (ground-state) parameters on the nature of the trans ligand. This is distinct from the "trans effect" which is related to bond labilization as measured by ligand substitution rates.

At very high fields (> 4.7 T), ^{35}Cl/^{37}Cl and ^{79}Br/^{81}Br isotopomers are resolvable (17) and, in principle, the number of halide ions bound to Pt can be deduced from the isotopomer splitting pattern. In practice, the shifts (0.167 ppm for Cl, 0.028 ppm for Br) are too small in comparison with the temperature dependence of ^{195}Pt shifts (0.3-1 ppm per °C rise in temp.) and natural linewidths of many complexes. Temperature gradients across samples are particularly marked when large sample tubes and ^{1}H decoupling are used.

Representative ^{195}Pt shifts for anti-tumour and related complexes are given in Table II. Figure 1 illustrates the regular pattern of NH$_3$ - H$_2$O substitution shifts in Pt(II) complexes. A similar graph is obtained for the NH$_3$ - Cl$^-$ system, giving the following incremental shifts:

$$\Delta\delta(NH_3 \text{ by } OH_2) = + 590 \text{ ppm}$$
$$\Delta\delta(NH_3 \text{ by } Cl^-) = + 270 \text{ ppm}$$

The sensitivity of ^{195}Pt NMR shifts to small changes in the types of bound ligands is very useful for the characterisation of new drugs. For example, the coordination of bis-carboxylates is often not convincingly detectable by ^{1}H or ^{13}C NMR, but Table II shows that replacement of two H$_2$O ligands by cyclobutanedicarboxylate gives a low frequency shift of 133 ppm (18).

Table II

^{15}N and ^{195}Pt NMR shifts and one-bond coupling constants for Pt(II) and Pt(IV) diamines

Complex	$\delta(^{195}Pt)$/ppm	$\delta(^{15}N)$/ppm	$^1J(^{195}Pt-^{15}N)$/Hz	Solvent
Pt(IV)				
$\underline{c},\underline{t}$-Pt(NH$_3$)$_2$(mal)(OH)$_2$	+1570	-	-	D$_2$O/H$_2$O$_2$
$\underline{c}$-Pt(C$_3$H$_7$NH$_2$)$_2$(OH)$_4$	+1521	-	249	D$_2$O
$\underline{c},\underline{c},\underline{t}$-Pt(C$_3H_7NH_2$)$_2Cl_2(OH)_2$	+881	-	266	D$_2$O
$\underline{c},\underline{c},\underline{t}$-Pt(NH$_3$)$_2Cl_2(OH)_2$	+860	-37.9	275	H$_2$O/H$_2$O$_2$
$\underline{c}$-Pt(NH$_3$)$_2$Cl$_4$	-145	-30.5	247	H$_2$O
Pt(II)				
[Pt(NH$_3$)$_2$(OH)]$_2$$^{2+}$	-	-81.7	342	H$_2$O
[Pt(NH$_3$)$_2$(OH)]$_3$$^{3+}$	-1499	-79.1	339	H$_2$O
$\underline{c}$-Pt(NH$_3$)$_2$(H$_2$O)$_2$$^{2+}$	-1590	-89.0	387	H$_2$O
Pt(NH$_3$)$_2$(Etmal)	-1694	-83.7	366	H$_2$O
Pt(NH$_3$)$_2$(CBDCA)	-1723	-	360	H$_2$O
Pt(en)(H$_2$O)$_2$$^{2+}$	-1914	-51.9	411	H$_2$O
$\underline{c}$-Pt(NH$_3$)$_2$Cl$_2$	-2048	-	302	DMF
	-2097	-	312	DMSO
	-2168	-	312	H$_2$O

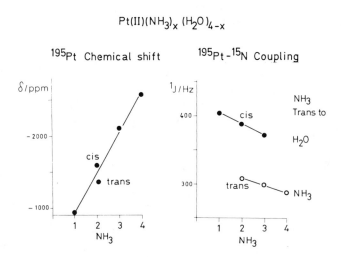

Figure 1.   Plots of the variation in ^{195}Pt chemical shift (left) and $^{195}Pt–^{15}N$ one-bond coupling constants with the number of NH_3 ligands in the complexes $[Pt(NH_3)_x$-$(H_2O)_{4-x}]^{2+}$ (right). The values for trans-$Pt(NH_3)_2(H_2O)_2^{2+}$ are those reported in Ref. 12.

^{195}Pt - ^{14}N, ^{15}N Couplings

One bond ^{195}Pt - ^{15}N coupling constants depend on the s character of the Pt orbitals used in bonding to N, and are expected to be smaller for a N ligand <u>trans</u> to a ligand which has a large <u>trans</u> influence since this tends to weaken the <u>trans</u> bond (9,10,11). The remarkable regularity of couplings in Pt(II)NH₃/ H₂O complexes is shown in Figure 1, where it can be seen that small <u>cis</u> effects also occur.

For <u>cis</u>-Pt(NH₃)₂ complexes, the order of <u>trans</u> influences based on ^{1}J is:

ligand :	H_2O	$<CO_2^-$	$<OH^-$	$<Cl^-$	$<NH_3$	$<S-Met$
^{1}J/Hz :	390	360	340	310	285	265

The ratio of Pt(II) : Pt(IV) ^{195}Pt - ^{15}N couplings would be expected to be 1.5, based on a hybridization change from dsp^2 to d^{2}sp^3 (9). From our limited data, Table II, it is apparent that <u>cis</u> effects from the additional axial ligands in Pt(IV) play a role. Many of the Pt(IV) couplings are higher than predicted, giving ratios of ca. 1.2.

^{15}N and ^{14}N couplings to ^{195}Pt are related by their gyromagnetic ratios:

$$^1J(^{195}Pt-^{15}N)/^1J(^{195}Pt - ^{14}N) = 2.711/1.932 = 1.40$$

However directly bonded ligand ^{14}N nuclei often cause severe broadening of ^{195}Pt resonances and hence couplings are unresolved. This leads us to a consideration of some important relaxation mechanisms for ^{195}Pt.

^{195}Pt Relaxation

Scalar Relaxation of the Second Kind. The linewidths of ^{195}Pt resonances from complexes with ^{14}N ligands are determined by the quadrupolar relaxation rate of ^{14}N, $(T_{1q})^{-1}$ where

$$(T_{1q})^{-1} = (T_{2q})^{-1} = \frac{3\pi^2(2I + 3)}{10I^2(2I-1)} \chi^2(1 + 1/3\eta^2)\tau_c$$

At high temperatures $(T_{1q})^{-1}$ decreases as the motional correlation time τ_c decreases. Provided that field gradients are small, (usually the case for coordinated primary amines), then T_{1q} may become long enough to allow resolution of ^{195}Pt - ^{14}N couplings. This is illustrated in Figure 2. Similarly, [<u>cis</u>-Pt(NH₃)₂(H₂O)₂]$^{2+}$ gives a broad resonance at 300 K, but at 343 K couplings are resolved (6). Conversely, at low temperatures, or in large molecules, effective decoupling of ^{14}N from ^{195}Pt may occur.

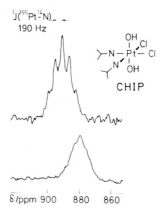

Figure 2. {^{1}H}–^{195}Pt-NMR spectra (43 MHz) of cis,cis,trans-Pt(isopropylamine)$_2$-Cl$_2$(OH)$_2$ in D$_2$O at 333 K (top) and 298 K (bottom) showing resolution of ^{195}Pt–^{14}N coupling at high temperature. The shift is temperature dependent. (Reproduced with permission from Ref. 6.)

Chemical Shift Anisotropy (CSA). CSA relaxation increases with the square of the applied field (B_0^2), nuclear screening anisotropy ($\Delta\sigma^2$), and with molecular weight and lowering of the temperature (τ_c increases):

$$[T_1(Pt)]^{-1}(CSA) = 6/7\ [T_2(Pt)]^{-1}(CSA)$$
$$= (2/15)\ \gamma_{Pt}^2\ B_0^2\ \Delta\sigma^2\ \tau_c$$

This has restricted many of our ^{15}N studies of Pt(II) complexes to intermediate fields (e.g. 4.7 T). Pt(IV) complexes are less anisotropic and the effect is less marked. It is probable that CSA relaxation is partly responsible for our failure to observe ^{195}Pt signals directly from Pt bound to macromolecules. CSA relaxation of ^{195}Pt can also lead to the disappearance of ^{195}Pt satellites from ^{1}H, ^{13}C or ^{15}N spectra. These are normally used as indications of binding sites. ^{195}Pt couplings appear in the spectra of coupled ligand nuclei as 1:4:1 multiplets only if relaxation times are the same in Pt(I=0) and ^{195}Pt species. Indications that differences could exist were noted in ^{1}H NMR studies by Erickson et al (4) on 1,2-diaminoethane complexes, and Lallemand et al (5) for nucleoside complexes. We have recently shown (6) for trans-Pt(ethene)(2-carboxy-pyridine)Cl$_2$ that the broadening of ^{1}H satellites at high field arises from ^{195}Pt relaxation via the CSA mechanism. The effect on the satellite linewidths is proportional to the spin-lattice relaxation rate of ^{195}Pt, $[2\pi T_1(Pt)]^{-1}$, and therefore to B_0^2 as shown above.

Spin-rotation. This relaxation mechanism is important for small complexes and unlike the others, increases with temperature. It appears to be dominant for PtCl$_4^{2-}$ and PtCl$_6^{2-}$ (19).

^{15}N Chemical Shift Range

^{15}N NMR shifts of amines bonded to Pt(II) appear to be determined largely by the nature of the trans ligand. We find the following approximate ranges for ligands trans to ^{15}NH$_3$:

δ/ppm :	-40 to -50 ;	-50 to -70 ;	-80 to -90
ligand :	S (Met, DMSO)	NH$_3$, Cl$^-$	H$_2$O, CO$_2^-$

It is notable that this order parallels trans influences in a similar manner to $^1J(^{195}Pt-^{15}N)$. Motschi and Pregosin (11a) have previously noted a strong correlation between $\delta(^{15}N)$ and $^1J(^{195}Pt-^{15}N)$ for a range of Pt(II) Schiff's base complexes.

Alei et al (20) clearly demonstrated that changes in ^{15}N shifts and $^{195}Pt-^{15}N$ couplings can be used to follow reactions of ^{15}N-enriched cis-diamine Pt(II) diaquo complexes with 1-methyl-imidazole (also enriched). The shift ranges for ethylenediamine complexes are similar to those above for NH$_3$ except that all peaks are shifted to high frequency by about 30 ppm.

Hydroxide-bridged Dimers and Trimers

An elegant use of ^{195}Pt NMR has been in kinetic studies of the oligomerization of Pt(II) diamines around neutral pH. ^{195}Pt spectra of ^{15}N-enriched [cis-Pt(NH$_3$)$_2$(H$_2$O)(OH)]$^+$ show well resolved resonances for monomer, dimer and trimer (hydroxide-bridged) species (21a). From these studies the half-life for disappearance of the monomer at pH 7 was calculated to be about 7 min. This system has also been studied by Boreham et al (22).

Gill and Rosenberg have recently reported (21b) a similar ^{195}Pt study for unenriched 1,2-diaminocyclohexane complexes. Although ^{14}N scalar coupling broadens the resonances, T_1 is now short enough to enable rapid pulse rates to be used without saturation. Spectra with good signal-to-noise ratios were acquired from 50 mM solutions in just a few minutes. The shift of the dimer is about 436 ppm to high frequency of the diaquo monomer. This is probably due to the short Pt - Pt contact (3.1 Å) since the resonance for the trimer (Pt - Pt, 3.7 Å) is shifted back to within 141 ppm of the diaquo complex. The stronger trans influence of bridging OH$^-$ compared to H$_2$O is reflected in a 40 Hz decrease in $^1J(^{195}$Pt-^{15}N), Table II. Terminal OH$^-$ ligands apparently have comparable trans influences to NH$_3$ (22).

Interaction of cis-Pt(NH$_3$)$_2$$^{2+}$ with Nucleic Acid Bases

Using a combination of ^{195}Pt and ^{15}N NMR, we have recently shown (23) that cis-Pt(NH$_3$)$_2$(H$_2$O)$_2$$^{2+}$ and its ethylenediamine (en) analogue react rapidly with acetamide to give a product in which the C=O group is bound to Pt through O with H$_2$O displacement. A 2 ppm shift of the ^{15}N NH$_3$ or en resonance to high frequency was observed in addition to a 47 ppm ^{195}Pt shift (23). We therefore sought to use similar methods to detect possible N7-O6 chelation with nucleic acid bases, the subject of much speculation.

For our initial studies, we chose inosine (I) and adenosine monophosphate (AMP), Figure 3. Only the former has the possibility of N7-O6 chelation. We chose to work at low pH's of ca. 2 where all the literature evidence seemed to point to N7 as the only binding site on both I and AMP (24,25). Acidic solutions also avoid any competing oligomerization reactions through OH$^-$ bridging. A ^{195}Pt NMR spectrum of a 1:1 mixture of I and cis-Pt(^{15}NH$_3$)$_2$Cl$_2$ which had reacted for 7 days at pH 2.3 in the dark is shown in Figure 4. The long reaction time was chosen merely to ensure the attainment of equilibrium. Unreacted complex (triplet, J = 312 Hz) as well as two sets of signals with shifts near those expected for PtN$_3$(H$_2$O) (-2330 ppm) and PtN$_4$ (-2440 ppm) species are seen. The broadening of these suggests coordination of I via ^{14}N. Curiously there appear to be two different PtN$_3$(H$_2$O) complexes possibly due to coordination of both N7 and N1. The shift of the proposed 1:2 complex compares well with the product of a similar reaction we have carried out with 2 equivalents of GMP.

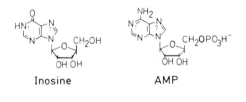

Figure 3.   Molecular structures of inosine (left) and adenosine 5'-monophosphate (right). At acidic pH values, the only Pt binding site expected is N7.

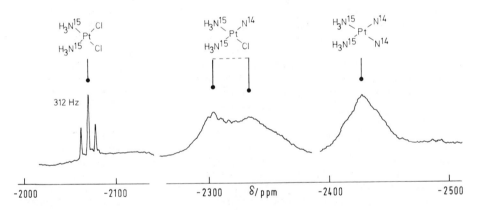

Figure 4.   {^{1}H}–^{195}Pt-NMR spectrum (43 MHz) of a 1:1 solution of cis-Pt-($^{15}NH_3$)$_2$Cl$_2$ and inosine (50 mM in H$_2$O/10% D$_2$O). Some of the Pt complex was present in suspension at the start of the reaction but almost all of it had dissolved after 7 d at 40 °C when this spectrum was recorded (pH 2.3).

A $\{^1H\}$ - ^{15}N NMR spectrum of the same inosine solution is shown in Figure 5. There is <u>no</u> observable signal in the 80-90 ppm range (not shown). This is the region expected for NH_3 <u>trans</u> to C=O if chelation occurs.   The resonance of 64.7 ppm (J=312 Hz) confirms the presence of unreacted <u>cis</u>-Pt$(NH_3)_2Cl_2$. All the resonances in the 61-69 ppm region are assigned to NH_3 ligands <u>trans</u> to N or Cl^-. There seems to be at least 7 resolved peaks, 5 of which have visible satellites. Resonance <u>5</u> has a coupling most appropriate to a PtN_4 complex (288 Hz) the other couplings lie between 304 and 335 Hz. No liberation of NH_4^+ is observed.   If [<u>cis</u>-Pt$(NH_3)_2$(N7-I)Cl]$^+$ and [<u>cis</u>-Pt$(NH_3)_2$(N7-I$_2$]$^{2+}$ were the only products, only three resonances would be expected. The presence of four additional peaks suggests either that there are additional binding sites (N1 or N3, not O), or that species with different base orientations or H-bonding interactions involving NH_3 are being detected. The sharpness of the satellite peaks suggests that all species are of low molecular weight.

Chu and Tobias (<u>24</u>) were unable to detect N7-O6 chelation for inosine by Raman spectroscopy, and suggested that a special stability was associated with <u>cis</u>-Pt$(NH_3)_2$(I)$_2$ perhaps through stacking of coordinated inosines. Their work on acidic solutions of <u>cis</u>-Pt$(NH_3)_2$(H$_2$O)$_2$$^{2+}$ suggested that only N7- coordinated 1:1 and 1:2 complexes were formed. Our ^{15}N spectra of similar solutions are shown in Figure 6 where inosine is compared to AMP. Peaks are now present in the 85-95 ppm range as expected for $^{15}NH_3$ <u>trans</u> to H$_2$O. If we ignore n.O.e. effects on intensities (although there is little justification for this) then there is a similar amount of unreacted diaquo complex in both cases. This is curious in view of the second binding site available on AMP, <u>although Pt has to displace a proton</u> (pK$_a$ of N1 ca. 4). Indeed, although peaks 1 and 3 are common to both spectra, peak 5 is unique to the AMP reaction and maybe due to the NH_3 <u>trans</u> to H$_2$O in [Pt$(NH_3)_2$ (N1-AMP)(H$_2$O)]$^{2+}$.   Again in the 60-70 ppm region there are more resonances than can be simply accounted for by N7 coordination alone for I, unless H-bonding, base-orientation or inter-molecular assocation are also involved.

We predicted that closure of the N7-O6 chelate ring would lead to a ca. 2 ppm shift of the <u>trans</u> NH_3 to high frequency. Possible candidates are resonances 1 (ring open) and 2 (closed) for I (Figure 6). Resonance 2 is absent for the AMP system as would be expected.

^{15}N NMR is therefore a powerful method for studying the interaction between nucleic acid bases and platinum drugs in solution. When combined with ^{195}Pt and ^1H NMR, more details of the interactions in solution should be revealed. Further work along these lines is in progress.

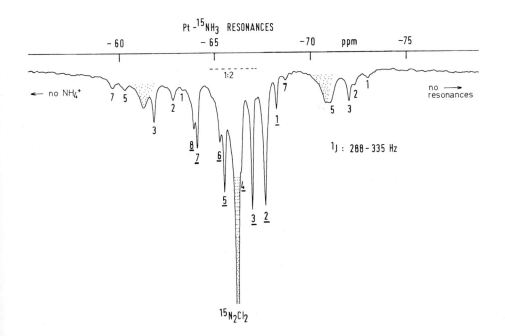

Figure 5.   {1H}–15N-NMR spectrum (20.3 MHz) of the same 1:1 solution of cis-Pt(15NH3)2Cl2 and inosine used in Figure 4. Main peaks and their 195Pt satellites are numbered.

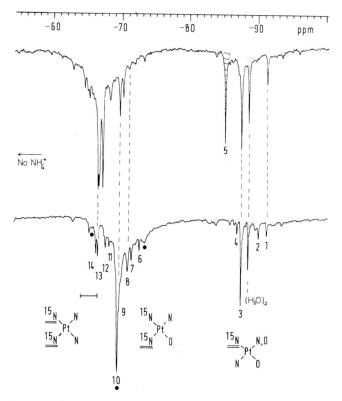

Figure 6. {¹H}–¹⁵N-NMR spectra (40.6 MHz) of 0.32 M cis-Pt(¹⁵NH₃)₂(H₂O)₂²⁺ in the presence of 0.5 molar equivalents of AMP (top, pH 2.2) and inosine (bottom, pH 1.9) 1 d after mixing. Resonances from ca. —65 to —75 ppm and —85 to —95 ppm are assigned to ¹⁵NH₃ ligands trans to N or Cl⁻ and O, respectively. A resonance due to unreacted Pt complex appears in both spectra at —89 ppm.

Drug Binding to Methionine in Peptides and Proteins: Release of Coordinated Amines

Our interest in Pt binding to methionine residues of proteins was first aroused by the observations of crystallographers (26) that $PtCl_4^{2-}$ and cis-Pt(NH$_3$)$_2$Cl$_2$ bind specifically to the Met S atoms in protein crystals, sometimes with secondary binding to His if the pH is high enough (pH 6-7). However, the resolution in electron density maps of proteins is rarely high enough to allow complete definition of the coordination sphere of Pt. This lead Dickerson to propose that on binding to cytochrome c, $PtCl_4^{2-}$ becomes 6-coordinate: a Pt(IV)Cl$_4$(SMet)L adduct (26). Chemically this seemed very unlikely, as discussed by Petsko et al (27), and we sought to use a combination of ^{195}Pt NMR shifts and ^{15}N couplings to define the binding sites.

All our attempts to observe ^{195}Pt NMR signals from either $PtCl_4^{2-}$ or cis-Pt(^{15}NH$_3$)$_2$Cl$_2$ bound to reduced cytochrome c or ribonuclease A (RNase) have so far failed. These platinum complexes are known to bind to the sulphur atoms of exposed methionines (residues 65 and 29 of Cyt c and RNase respectively) as shown by our previous ^{1}H NMR studies on RNase (28) and those of Boswell et al on Cyt c (29) and x-ray crystallography. We assume therefore that the resonances are broadened beyond detection via chemical shift anisotropy relaxation. The restriction of Pt mobility on the protein will lead to a large increase in τ_c (see CSA equation above). The anisotropy term would also be expected to increase. Scalar coupling to ^{14}N will also contribute to the increase in linewidths if nitrogen binding sites are involved.

To make sure that our search of the ^{195}Pt chemical shift range was concentrated in the correct regions, we studied a number of model reactions. Displacement of one Cl$^-$ by S of Met leads to a high field shift of ca. 1000 ppm, whereas introduction of further S to give PtN$_2$S$_2$, PtNS$_3$ and PtS$_4$ gives further incremental shifts of 600, 300 and 0 ppm respectively. The most interesting feature of the ^{15}N NMR spectrum of a solution containing cis-Pt(NH$_3$)$_2$Cl$_2$ and N-acetyl-L-Met (1:2) pH 2.2, after 3.5 hr reaction at 298 K, is the large peak for NH$_4^+$. All the other peaks are explicable by S coordination: cis-Pt(NH$_3$)$_2$(S-NAcMet)Cl and cis-Pt(NH$_3$)(S-NAcMet)Cl$_2$.

Reactions of cis-Pt(NH$_3$)$_2$Cl$_2$ with RNase A at pH 6.5 also lead to the release of coordinated NH$_3$, Figure 7. Unlike the N-Ac-Met system above, no signals are observed for ^{15}NH$_3$ trans to S. It seems that NH$_4^+$ production induced by the high trans influence of S is a general reaction and, in particular, does not require a low pH. Once S displaces Cl$^-$, NH$_3$ release appears to be more favourable with the protein, although in analogous reactions of cis-Pt(NH$_3$)$_2$(H$_2$O)$_2^{2+}$ added to RNase A at pH 6, intermediates with NH$_3$ trans to S are detectable.

Our report seems to be the first direct demonstration of NH$_3$ release on reaction of Pt drugs with peptides and proteins, although Volstein et al (30,31) have isolated analogous products from reaction of methionine itself (which can chelate via S and NH$_2$) with cis-Pt(NH$_3$)$_2$Cl$_2$.

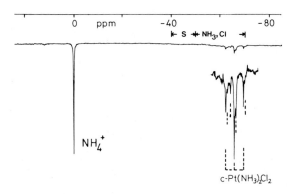

Figure 7.   {^1H}–^{15}N-NMR spectrum (40.6 MHz) of a 6 mM solution of RNase A that had reacted with 5 molar equivalents of cis-Pt($^{15}NH_3$)$_2$Cl$_2$ for 8 d (final pH 6.5).

This raises the question of whether the differing biological activities of cis and trans Pt(II) diamines could be related to S-induced amine release. This would be a kind of biological Kurnakov test! Kurnakov distinguished (32) between cis and trans-Pt(NH$_3$)$_2$Cl$_2$ by their reactions with thiourea: the cis isomer gives a yellow tetrakisthiourea species, whereas no NH$_3$ is released from the trans complex giving the white product, [trans-Pt(NH$_3$)$_2$(thiourea)$_2$]$^{2+}$. However, for this to be an important biological event, it would need to apply to chelated diamine complexes also, and this seemed less likely. Indeed, Romeo et al reported (33) that significant amounts of the ring-opened form of [Pt(en)(DMSO)Cl]$^+$ are present in solution only at high H$^+$ (molar) and Cl$^-$ concentrations, based on uv-visible spectra.

Thus we were somewhat surprised to find that reations of cis-Pt(en)Cl$_2$ with both N-acetyl-L-methionine (as a model system) and with RNase A lead to significant release of free ethylenediamine, Figures 8 and 9. The greater difficulty in displacing en relative to NH$_3$ is reflected in the presence of peaks for ^{15}N trans to S in the spectrum. A curious feature in Figure 9 is the additional peak ca. 3 ppm to low field of enH$_2$$^{2+}$. Only further experiments will determine whether this is monodentate (dangling-arm) en, or perhaps en bound to the protein.

Finally, we describe a model reaction which suggests that some binding sites in proteins could lead to very efficient amine release. Reaction of one equivalent of the dipeptide Gly-L-Met with cis-Pt(NH$_3$)$_2$Cl$_2$ at pH 5.5 leads to a very efficient release of NH$_3$. This is attributable to the tridentate binding of the peptide via S, deprotonated NH, and NH$_2$ groups: a mode of coordination found by Freeman and Golomb (34) in the crystal structure of Pt(Gly-L-Met)Cl with deprotonation of NH even at pH 2.5. This raises the question as to whether binding of Pt to Met residues of proteins can be followed by binding to N$^-$ (deprotonated NH) of the neighbouring peptide linkage, although it seems likely that this reaction needs to be driven by additional NH$_2$ coordination. It is pertinent to note that the SCH$_3$ ^{1}H NMR shift of Fe^{2+} cytochrome c on reaction with Pt complexes differs markedly from that observed in a model system of N-Ac-Met where coordination is to S only (29).

Biological Significance of Amine Release. Our suggestion that amine release may be an important in vivo event for Pt antitumour drugs was not supported by animal studies, until recently. The early work of Talyor et al (35) appeared to establish that ^{195}Pt and ^{14}C-labelled Pt(en)Cl$_2$ were metabolised similarly in rats. However this study, which was based on a single 24h time point, has recently been extended. Robins and Leach now find (36), using ^{191}Pt and ^{14}C-labelled Pt(en)Cl$_2$ and cis-Pt(NH$_3$)$_2$Cl$_2$, that dissociation of ligand from Pt occurs as soon as 1 hr after administration to mice bearing ADJ/PC6 plasma cell tumours. Proliferating tissues of the gut and tumour take up ^{14}C into DNA

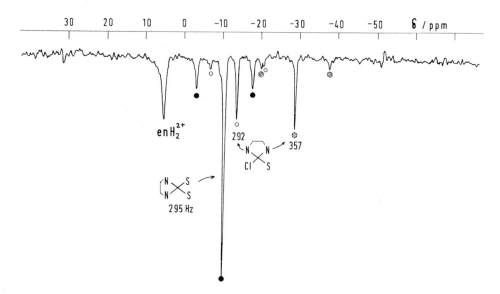

Figure 8. $\{^1H\}-^{15}N$-*NMR spectrum (20.3 MHz) of a 0.1 M solution of Pt(^{15}N-en)Cl$_2$ containing two molar equivalents of N-acetyl-L-methionine at pH 2.8 and reaction time of 1 wk, although equilibrium may be reached earlier than this.*

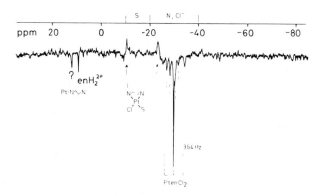

Figure 9. $\{^1H\}-^{15}N$-*NMR spectrum (40.6 MHz) of Pt(^{15}N-en)Cl$_2$ after reaction with RNase A (6 mM) in a 5:1 molar ratio for 7 d (3 d at 37 °C and 4 d at 20 °C in darkness). Initially much of the Pt complex was present as a suspension. Peaks for unreacted complex appear in the spectrum. The phases of peaks were checked against a phase reference. The loss of n.0.e. on the signals from the proposed Pt(en)Cl(S–Met–Protein) species is consistent with a lowered mobility (longer τ_c) for these ^{15}N nuclei. Relaxation via mechanisms other than dipolar coupling to ^{1}H may also be occurring.*

from day 4 in parallel with the rise in synthetic activity, but this is not paralleled by an uptake of [191]Pt. Levels of [191]Pt in the gut and tumour from cis-Pt(NH_3)_2Cl_2 are much greater than those from PtenCl_2, perhaps a reflection of the ease of release of NH_3 compared to en. We therefore conclude that studies of the mechanism of action of Pt anti-tumour complexes should include consideration of the consequences of protein as well as nucleotide binding. The active metabolites may well be different from those currently considered. A controlled transfer of Pt from proteins to DNA could occur, and it is pertinent to note that methionine is thought to play a key role in the initiation of protein synthesis. The fate of released amines also requires further attention. Taken together, these new approaches may lead to a better understanding of structure-activity relationships.

Acknowledgments

We thank the SERC, MRC, Johnson Matthey Ltd and the University of London Intercollegiate Research Service for support. We are also grateful to Mr. P. Hydes and Dr. C. Barnard (Johnson Matthey) for discussions and loan of Pt compounds, Mr. M. Buckingham and Dr. G. Hawkes (ULIRS High Field NMR Service), Dr. J. Feeney and Dr. P. Morris (MRC Biomedical NMR Centre) for assistance with some NMR measurements, and Dr. A.B. Robins (Royal Marsden) for discussion of his unpublished results. PJS is a Nuffield Foundation Science Research Fellow 1981-82.

Literature Cited

1.   Connors, T.A., Jones, M., Ross, W.C.J., Braddock, A.R., Khokhar, A.R., Tobe, M.L.   Chem.-Biol. Interact.,1972,5,415.
2.   Cleare, M.J., Hughes, E.G., Jacoby, B., Pepys, J.   Clin. Allergy,1976,6,183.
3.   Cleare, M.J.   Coord. Chem. Rev.,1974,12,349.
4.   Erickson, L.E., Sarneski, J.E., Reilley, C.N.   Inorg. Chem., 1975,14,3007.
5.   Lallemand, J-Y., Soulié, J., Chottard, J-C., J.C.S. Chem. Commun.,1980,436.
6.   Ismail, I.M., Kerrison, S.J.S., Sadler, P.J.   Polyhedron, 1982,1,57.
7.   Laverick, M., Nias, A.H.W., Ismail, I.M., Sadler, P.J. Br. J. Cancer Res.,1981,732.
8.   Garth Kidd, R., Goodfellow, R.J.   "NMR and the Periodic Table", Harris, R.K., Mann, B.E. Ed, Academic 1978, 249.
9.   Pregosin, P.S., Omura, H., Venanzi, L.M.   J. Amer. Chem. Soc., 1973,95,2047.
10. Kerrison, S.J.S., Sadler, P.J.   J.C.S. Chem. Commun.,1977,861.
11. (a) Motschi, H., Pregosin, P.S.   Helv. Chim. Acta, 1980,40, 141.
     (b) Motschi, H., Pregosin, P.S., Venanzi, L.M.   Helv. Chim. Acta, 1979,62,667.

12. (a) Kerrison, S.J.S. Ph.D. Thesis, London University,
        London, 1982.
    (b) Kerrison, S.J.S., Sadler, P.J. J. Chem. Soc. Dalton,
        1982, in press.
13. Freeman, W., Pregosin, P.S., Sze, S.N., Venanzi, L.M. J.
    Magn. Res.,1976,22,473.
14. Al-Najjar, I.M., Green, M., Kerrison S.J.S., Sadler, P.J.
    J. Chem. Res. (S),1979,206.
15. Goggin, P.L., Goodfellow, R.J., Haddock, S.R., Taylor, B.F.,
    Marshall, I.R.H. J.C.S. Dalton,1976,459.
16. Kerrison, S.J.S., Sadler, P.J. J. Magn. Res.,1978,31,321.
17. Ismail, I.M., Kerrison, S.J.S., Sadler, P.J. J.C.S. Chem.
    Commun.,1980,1175.
18. Neidle, S., Ismail, I.M., Sadler, P.J. J. Inorg. Biochem.,
    1980,13,205.
19. Pesek, J.J., Mason, W.R. J. Magn. Res.,1977,25,519.
20. Alei, M., Vergamini, P.J., Wageman, W.E., J. Amer. Chem. Soc.,
    1979,101,5415.
21. (a) Rosenberg, B. Biochimie,1978,60,859.
    (b) Gill, G.S., Rosenberg, B. J. Amer. Chem. Soc.,1982,in
        press.
22. Boreham, C.J., Broomhead, J.A., Fairlie, D.P. Aust. J. Chem.
    1981,34,659.
23. Kerrison, S.J.S., Sadler, P.J. J.C.S. Chem. Commun.,1981,61.
24. Chu, G.Y.H., Tobias, R.S. J. Amer. Chem. Soc.,1976,98,2641.
25. Barton, J.K., Lippard, S.J. in "Nucleic Acid-metal Ion
    Interactions", Spiro, T.G. Ed, Wiley Inter. Sci., New York,
    1980,1,(Metal Ions in Biology Series, p.32).
26. Dickerson, R.E., Eisenberg, D.E., Varnum, J., Kopka, M.L.
    J. Mol. Biol.,1969,45,77.
27. Petsko, G.A., Phillips, D.C., Williams, R.J.P., Wilson, I.A.
    J. Mol. Biol.,1978,120,345.
28. Sadler, P.J., Benz, F.W., Roberts, G.C.K. Biochim. Biophys.
    Acta,1974,359,13.
29. Boswell, A.B., Moore, G.R., Williams, R.J.P. Biochem. J.,
    1982,201,523.
30. Volshtein, L.M., Krylova, L.F., Mogilevkina, M.F. Russ. J.
    Inorg. Chem.,1965,10,1077.
31. Volshtein, L.M., Krylova, L.F., Mogilevkina, M.F. Russ. J.
    Inorg. Chem.,1963,8,304.
32. Kurnakov, N.S. J. Russ. Phys. Chem. Soc.,1893,25,565.
33. Romeo, R., Lanza, S., Tobe, M.L. Inorg. Chem.,1977,16,785.
34. Freeman, H.C., Golomb, M.L. J.C.S. Chem. Commun.,1970,1523.
35. Talyor, D.M., Jones, J.D., Robins, A.B. Biochem. Pharmacol.,
    1973,22,833.
36. Robins, A.B., Leach, M.O. Cancer Chemother. and Pharmacol.,
    1982, in press.

RECEIVED October 4, 1982

Conformational Properties of Purine and Pyrimidine Complexes of *cis*-Platinum

Implications for Platinum(II)–DNA Crosslinking Modes

THOMAS J. KISTENMACHER and JOHN D. ORBELL
The Johns Hopkins University, Department of Chemistry, Baltimore, MD 21218

LUIGI G. MARZILLI
Emory University, Department of Chemistry, Atlanta, GA 30322

The stereochemical properties of a variety of cis
complexes of Pt(II) containing purine or pyrimidine
ligands are examined. The critical intramolecular
conformational parameters [the interbase dihedral
angle and the base/coordination plane dihedral
angles] are systematically studied and trends sought.
Where intramolecular interactions are determinative
of the adopted molecular conformation, the nature of
the steric demands imposed by increasing numbers of
exocyclic functional groups contiguous to the Pt
binding site are clearly of major import.

Within the past several years, there has been literally an
explosion of chemical and biochemical studies (1) directed toward
elucidating the mode of action of platinum(II) anti-tumor drugs,
typified by cis-Pt(NH$_3$)$_2$Cl$_2$ (2). It is perhaps not inappropriate
to suggest, however, that while significant progress has been
made, the mode (or modes) of action of such Pt(II) reagents at
the molecular level remains elusive. A leading hypothesis is
that the primary molecular targets for active Pt(II) complexes
are the nucleobases of cellular DNA. In the event that DNA is
the "active" macromolecular target, several experimental results
can be cited (3-6) which implicate metal-base binding at regions
rich in guanosine-cytidine (G-C) residues as both prevalent and
possibly of mechanistic importance.
     The various results accumulated thus far have led to
numerous proposals for ways in which Pt(II) agents may bind to
the nucleobases of DNA so as to cause mutagenesis (by inducing
base-mispairing) or cell death (by introducing one or more
"defects" which cancer cells may find difficult or impossible to
repair). Both the cis and trans isomers of a reagent such as
Pt(NH$_3$)$_2$Cl$_2$ are mutagenic, and to some extent carcinogenic, but
only the cis isomer has significant anti-tumor activity (1). One
of the requirements for anti-tumor activity in these systems,

0097-6156/83/0209-0191$06.00/0

then, centers about the availability of two adjacent sites at the
Pt(II) center. The possibility has naturally arisen that each of
these sites is utilized to form a covalent bond to a nucleobase -
leading to the formation of an interstrand or an intrastrand
metal-mediated cross-link.

One chemical approach toward achieving resolution of the
mode of action of cis-Pt(II) complexes at the molecular level has
been to synthesize various model complexes of the general formulation cis-A_2PtB_2, where A is NH_3 or A_2 is a bidentate chelate
such as ethylenediamine (en) or trimethylenediamine (tn) and the
B ligands are nucleobases, nucleosides or nucleotides. The principal advantage of this approach is that these complexes are
usually isolable (often in crystalline form) and readily studied
both in solution and the solid state by a variety of spectroscopic techniques (e.g., NMR, IR, RAMAN, ORD/CD, and X-ray
scattering - both EXAFS and single crystal). The major disadvantage of these model systems lies in deducing to what degree
correlations that arise from such systematic studies can be
carried over with fidelity to a Pt(II)-DNA complex.

In this report, we briefly summarize some of the major correlations, emphasizing molecular conformational properties, for
cis-A_2PtB_2 complexes which have become available through single-
crystal X-ray diffraction studies. An attempt is also made to
suggest which of these deductions are most likely to be worthy of
consideration as possible elements of any detailed description of
an "in vivo" Pt(II)-DNA complex and its possible role in antitumor activity.

Nucleobase Binding Sites

In any systematic analysis of the binding of a metal to the
nucleobases of DNA, a careful scrutiny of the variety of endocyclic nitrogen atom sites available or potentially available at
physiological pH is of central importance. In this section, we
enumerate for each nucleobase the various metal binding sites,
paying particular attention to the number and the nature of the
exocyclic functional groups near to these sites. To this end, we
present in Figure 1 illustrations of four commonly employed
nucleobases (9-methylguanine, 9-methyladenine, 1-methylcytosine
and the thymine monoanion). Also presented in Figure 1 are in-
plane electrostatic potential energy maps for these bases. These
maps are ready visualizations of the availability of the lone
pair density for each base and the possible role of electro-
statics in any particular metal binding mode.

Guanosine. Near pH 7, the N(7) site (Figure 1) on a guanine
base has an available pair of electrons and is known to bind
metals (notably Pt(II) and Pd(II)) to produce stable complexes
(7, 8, 9). The presence of the nearby O(6) carbonyl oxygen atom
has led to a continuing speculation (10-13) that this exocyclic

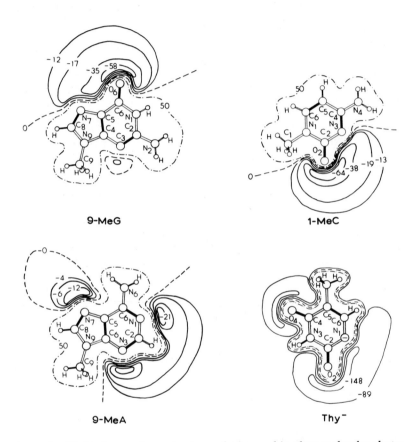

Figure 1.   Molecular topology, atomic numbering, and in-plane molecular electrostatic potential energy maps for a, 9-methylguanine (9-MeG); b, 9-methyladenine (9-MeA); c, 1-methylcytosine (1-MeC); and d, the N1-deprotonated thymine monoanion (Thy⁻). Contour levels for the electrostatic potential energy maps are given in kcal/mol as in Ref. 21 and 26.

oxygen atom may play an important role in M-N(7)-bound guanosine systems (e.g., the possible presence under certain conditions of a M-N(7),O(6) chelation binding mode).

The N(1) site on guanosine (Figure 1) is protonated at pH 7. It is known, however, that both alkylation (14) and Pt(II) binding (14, 15, 16) at N(7) can reduce the pKa of the N(1)-H proton by ca. 2 log units, leading to significant N(1) deprotonation at pH 7. As for the case of N(7) metal binding, the possible role of O(6) for metal attack at N(1) has been considered (17-22). (It is worthwhile to note that there is one example in the literature of a Cu(II) complex which exhibits a direct M-O(6) binding mode (23) and recent spectroscopic evidence which suggests O(6) binding by N(1)-deprotonated guanine derivatives in solution (22)). A point of particular interest to us here, however, is that the deprotonated N(1) site of guanosine is expected to be a strong nucleophile. In addition, we note that this site is flanked by an exocyclic amino group as well as an exocyclic oxo group (Figure 1). (For the less common nucleoside inosine, the exocyclic amino group at C(2) is missing, and the deprotonated N(1) binding site has only the adjacent oxo group nearby).

Adenosine. Unlike guanosine, both the N(7) and N(1) base binding sites of adenosine have lone pair density available for metal binding at pH 7 (Figure 1). These two sites are, for N(9)-substituted 6-aminopurines, of about equal metal binding strength (9, 24), and there is reason to speculate (25, 26) that the availability of these two metal binding sites leads to multiple metal binding and polymer formation in metal-adenosine systems.

The major stereochemical difference in the environments about the N(7) and N(1) sites of adenosine is that, for the latter site, the exocyclic amino group is adjacent to the site of potential metal attack, while for M-N(7) binding this amino group lies off a β-carbon atom (Figure 1).

Cytidine. Near neutral pH, only the N(3) site on a cytosine base has lone pair density available for metal binding (Figure 1). We wish to emphasize that the N(3) site on a cytosine base is directly analogous to the N(1)-deprotonated site on guanosine, in that both have an exocyclic amino and an exocyclic oxo group on their respective α-carbon atoms. (It has also been shown that under relatively mild conditions (27, 28) deprotonation of the exocyclic amino group of cytosine can occur followed by metal binding at this group).

Thymidine. Under basic conditions, thymine exists as a tautomeric mixture of monoanions (29), with either N(1) or N(3) deprotonated (the N(1) deprotonated tautomer and its electrostatic potential map are illustrated in Figure 1). Deprotonation of a thymidine residue in a polynucleotide allows the potential for metal attack at N(3). This site is contiguous to two oxo

functional groups; the possible utilization of these carbonyl
oxygen atoms in the formation of dimeric and polymeric metallo
species has been an active area of investigation (17, 18, 30-32
and references therein).

In Table I, we summarize the endocyclic base binding sites
for the common nucleosides discussed above and reiterate the
nature of the exocyclic functional groups near these sites.

Table I

Nucleobase Metal Binding Sites and the Nature of the
Substituents Contiguous to the Binding Site

Nucleoside	Binding Site	Adjacent Substituents
Adenosine	N(7)	-H;
	N(1)	-H; -N(6)H$_2$
Guanosine	N(7)	-H;
	N(1)*	-N(2)H$_2$; =O(6)
Inosine	N(7)	-H;
	N(1)*	-H; =O(6)
Cytidine	N(3)	-N(4)H$_2$; =O(2)
Thymidine	N(3)*	=O(2); =O(4)

*Requires deprotonation prior to or concomitant with metal binding

Stereochemical Properties of cis-A$_2$PtB$_2$ Complexes

For the class of complexes symbolized by cis-A$_2$PtBB' (where
B and B' are potentially different nucleobases, nucleosides or
nucleotides), the principal intramolecular conformational parameters are the following: (1) the interbase dihedral angle (B/B');
and, (2) the base/PtN$_4$ coordination plane dihedral angles (B/PtN$_4$
and B'/PtN$_4$). It became clear to us in the course of attempting
to compare these conformational parameters over a wide variety of
complexes studied by single-crystal X-ray diffraction methods
that some convention needed to be advanced (33). For example,
the B/B' dihedral angle, as with other dihedral angles, may be
defined as an angle or its supplement, leading to potential con-
fusion and inappropriate comparisons.

In order to achieve a meaningful comparison among different
complexes, it was decided that a visual as well as an analytical
description of these dihedral angles was essential. As our proposed convention has been detailed elsewhere (33), we offer here
a simplified illustration sufficient for the appreciation of the
comparisons and trends presented later. In Figure 2, the B/B',
B/PtN$_2$Cl$_2$ and B'/PtN$_2$Cl$_2$ dihedral angles are illustrated for the
complex cis-dichlorobispyridineplatinum(II) (34). The B/B' draw-
ing, for example, is achieved by confining one of the two cis
pyridine bases (the one containing atom N(2) has been chosen) to

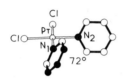

BASE/BASE DIHEDRAL ANGLE

(1) PLACE ONE BASE IN-PLANE

   SO $\overrightarrow{N-Pt}$ IS LEFTWARD

(2) SECOND BASE OUTWARD

(3) DEDUCE IF ANGLE IS ≥90°

BASE/PTN$_4$ DIHEDRAL ANGLE

(1) ORIENT ONE $\overrightarrow{N-Pt}$ NORMAL

   TO THE VIEWING PLANE

(2) SECOND $\overrightarrow{Pt-N}$ LEFTWARD

(3) SENSE OF ANGLE(≥90°) AS

   INDICATED

*Figure 2.   Systematic molecular conformational drawings for cis-dichlorobispyri-
dineplatinum(II) and the essence of the proposed conformational convention.*

the plane of the paper and to the right of the second base (containing atom N(1)), which projects outward toward the viewer.

The convention (33) yields a B/B' interbase dihedral angle of 72° for the present complex as the pyridine ring containing N(1) is obviously tilted toward that containing N(2). It is clear to us that the definition of the interbase dihedral angle at 72° is superior to that of its supplement 108°. By a similar procedure (see Figure 2), one obtains base/PtN$_2$Cl$_2$ dihedral angles of 124° (N(1)-ring) and 118° (N(2)-ring). In this case (and all others considered subsequently), we have employed least-squares planes obtainable from published fractional coordinates to derive numerical values for the dihedral angles.

Applications to cis-Bis(purine)Pt(II) Complexes. There are presently available a large number of cis-bis(N(7)-bound purine base)Pt(II) complexes whose molecular structures have been determined by X-ray diffraction techniques. For the most part, the nucleobase in these systems is a 6-oxopurine derivative (7). Figure 3 presents conformational drawings for three of these complexes: the cis-[Pt(en)(1,3,9-trimethylxanthine)$_2$]$^{2+}$ cation (35); the [Pt(en)(guanosine)$_2$]$^{2+}$ cation (36); and [Pt(tn)(Me-5'-GMP$_2$)]$^{\circ}$ (37), where Me-5'-GMP is the phosphate methyl ester of guanosine 5'-monophosphate. Since each of these three complexes is required to possess C$_2$ molecular symmetry in the solid state, only one of the B/PtN$_4$ dihedral angles is illustrated in Figure 3.

From Figure 3, it is clear that the B/B' interbase conformational angle (as well as the B/PtN$_4$ dihedral angle) decreases significantly on going from the bis(nucleobase) complex, through the bis(nucleoside) complex, to the bis(nucleotide) complex. This trend has been rationalized by suggesting that across the series there is an increasing amount of attractive intracomplex base/base interaction which culminates with the nucleotide complex. Specific interbase interactions involving the carbonyl oxygen atom O(6) of one base and the Pt-bound imidazole ring of the two-fold related nucleotide have been cited (37) as possibly of particular importance. Such interbase interactions are also of notable strength in several Pt(II) complexes containing two cis-bound inosine 5'-monophosphate ligands (12, 38, 39). A factor which may also be of some importance with regard to these bis(nucleotide) complexes is the common occurrence (35, 37) of a O(phosphate)···H-O-H···O(6) intracomplex hydrogen bonding scheme which is favored by (favorable to) a small interbase dihedral angle.

Nonetheless, it has been suggested (35) that it is unlikely that these intracomplex interactions are of sufficient strength to be determinative of the adopted molecular conformation under a variety of conditions. If so, it is likely that the molecular conformation of such N(7)-bound 6-oxopurine complexes (and N(7)-bound 6-aminopurine systems (26)) will be dictated by a competition between intracomplex (base/base, hydrogen bonding) and

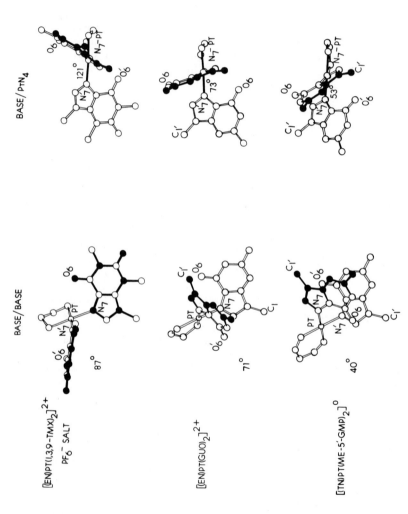

Figure 3. Base/base and base/PtN₄ dihedral angles for three N7-bound bis(purine)Pt(II) complexes. 1,3,9-TMX is 1,3,9-trimethylxanthine; Guo is guanosine; and Me-5'-GMP is the monoanion of the phosphate methyl ester of guanosine 5'-monophosphate.

intercomplex (base/base stacking, base/counterion, hydrogen bonding) interactions.

Applications to cis-bis(pyrimidine)Pt(II) Complexes. Considerably less stereochemical data are presently available for cis-bis(pyrimidine)Pt(II) complexes from X-ray diffraction studies (20, 33, 40-42). Of these, we have chosen to present conformational drawings in Figure 4 for the cis-[Pt(NH$_3$)$_2$(1-methylcytosine)$_2$]$^{2+}$ cation (33), the mixed base cation cis-[Pt(NH$_3$)$_2$(1-methylcytosine)(N(1)-deprotonated thymine monoanion)]$^+$ (41) and the [Pt(en)(7,9-dimethylhypoxanthine)$_2$]$^{2+}$ cation (20). In the latter complex, the nucleobases are actually modified purines; however, since the pyrimidine ring site N(1) of the purine base is bound to the Pt(II) center, this complex is included in the present series.

It is evident from a study of Figure 4 that there are exactly opposite trends observed for the B/B' and the B/PtN$_4$ dihedral angles. The interbase dihedral angle increases smoothly and the base/coordination plane dihedral angle decreases progressively as the number of exocyclic functional groups adjacent to the Pt atom binding site increases from (1 + 1) for the 7,9-dimethylhypoxanthine cation to (2 + 1) for the mixed 1-methylcytosine/thymine monoanion complex to (2 + 2) for the bis(1-methylcytosine) complex cation. These trends suggest that as the number of exocyclic substituents ortho to the Pt atom binding site increases, intracomplex steric factors become increasingly more determinative of the adopted molecular conformation.

These trends culminate in the sterically crowded cis-[Pt(NH$_3$)$_2$(1-methylcytosine)$_2$]$^{2+}$ cation (33). It can be contended that the conformational parameters in this cation are primarily dictated by intracomplex steric effects. In conjunction with earlier remarks (vide supra), this deduction is expected to carry over directly to cis-bis(N(1)-bound)Pt(II) complexes of deprotonated guanine as the nature and number of functional groups ortho to the N(1) binding site are exactly those for the N(3) binding site of cytosine.

Mixed Purine/Pyrimidine Complexes. Unfortunately, only very limited structural information is available (15, 16) for mixed purine/pyrimidine complexes of Pt(II). In fact, so far only complexes containing N(7)-bound 9-ethylguanine (or its N(1)-deprotonated monoanion) and N(3)-bonded 1-methylcytosine have been structurally characterized. Conformational drawings for these complexes are presented in Figure 5.

Following the empirical trends offered in the previous two sections, it might be expected that the role of intracomplex steric factors for such complexes would be intermediate between those for a cis-bis(N(7)-bound guanine) complex and those for a cis-bis(N(3)-bound cytosine) complex. The conformational parameters displayed in Figure 5 seem to be in accord with this

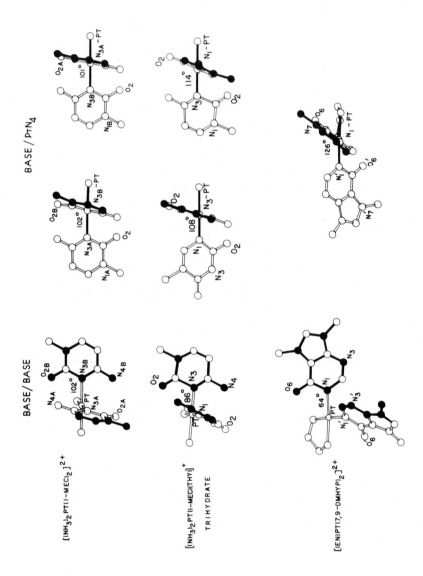

Figure 4.   Base/base and base/PtN₄ dihedral angles for three bis(pyrimidine-ring-bound)Pt(II) complexes. 1-MeC is 1-methylcytosine; Thy⁻ is the N1-deprotonated monoanion of thymine; and 7,9-Dmhyp is 7,9-dimethylhypoxanthine.

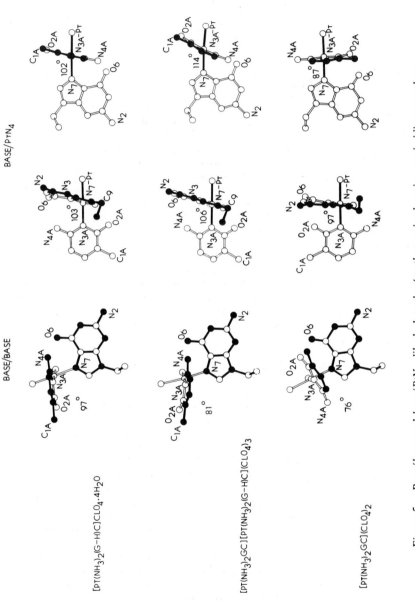

Figure 5. Base/base and base/PtN₄ dihedral angles for three mixed purine–pyrimidine complexes of Pt(II). G–H is the N1-deprotonated monoanion of 9-ethylguanine; G is 9-ethylguanine; and C is 1-methylcytosine.

notion. The B/B' interbase dihedral angles are large for all
three complexes. There is, however, clearly some degree of vari-
ability in the interbase dihedral angle, probably owing to the
relatively different environment (especially the presence of 9-
ethylguanine:9-ethylguanine monoanion interbase hydrogen bonding
in some cases) about each of the species in their respective
crystalline solids (15, 16).

     Environmental Effects. To further expose the varying effects
of crystalline environment on molecular conformation, we present
in Figure 6 two complexes where only the charge-balancing counterion has been changed (35) or the degree of hydration modified
(41, 42).
     In the first example of the [Pt(en)(1,3,9-trimethylxan-
thine)$_2$]$^{2+}$ cation, the change in counterion from PF$_6^-$ to NO$_3^-$
causes a reasonably dramatic reduction in the B/B' dihedral angle
by ca. 16°. Similarly, addition to the crystalline structure of
three water molecules per complex of the cis-[Pt(NH$_3$)$_2$(1-methyl-
cytosine)(N(1)-deprotonated thymine monoanion)]$^+$ (as the per-
chlorate salt in each case) causes a decrease in the interbase
dihedral angle by some 11°. That the alteration in the B/B'
dihedral angle owing to environmental effects is less for the
mixed pyrimidine complex than for the bis(purine) complex would
certainly be consistent with the stereochemical influence of the
number of exocyclic functional groups adjacent to the metal binding site for each of the nucleobases. However, the paucity of
the data presently available limits our confidence in such a
proposal.

Implications for Pt-DNA Cross-linking Modes

     In the foregoing sections, we have described a convention
for the systematic appraisal of the conformational (notably, the
interbase dihedral angle) properties of cis complexes of Pt(II)
containing purine or pyrimidine bases or their nucleosides or
nucleotides as ligands. From an analysis of these conformational
parameters, the principal empirical deduction is that the role of
intramolecular forces in determining the adopted molecular conformation is most strongly in effect when there are two ortho
substituents adjacent to the Pt binding site on each of the cis-
bound nucleobase ligands.
     In this section, we will attempt to apply this deduction to
an "in vivo" Pt(II)-DNA complex. In particular, we will concentrate our attention on regions of a DNA duplex which are rich in
(G-C) residues. These regions are kinetically favorable to
Pt(II) binding, and, therefore, most likely initial sites for
attack by a Pt(II) anti-tumor drug. Our attention will be further focused onto potential intrastrand or interstrand metal-
mediated cross-links in these (G-C) rich regions.
     In Table II, the six different types of cross-linking modes

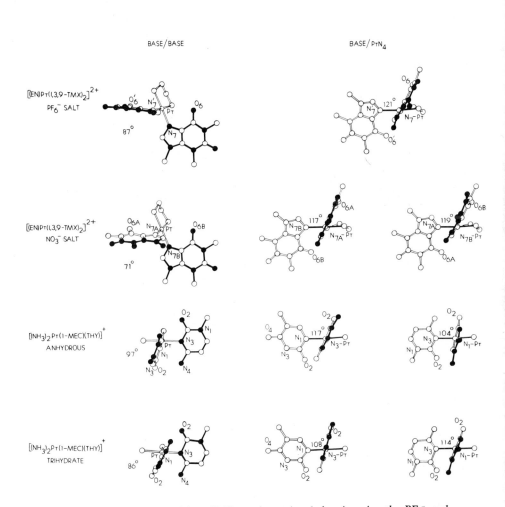

Figure 6. Base/base and base/PtN₄ conformational drawings for the PF₆⁻ and NO₃⁻ salts of [Pt(en)(1,3,9-trimethylxanthine)₂]²⁺ and the anhydrate and trihydrate of cis-[Pt(NH₃)₂(1-methylcytosine)(N1-deprotonated thymine anion)]⁺.

Table II

Cross-linking Modes in Regions of High (G-C) Content

(1) $N(7)_G$-Pt-$N(7)_G$ (Periphery-Periphery)

(2) $N(7)_G$-Pt-$N(1)_G$ (Periphery-Core)

(3) $N(1)_G$-Pt-$N(1)_G$ (Core-Core)

(4) $N(7)_G$-Pt-$N(3)_C$ (Periphery-Core)

(5) $N(1)_G$-Pt-$N(3)_C$ (Core-Core)

(6) $N(3)_C$-Pt-$N(3)_C$ (Core-Core)

which can be envisioned in a region of high (G-C) content are
enumerated. In each case, the endocyclic N-atom binding site
utilized for each nucleobase is indicated, as well as the relative position of this binding site at the "periphery" or "core"
of a DNA duplex (these latter labels are most appropriate for a
B-DNA helix (43) and least appropriate for a Z-DNA helix (44,
45)). In this context, only the N(7) site on a guanine base is
considered to be near the periphery of the helix (these sites are
often exposed to the surrounding medium in the major grove of a
B-DNA helix); the core sites (N(3) of cytosine and N(1) of
guanine), are, of course, involved in the G-C triple hydrogen-
bond scheme. Clearly, the utilization of either of these core
sites by a Pt(II) reagent will disrupt, at least locally, the
continuity of the DNA helix.

A particular point we wish to make is that the core-core
cross-linking modes of Table II will be restricted, in the
absence of steric strain, by intramolecular forces to large
(>100°) interbase dihedral angles, owing to the presence of the
exocyclic amino and oxo groups adjacent to the metal binding site
on each base. The intramolecular steric demands for the core-
core cross-linking modes are expected to exceed those for the two
stereochemically equivalent periphery-core modes and almost certainly exceed those for the lone periphery-periphery cross-link
of Table II. It is difficult to predict, at this time, how the
overall structure of the DNA polymer would influence the interbase dihedral angle.

The formation of a core-core cross-linking mode requires the
penetration of the DNA duplex by the Pt(II) reagent; in addition,
for those modes involving N(1) of guanine, proton release must
take place prior to or concomitant with metal attack. One possible means by which proton release at N(1) of a guanine base can
be facilitated is through binding of the Pt(II) reagent at N(7)
of the same base (14, 15, 16). In such a model, the Pt(II) agent
would act in an auto-synergistic mode, in which its role would be
twofold - to facilitate proton release at N(1) of G through binding at N(7) and to form a critical intrastrand or interstrand

core-core cross-link which is expected to cause a severe local deformation of a DNA duplex. In a similar vein, in a synergistic combination of a Pt(II) agent with a nitrogen mustard (1), the role of the latter component could also be construed as facilitating N(1) deprotonation through covalent cross-links involving N(7) of G. However, the attack of two agents at a similar location may be statistically improbable.

In summary, it is at least a permissible possibility that the critical lesions in a Pt(II)-DNA complex are those involving Pt binding at core sites of a DNA helix. In regions of high (G-C) content, intrastrand or interstrand core-core cross-linking modes are expected to place severe demands on the local continuity (vis-a-vis, the normal base stacked configuration) of a DNA helix, owing to the large interbase dihedral angle favored by intramolecular steric effects. It is also important to note that all possible core-core cross-links in regions of high (G-C) content are equivalently demanding in the vicinity of the Pt center. Certainly for these cross-links, the interbase dihedral angle will be modified by forces present in the polymer. Since the polymer backbone is attached to the bases in a different manner for C and G, specific differences in the disruption of the DNA structure is expected. Inadequate information is presently available to fully assess these perturbations, but it is highly unlikely that dihedral angles approaching 0°, as found in native DNA, will exist at metallated cross-linking sites. It is reasonable to believe that the degree of perturbation in the Pt-DNA complex will parallel the trend found for small molecules. This in turn could mean that the initial attack of the Pt agent will be selective. That is, if the steric strain influence of adjacent exocyclic groups near the potential metal binding site is too great, that particular lesion might not form.

Finally, if one accepts the prevalent notion (13) that cancer cells are deficient in their ability to excise defects from strands of DNA, then such cells may find defects imposed by core-core or even periphery-periphery cross-links in regions of high (G-C) content difficult to repair.

Acknowledgments

This investigation was supported by the National Institutes of Health, Public Health Service Grant No. GM 29222. We are indebted to Drs. C. J. L. Lock and B. Lippert for making many of their results known to us prior to publication.

Literature Cited

1. Prestayko, A. W.; Crooke, S. T.; Carter, S. K., Eds.; "Cis-platin - Current Status and New Developments"; Academic Press: New York, 1980.
2. Rosenberg, B. In "Nucleic Acid-Metal Ion Interactions"; Spiro, T. G., Ed.; Wiley: New York, 1980, Chapter 1; Roberts, J. J. In "Metal Ions in Genetic Information Transfer", Adv. Inorg. Biochem. 1981, 3, 274.
3. Stone, P. J.; Kelman, A. J.; Sinex, F. M. Nature(London) 1974, 251, 736.
4. Kelman, A. D.; Buchbinder, M. Biochimie 1978, 60, 893.
5. Cohen, G. L.; Ledner, J. A.; Bauer, W. R.; Ushay, H. M.; Caravana, C.; Lippard, S. J. J. Am. Chem. Soc. 1980, 102, 2487.
6. Tullius, T. D.; Lippard, S. J. J. Am. Chem. Soc. 1981, 103, 4620.
7. de Castro, B.; Kistenmacher, T. J.; Marzilli, L. G. In "Trace Elements in the Pathogenesis and Treatment of Inflammatory Conditions"; Rainsford, K. D.; Brune, K.; Whitehouse, M. W., Eds.; Agents and Actions: Basel, 1981, Chapter 21.
8. Vestues, P. I.; Martin, R. B. J. Am. Chem. Soc. 1981, 103, 806.
9. Scheller, K. H.; Scheller-Krattiger, V.; Martin, R. B. J. Am. Chem. Soc. 1981, 103, 6833.
10. Dehand, J.; Jordanov, J. J. Chem. Soc. Chem. Commun. 1976, 589.
11. Millard, M. M.; Macquet, J. P.; Theophanides, T. Biochim. Biophys. Acta 1975, 402, 166.
12. Goodgame, D. M. L.; Jeeves, I.; Phillips, F. L.; Skapski, A. C. Biochim. Biophys. Acta 1975, 378, 153.
13. Rosenberg, B. Biochimie 1978, 60, 859.
14. See discussion in Chu, G. Y. H.; Mansy, S.; Duncan, R. E.; Tobias, R. S. J. Am. Chem. Soc. 1978, 100, 593.
15. Faggiani, R.; Lock, C. J. L.; Lippert, B. J. Am. Chem. Soc. 1980, 102, 5419.
16. Faggiani, R.; Lippert, B.; Lock, C. J. L.; Speranzini, R. A. Inorg. Chem., in press.
17. Barton, J. K.; Lippard, S. J. Ann. N. Y. Acad. Sci. 1978, 313, 686.
18. Barton, J. K.; Szalda, D. J.; Rabinowitz, H. N.; Waszczak, J. V.; Lippard, S. J. J. Am. Chem. Soc. 1979, 101, 1434.
19. Marzilli, L. G.; Wilkowski, K.; Chiang, C. C.; Kistenmacher, T. J. J. Am. Chem. Soc. 1979, 101, 7504.
20. Kistenmacher, T. J.; Wilkowski, K.; de Castro, B.; Chiang, C. C.; Marzilli, L. G. Biochem. Biophys. Res. Commun. 1979, 91, 1521.
21. Orbell, J. D.; Wilkowski, K.; Marzilli, L. G.; Kistenmacher, T. J. Inorg. Chem., in press.

22. Marzilli, L. G.; de Castro, B.; Solorzano, C.. J. Am. Chem. Soc. 1982, 104, 461.
23. Gellert, R. W.; Fischer, B. E.; Bau, R. J. Am. Chem. Soc. 1980, 102, 7812.
24. Marzilli, L. G.; Trogler, W. C.; Hollis, D. P.; Kistenmacher, T. J.; Chang, C. H.; Hanson, B. E. Inorg. Chem. 1975, 14, 2568.
25. Lock, C. J. L.; Speranzini, R. A.; Turner, G.; Powell, J. J. Am. Chem. Soc. 1976, 98, 7865.
26. Orbell, J. D.; Solorzano, C.; Marzilli, L. G.; Kistenmacher, T. J. Inorg. Chem., in press.
27. Graves, B. J.; Hodgson, D. J. J. Am. Chem. Soc. 1979, 101, 5608.
28. Faggiani, R.; Lippert, B.; Lock, C. J. L.; Speranzini, R. A. J. Am. Chem. Soc. 1981, 103, 1111.
29. Lippert, B. Raman Spectrosc. 1980, 9, 324 and references therein.
30. Faggiani, R.; Lock, C. J. L.; Pollock, R. J.; Rosenberg, B.; Turner, G. Inorg. Chem. 1981, 20, 804 and references therein.
31. Hollis, L. S.; Lippard, S. J. J. Am. Chem. Soc. 1981, 103, 1230.
32. Hollis, L. S.; Lippard, S. J. J. Am. Chem. Soc. 1981, 103, 6761.
33. Orbell, J. D.; Marzilli, L. G.; Kistenmacher, T. J. J. Am. Chem. Soc. 1981, 103, 5126; this same compound has been studied by Faggiani, R.; Lippert, B.; Lock, C. J. L. Inorg. Chem., in press. This latter report contains extensive characterization by IR and Raman methods.
34. Colamarino, P.; Orioli, P. L. J. Chem. Soc. Dalton 1975, 1656.
35. Orbell, J. D.; Wilkowski, K.; de Castro, B.; Marzilli, L. G.; Kistenmacher, T. J. Inorg. Chem. 1982, 21, 813.
36. Gellert, R. W.; Bau, R. J. Am. Chem. Soc. 1975, 97, 7379.
37. Marzilli, L. G.; Chalilpoyil, P.; Chiang, C. C.; Kistenmacher, T. J. J. Am. Chem. Soc. 1980, 102, 2480.
38. Kistenmacher, T. J.; Chiang, C. C.; Chalilpoyil, P.; Marzilli, L. G. Biochem. Biophys. Res. Commun. 1978, 84, 70.
39. Kistenmacher, T. J.; Chiang, C. C.; Chalilpoyil, P.; Marzilli, L. G. J. Am. Chem. Soc. 1979, 101, 1143.
40. Wu, S. M.; Bau, R. Biochem. Biophys. Res. Commun. 1979, 88, 1435.
41. Lippert, B.; Pfab, R.; Neugebaur, D. Inorg. Chim. Acta 1979, 37, 1495.
42. Faggiani, R.; Lippert, B.; Lock, C. J. L.; Pfab, R. Inorg. Chem. 1981, 20, 2381.
43. Arnott, S.; Hukins, D. W. L. J. Mol. Biol. 1973, 81, 93.
44. Crawford, J. L.; Kolpak, F. J.; Wang, A. H.-J.; Quigley, G. J.; van Boom, J. H.; van der Marel, G.; Rich, A. Proc. Natl. Acad. Sci. USA 1980, 77, 4016.
45. Drew, H.; Takano, T.; Tanaka, S.; Itakura, K.; Dickerson, R. E. Nature(London) 1980, 286, 567.

RECEIVED October 4, 1982

Platinum Complexes with DNA Bases, Nucleotides, and DNA

A. P. HITCHCOCK, C. J. L. LOCK, and W. M. C. PRATT

McMaster University, Institute for Materials Research, Hamilton, Ontario, L8S 4M1 Canada

B. LIPPERT

Technische Universität München, Anorganisch-Chemisches Institut,
Lichtenbergstrasse 4, 8046 Garching, Federal Republic of Germany

Models for the interaction of cis-platin and its
hydrolysis products with DNA are discussed. The
models are the interstrand cross-link, intrastrand
cross-link, N7–O6 clip, platinum dimer interaction,
Eichhorn costacking, and N1 pK shift. Interactions
observed in model compounds have been observed to
occur in DNA for most of the models, but it is not
possible to say which, if any, is the important
lesion in the anti-cancer action of cis-platin.

In this paper we intend to discuss various ways in which
platinum complexes may interact with DNA bases and perhaps with
DNA. In previous papers in this symposium much has been said
about interstrand and intrastrand cross-links involving one
platinum atom. We shall consider these only briefly and concentrate on other methods of interaction. Whether these other modes
of binding are relevant to the anti-cancer action of platinum
complexes cannot be said at this point, but we have concentrated
on interactions which are peculiar to the cis-form of $Pt(NH_3)_2Cl_2$,
and which do not occur with the trans form.

Platinum complexes have been shown to bind to either the
neutral or anionic forms of adenine at N(1) and N(7) (1), thymine
at O(2), N(3), O(4), (2, 3), cytosine at N(3), N(4) (4) and
guanine at N(7) (5), N(1) (6) and possibly O(6) (7) when the
deoxyribose positions are blocked. Platinum complexes can be
considered to bind to these bases in DNA in four ways. Binding
can occur to one base, either monofunctionally or bifunctionally
when the base acts as a chelating agent, and to two bases, in
which case a base from each DNA strand may be bound forming an
interstrand cross-link or the two bases may be on the same DNA
strand forming an intrastrand clip. Considering all the
possibilities, six possible models of interaction have been
proposed. These are:

      (i)   Interstrand cross-link
     (ii)   Intrastrand cross-link

0097-6156/83/0209-0209$06.00/0

(iii)   N7-O6 clip
   (iv)   Dimer-DNA interaction
    (v)   Eichhorn co-stacking
   (vi)   N1 pK shift
and below we shall consider them separately.

Interstrand Cross-Link

The interstrand cross-link can occur for both cis and trans complexes and recent work has confirmed our postulate that trans complexes can be accomodated in the DNA double helix much more easily than cis (1). If we consider the complex [cis-Pt(NH$_3$)-GC]$^{2+}$ (G, C etc. are used to indicate the bases guanine, cytosine, etc. blocked at the deoxyribose position with either a methyl or ethyl group), as shown in Figure 1, the bases are roughly at right angles to each other and to the ligand square plane (8). Large dihedral angles are found in all complexes of this type. The effect on the DNA structure is shown in Figure 2. Either the bases will have to "bend down" (2b) to coordinate the platinum or they will have to "turn on edge" (2c). Either will cause marked distortion of the DNA structure. Such distortion is consistent with the destabilization of the DNA structure and lowering of the melting point (9). Our argument that the trans-complex would pack better into the DNA structure was based on the model shown in Figure 3. Binding of the type shown will increase the N(1)...N(3) distance in a GC pair from 2.8 Å to 4.1 Å. The picture was based on the structure of [trans-Pt(NH$_3$)$_2$(C)$_2$](NO$_3$)$_2$ (10), illustrated in Figure 4, which has the two bases co-planar, with an N(3)...N(3)' distance of 4.1 Å. The nitrate groups (these would be other bases in DNA) lie parallel to the C bases 3.4 Å above and below. The ammonia groups, which lie above and below the plane of the bases, hydrogen bond to the nitrate groups (these would be bases in DNA). In practice, the packing of a trans complex will likely be even more efficient, as we have shown in Figure 5 (11). The deoxyribose positions are in similar positions to those in a Watson-Crick GC pair but the guanine molecule has been rotated 180° about the deoxyribose-N9 bond, allowing both N7 of guanine and N3 of cytosine to bond to platinum. The structure is further stabilized by a weak internal O6(G)...N4(C) hydrogen bond. The distance between the deoxyribose positions is 10.38 Å, very close to the distance of 10.85 Å for a normal GC pair. The group will therefore pack neatly into the DNA double helix. Any destabilizing effect will come only from the ammonia groups lying above and below the base plane, but since these are almost certainly involved in hydrogen bonding to the base pairs above and below the platinum atom, this destabilization may be negligible. The whole packing may indeed stabilize the DNA and explain why trans-Pt(NH$_3$)$_2$Cl$_2$ raises the melting point of DNA (13).

Intrastrand Cross-Link

The intrastrand cross-link has been discussed at length, particularly the one involving an interaction with the N7

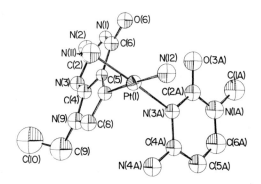

Figure 1.   The $(NH_3)_2PtGC^{2+}$ cation showing the large dihedral angles between the bases and the ligating atom square plane.

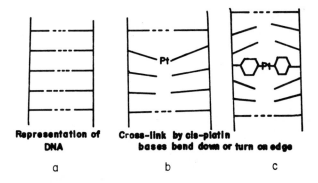

Figure 2.   The interaction of the cis-platinum complex with DNA. Key: a, DNA; b, crosslink with bases bent down to accommodate the large dihedral angles; and c, crosslink with bases turned on edge to accommodate the large dihedral angles.

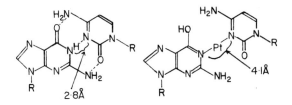

Figure 3.   The packing of the trans-$Pt(NH_3)_2^{2+}$ moiety in a GC pair lengthening the N3–N1 distance. N3,N1 binding is assumed.

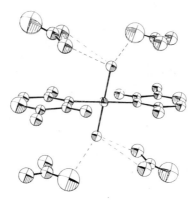

Figure 4.   Part of the packing of trans-$[Pt(NH_3)_3C_2](NO_3)_2$ *showing the* NO_3^- *ions packed parallel to the bases at 3.4 Å above and below and showing the hydrogen bonding to the* NH_3 *groups.*

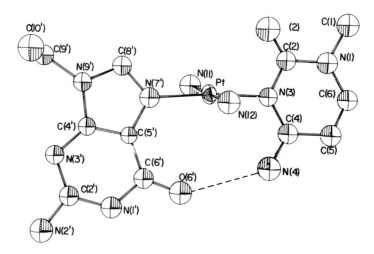

Figure 5.   The trans-$[Pt(NH_3)_2GC]^{2+}$ *cation. The two bases and Pt are coplanar.*

positions of two adjacent guanine molecules on a single strand. We shall only remind you that in such binding the requirements of the large dihedral angles cause marked distortion of the DNA structure because the bases can no longer lie parallel. It has been suggested (14) that this binding causes the bases to "fold-out" of the double helix. The attraction of such an interaction as the primary lesion in DNA is that it can only occur for the cis form of $Pt(NH_3)_2Cl_2$, and not for the trans form.

The N7-06 Clip

Another model which can only occur for cis-complexes is the N7-06 clip of guanine (15). It is proposed that bonding of 06 to platinum interferes with hydrogen bonding to 06 in a manner similar to that achieved by methylation of 06 in DNA. This latter is a defect for which repair is very difficult in DNA (15). Evidence for such an interaction is sparse. Certainly such a clip does occur when 06 is replaced by a sulphur atom (16,17). An N7-06 clip is suggested in the structure of a copper complex determined by Kistenmacher et al. (18). Nevertheless the Cu-06 distance is long (see Figure 6) and one is faced with the question of whether the interaction is real or whether the oxygen cannot "get away" from the copper atom because of the geometric rigidity of the ligand. One test would be to compare the M-N7-C8 and M-N7-C5 angles with those in compounds in which no interaction is present. The former should be larger with Cu-06 binding than the standard (no interaction) and the latter smaller. Comparison of values for the copper complex (18) with those for two platinum structures we have determined (19) suggests that the interaction is real.

	Cu(18)	Pt(19)	Pt(19)	Δ
M-N7-C8	138.9(3)°	124(1)°	124(1)°	+15°
M-N7-C5	117.8(3)°	129(1)°	126(1)	-9
C5-N7-C8	102.9(3)°	107(1)°	109(2)	-5
	359.6	360	359	

Despite this, there is no evidence of a Pt-06 interaction in any of the dozen or so platinum-guanine compounds studied so far by crystallography, even if the guanine is anionic, where one would expect 06 to be a better donor. It can be argued that we have not yet looked at the ideal compound; namely, [cis-Pt(NH$_3$)$_2$- G(OH$_2$)]X$_2$. On making guanine anionic one might expect 06 to bind to platinum and water to be eliminated, if an N7-06 clip is possible. So far we and others have been unable to isolate the cation in a stable form.

We reject the argument that experiments in the solid state do not apply to solutions. We have shown that vibrational spectra of solids and solutions are similar, and shifts in $\nu(C=O)$ of 20-30 cm^{-1}, supposed to give evidence of the N7-06 clip, are caused by changing hydrogen bonding patterns. Deprotonation at N1 causes even bigger shifts in $\nu(C=O)$ of up to 70 cm^{-1}. The issue is still

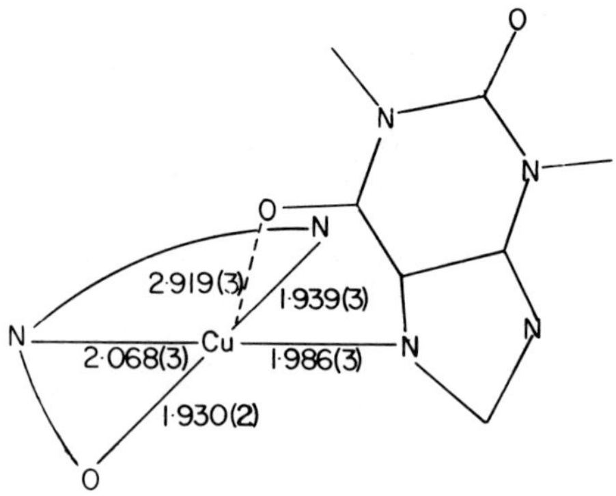

Figure 6.   The complex N3,4-benzosalicylidene-N¹,N¹-dimethylethylenediamine-(theophyllinato)copper(II) (18) showing the Cu–O6 interaction (dotted line).

in doubt but it is our feeling that the N7-O6 clip is not a
viable model.

The Dimer-DNA Interaction

A model we have spent some time examining is based on the
interaction of the dimeric cation $(NH_3)_2Pt(OH)_2Pt(NH_3)_2^{4}$ with
pyrimidines at N3 and at the exocyclic O4 or N4 position with the
consequent formation of an anion (2, 4, 20). Reaction also occurs
with guanine but the reaction product has not been characterized
so far. The formation of the complex with cytosine suggests how
reaction occurs. The pK of the NH_2 group which is deprotonated
is > 12, yet the complex is formed at near pH 7. This suggests
that a marked change in pK of the NH_2 group occurs upon initial
binding of platinum at the preferred N3 site. It should be
possible to detect such a pK shift by NMR. A downfield shift in
the NMR of the NH_2 group on coordination of platinum at N3 is
shown in Figure 7, where the spectra of 1-methylcytosine in
d_6-dimethylsulphoxide, and of the same system with K_2PtCl_4 added,
are compared. The shift is nearly 2 p.p.m. The platinum is
known to bond at N3 under the conditions of the experiment (21).
The splitting of the NH_2 protons into two peaks on platinum
coordination is not surprising; there is considerable multiple
bonding between the NH_2 group and the ring, and it is best
represented as ⟋ , with the two protons lying in the
plane of the ring, and thus in geometrically
different N3 ⟍ N positions with respect to a platinum
atom bonded at H N3. The probable reaction mechanism
is illustrated in Figure 8; in addition to the pK shift of the
NH_2 group the position of the proton-accepting hydroxide groups
probably aids the reaction.

The platinum-platinum distance in the three compounds
isolated so far is 2.95 Å. Both Lippard (22) and Mansy (23) have
suggested that a similar reaction could occur with guanine, in
the manner shown in Figure 9. It seemed that it should be
possible to detect such a reaction with bases in DNA by looking
for the Pt-Pt distance of 2.95 Å with extended x-ray absorption
fine structure (EXAFS) techniques. We have performed such
experiments on the Cornell High Energy Synchrotron Source.

We shall not discuss the theory of EXAFS (24), which has been
covered in other lectures, but briefly it is possible to subtract
a smooth background curve from the actual Pt L_3 absorption
spectrum (Figure 10) to give an oscillating function (Figure 11).
The energy scale of the first spectrum has been converted to
photoelectron wave number (k scale, $k = (0.263 (E-E_o))^{\frac{1}{2}}$ where E_o
is the midpoint of the absorption jump). It is then possible to
Fourier transform the EXAFS oscillations to give information about
distances to atoms surrounding the target platinum atom.

The information one can gain, however, is very dependent on
how much of the absorption spectrum is analysed. Three points
are marked on the Pt L_3 absorption spectrum of the dimer cation,

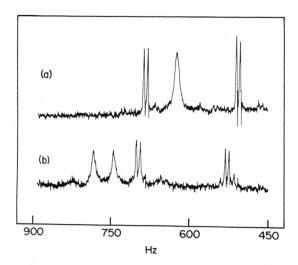

*Figure 7.   Part of the NMR spectra in d₆-DMSO of a, 1-methylcytosine; and b,
1-methylcytosine and K₂PtCl₄.*

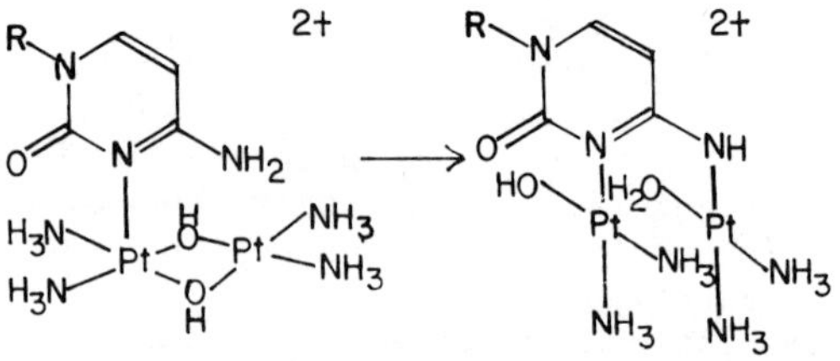

*Figure 8.   Binding of [(NH₃)₂Pt(OH)₂Pt(NH₃)₂]²⁺ at N3 of 1-methylcytosine and
subsequent reaction to form the 1-methylcytosinate anion bound to two platinum
atoms at N3 and N4.*

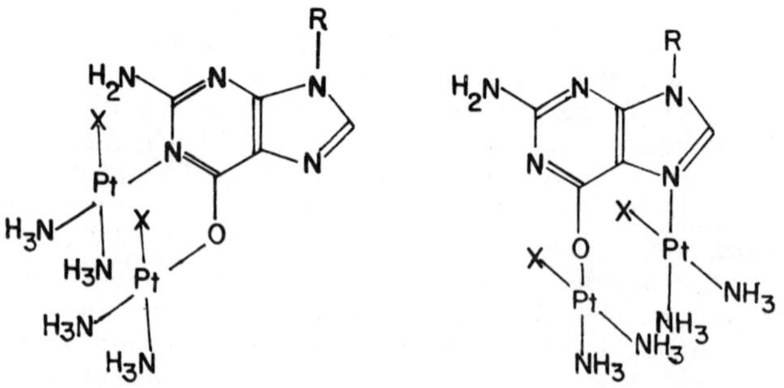

*Figure 9.   Binding of two platinum atoms to guanine at N1,O6 (22) and N7,O6
(23).*

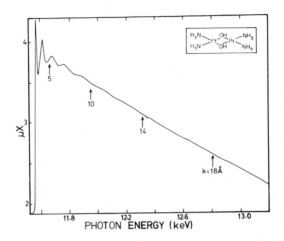

Figure 10. Pt L₃ x-ray absorption spectrum of [(NH₃)₂Pt(OH)₂Pt(NH₃)₂](NO₃)₂.

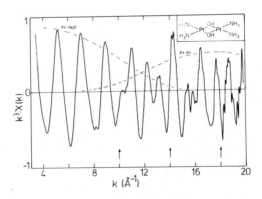

Figure 11. EXAFS spectrum of [(NH₃)₂Pt(OH)₂Pt(NH₃)₂](NO₃)₂ with background removed.

$(NH_3)_2Pt(OH)_2Pt(NH_3)_2^{2+}$, (Figure 10) and these are marked
similarly on the oscillating function (Figure 11). The
oscillations at low values of k arise primarily from backscattering of the ionized Pt L_3 electrons from the nearest neighbour
atoms N and O, whereas oscillations from the Pt-Pt interactions,
in which we are interested, arise primarily in the high k range,
where signal to noise effects become significant. Thus the
information in the Fourier transform is dependent on the k range
and k-weighting used. This effect is illustrated in Figure 12,
where a series of transforms over the wavenumber ranges 5-10,
5-14 and 5-18 ($Å^{-1}$) are plotted. The Pt-(N,O) peak at 1.8 Å is
easily visible in all plots but the Pt-Pt peak at $\sim$ 3 Å is only
marked in the 5-18 $Å^{-1}$ plot and is not observed in the 5-10 $Å^{-1}$
plot. This provides a potential problem in the DNA experiments
since the EXAFS data for the Pt-DNA complexes became excessively
noisy above 14 $Å^{-1}$. It should be noted (Figure 12) that the peak
maxima do not occur exactly at the known interatomic distances for
the cation (marked by vertical lines). This is because of phase
shifts in the backscattering which have the principal effect of a
shift in the Fourier transform spectrum of the Pt dimer of 0.31 Å
for Pt-(O,N) and 0.04 Å for Pt-Pt distances. We have assumed these
shifts are transferable from the dimer cation to the Pt-DNA complex
(25).

The DNA experiments (26) involved a comparison of the EXAFS
spectra of $[Pt(NH_3)_2C_2](NO_3)_2(C)$, C = 1-methyl cytosine, which
does not contain a short (<4 Å) Pt-Pt distance (27), $[(NH_3)_2Pt(OH)_2-Pt(NH_3)_2](NO_3)_2$ and the reaction product of the dimer cation
$[(NH_3)_2Pt(OH)_2Pt(NH_3)_2]^{2+}$ with DNA. This last sample was made by
reacting a solution of calf thymus DNA (buffered with 10mM $NaNO_3$,
5mM tris-NO_3) with $[(NH_3)_2Pt(OH)_2Pt(NH_3)_2](NO_3)_2$ for 1 and 8 days.
The dimer to PO_4^{2-} ratio was 1:10. After incubation the solutions
were centrifuged at 190,000g for twenty hours, the supernatant
decanted, and the DNA pellet washed with more buffer to remove any
excess platinum dimer. It was centrifuged again for twenty hours
at 190,000g, the supernatant removed and the DNA pellet dried under
nitrogen gas.

Fourier transform spectra of the Pt L_3 EXAFS of the cytosine
and dimer standards and the one-day DNA sample are shown in Fig.13.
For these results the data, over a k-range of 4-14 $Å^{-1}$, was
multiplied by k^3, k^4 or k^5 before Fourier analysis. A peak appears
in each of the spectra of the DNA sample at about 2.9 Å as compared
to 3.08 Å in the dimer standard, whereas none is observed in the
cytosine standard. The increase in the intensity of the $\sim$ 3 Å peak
with increased k-weighting supports identification of this feature
as a Pt-Pt distance since higher k-weighting emphasizes the large
k-regions where the EXAFS amplitude for a high Z atom is larger.
The 2.87(8) Å Pt-Pt distance observed is consistent with values
found in the model compounds (2, 4, 20), suggesting a similar
reaction takes place in DNA itself.

Comparison of the data (analysed over 4<k<14 $Å^{-1}$ with weight-

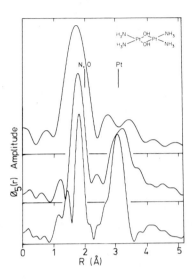

Figure 12. Fourier transform of the EXAFS spectrum of $[(NH_3)_2Pt(OH)_2Pt-(NH_3)_2](NO_3)_2$ over various k ranges. Key to k range in $Å^{-1}$: top, 5–10; middle, 5–14; and bottom, 5–18.

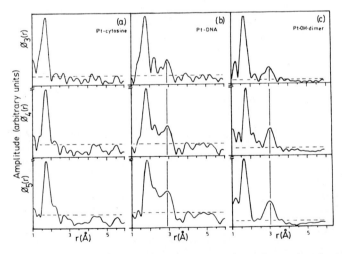

Figure 13. Comparison of the EXAFS results transformed over $4 < k < 14 \ Å^{-1}$ with a weighting of k^n, $n = 3, 4, 5$. Key: a, $[(NH_3)_2PtC_2](ClO_4)_2 \cdot C$, $C = 1$-methylcytosine; b, $[(NH_3)_2Pt(OH)_2Pt(NH_3)_2](NO_3)_2 + DNA$; and c, $[(NH_3)_2Pt(OH)_2Pt-(NH_2)_2](NO_3)_2$.

ing of k^3 and k^5) from the one day and eight day DNA samples, however, (Figure 14) reveals that the Pt–Pt vector is not present in the second sample, suggesting that the initial interaction is unstable and that the platinum atoms eventually move away from each other.

Although there is a difference in Pt–Pt distance in the dimer and the DNA reaction product, one would like to make sure that the peak does not arise from unreacted dimer. Additional information is obtained from the absorption edges of the various compounds (Figure 15). It is clear that the edge position for the dimer is quite different from that for the reaction product with DNA, suggesting a different chemical environment of the Pt atom. EXAFS studies of other Pt standards and of Pt–dimer–DNA samples prepared under a variety of conditions are in progress.

Eichhorn Co-stacking

Another model we have examined is based on Eichhorn's observation that cis-Pt(NH_3)$_2Cl_2$ and enPtCl$_2$ pack in the solid so that the square planes are ~ 3.4 Å apart, whereas this is not true for trans-Pt(NH_3)$_2Cl_2$. Because the distance between base pairs along the double helix in DNA is also 3.4 Å, Eichhorn suggested the cis-Pt(NH_3)Cl$_2$ molecules might "costack" (28). Since that time we have examined other complexes of cis-dihalo-platinum(II) and have found this type of packing is very common, whereas it has not been found in trans-complexes (Figure 16). We do not suggest that the 3.4 Å packing distance is found in all cis-dihaloplatinum(II) complexes; it is not (Figure 17). Now if platinum binding to two parallel adjacent bases is to occur in DNA it cannot be to the same platinum atom. It is true that a complex, with platinum bound to two guanosine monophosphate molecules, is known in which the dihedral angle between the bases is small, but as the authors point out (29) this structure cannot occur in DNA. The platinum atom is bound to two GMP nucleotides such that the phosphate groups lie on opposite sides of the molecule. The true analogue to the DNA situation would be binding to a dinucleotide which contains only one phosphate group. Thus in DNA the two phosphate groups would condense to one and would thus have to be on the same side of the molecule, preventing the type of structure observed.

If one examines Eichhorn's model in more detail to see how binding might occur, we see a difference between the action of cis and trans-Pt(NH_3)$_2Cl_2$. The reason for the 3.4 Å distance is that the molecules are held together by N-H...Cl or N-H...Br hydrogen bonds which are ~ 3.4 Å. In Figure 18 we show how cis- and trans-Pt(NH_3)$_2Cl_2$ ((a) and (b) respectively) might be bonded to two adjacent bases on DNA. Hydrogen bonding can still occur for the cis complex but cannot occur for the trans. Even allowing for the twist in DNA, when the bases are not one above the other we can still get one hydrogen bond for the cis-complex. One may reasonably ask whether the energy of a single hydrogen bond is

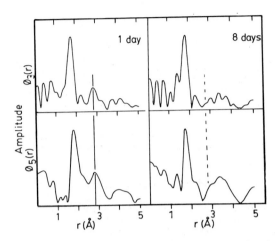

Figure 14. Comparison of EXAFS results transformed over $4 < k < 14\ Å^{-1}$ for the $[(NH_3)_2Pt(OH)_2Pt(NH_3)_2](NO_3)_2$–DNA complex after 1 d (left) and 8 d (right).

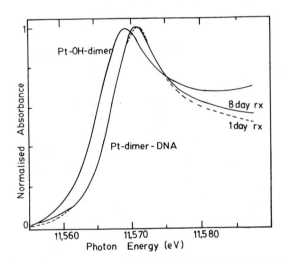

Figure 15. Pt L_3 absorption edge spectra for $[(NH_3)_2Pt(OH)_2Pt(NH_3)_2](NO_3)_2$ and the reaction product with DNA after 1- and 8-d reaction time.

No close contact (4Å)

trans-dichlorodiammineplatinum(II)
trans-dichlorobis(ethyleneimine)platinum(II)
trans-dichlorobis(cylco-butylamine)platinum(II)
trans-dichlorobis(cyclo-heptylamine)platinum(II)
trans-dichlorobis(cyclo-hexylamine)platinum(II)
trans-dibromobis(cyclo-hexylamine)platinum(II)

Figure 16.   List of known trans-dihalodiammineplatinum(II) *structures. Not one of these has a Pt–Pt contact less than 4 Å.*

No close contact (4Å)

cis-dichlorodi(cyclopropylamine)platinum(II)
cis-dichlorodi(cyclobutylamine)platinum(II)
cis-dichloro(1-methylamino-2(S)-aminopropane)platinum(II)
cis-dichlorodi(N-methylimidazole)platinum(II)
cis-dichlorodi(ethyleneimine)platinum(II)

Figure 17.   List of cis-dichlorodiammineplatinum(II) *structures with no Pt–Pt contact less than 4 Å.*

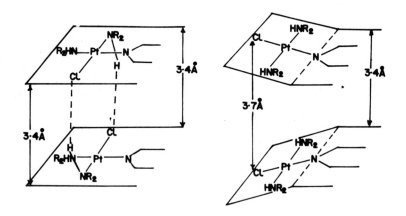

Figure 18.   Pairs of cis- *and* trans-[Pt(R₂NH)₂Cl₂] *molecules bound to adjacent bases on a DNA chain.*

enough to stabilize the system. We think not but Lippert, in a previous paper, has described a mono-hydroxide bridged two platinum atom complex which could act as a suitable model (Figure 19). Again, such an interaction, which would keep the bases parallel at 3.4 Å separation, can only occur for the hydrolysis products of <u>cis</u>=$Pt(NH_3)_2Cl_2$ and not for the <u>trans</u> complex.

N1 pK Shift Model

The question that arises is: How can binding at N7 on the outside of the DNA helix interfere with the hydrogen bonding region and cause mispairing? Work we have done on a series of complexes containing the cations and molecules $[Pt(NH_3)_2GC]^{2+}$, $[Pt(NH_3)_2(G-H)C]^+$, $[(Pt(NH_3)_2GC)(Pt(NH_3)_2(G-H)C]^{3+}$, $[Pt(NH_3)_2-(G-H)_2]$, $[Pt(NH_3)_2(G-H)_2]G$ has suggested how this might occur (8, 19, 30). Binding of platinum at N7 of guanine causes a marked change in the pK of N1 of guanine from about 9.4 to 8.0. Thus at physiological pH ($\sim$ 7.6) about 15% of all platinated guanine molecules are deprotonated at N1. It has thus proved possible to form complexes containing G-G$^-$ pair with three hydrogen bonds like the Watson-Crick G-C pair (Figure 20a). A comparison of hydrogen bond distances for various base pairs (Figure 21) shows the G-G$^-$ pair is strongly hydrogen-bonded and this is borne out by vibrational spectral studies in solution which suggest it is bonded much more strongly than the Watson-Crick base pair. The G-G$^-$ pair cannot fit into the DNA double helix because the deoxyribose positions are on the opposite side of the base pair (Figure 20) and the sugar-sugar distance is $\sim$ 14 Å. Nevertheless, it is possible to see how platinum induced base mis-pairing could occur. Using the example in Figure 20 deprotonated guanine should bond to thymine and in solution we have shown this occurs. Isolation of a solid has proved difficult, since thymine is much less soluble than any complex and separates first. What we have induced, however, is G$^-$-T mispairing by coordinating platinum to the N7 position of guanine

Because of the strength of the G$^-$-G bond we should examine how much bonding might occur in DNA. If we bond two guanine molecules to one platinum atom, the bases will "fold out" of the helix. Deprotonation of one guanine molecule might allow us to affect the DNA tertiary structure by a G-G$^-$ bond between two folded out positions. This might occur in a simple bond of the type shown in Figure 22(a) or alternatively involve a cruciform segment of DNA as shown in Figure 22(b). Such cruciform structures, although common in RNA, are only normal in DNA where one finds inverted sequence repeats. These usually occur in the control regions of DNA (Figure 23). In this case such binding would not cause base mispairing in the DNA but would prevent replication completely.

In summary, we have discussed some ways in which cis-platin, cis-$Pt(NH_3)_2Cl_2$, and its aquation products react with DNA bases.

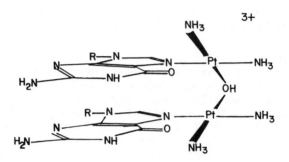

Figure 19.   A hydroxide-bridged platinum dimer bound to two guanine molecules co-stacked as in a dinucleotide.

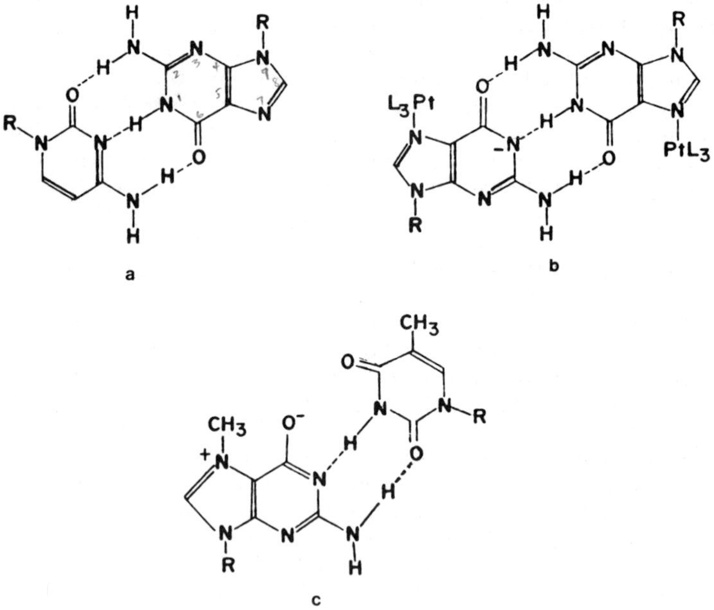

Figure 20.   Structural formulas of a, Watson–Crick GC base pair; b, N7-platinated G–G⁻ base pair; c, methylated G–T base pair.

Hydrogen bond distances in Å

	N2···O6, N4···O2 or N2···O6	N1···N1, N3···N3 or N3···N1	O6···N2, O2···N4 or O2···N2
$(NH_3)_2Pt(G-H)_2G$	2·88(2)	2·95(2)	2·87(2)
$(NH_3)_2PtGC^{2+}$ $(NH_3)_2Pt(G-H)C^+$	2·99(1)	2·73(1)	2·99(1)
GC	2·81(1)	2·92(1)	2·94(1)
GFC	2·82(1)	2·94(1)	2·96(1)
C_2H^+	2·76	2·83	2·93

Figure 21. Hydrogen-bond distances in Å for various triply hydrogen-bonded base pairs (FC = 5-fluorocytosine).

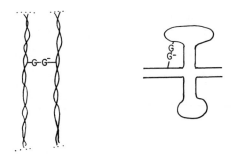

Figure 22. Possible ways in which G–G⁻ pairs could occur.

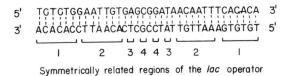

Symmetrically related regions of the *lac* operator

Figure 23. An inverted sequence repair in the control region of the lac *gene.*

Because of the complexity of the aquation and hydrolysis reaction the possible modes of interaction are more numerous and complex than had previously been realized. In some cases it has been shown that the interaction of cis-platin with DNA is accurately described by the model compounds. It has not been established which, if any, of the above models describes the primary lesion in the anti-cancer activity of cis-platin.

Acknowledgments

We acknowledge with thanks the contributions of our co-workers. Currently at McMaster these are J. Britten, B. Brown, R. Faggiani, Dr. H.E. Howard-Lock, P. Pilon and M.A. Turner and those who have graduated are Dr. J. Bradford, Dr. R.A. Speranzini, Dr. G. Turner and Dr. M. Zvagulis. Other cooperation has taken place with the research groups of Profs. B. Rosenberg, F. Ghadially, J. Powell and T. Theophanides.

Literature Cited

1. Lock, C.J.L.; Speranzini, R.A.; Turner, G.; Powell, J.
    J. Amer. Chem. Soc. 1976, 98, 7865.

2. Lock, C.J.L.; Peresie, H.J.; Rosenberg, B.; Turner, G.
    J. Amer. Chem. Soc. 1978, 100, 3371.

3. Faggiani, R.; Lippert, B.; Lock, C.J.L. Unpublished work.

4. Faggiani, R.; Lippert, B.; Lock, C.J.L.; Speranzini, R.A.
    J. Amer. Chem. Soc. 1981, 103, 1111.

5. Gellert, R.W.; Bau, R. J. Amer. Chem. Soc. 1975, 97, 7379
    J. Clinical Hemat. Oncol. 1977, 7, 51.

6. DeCastro, B.; Chiang, C.C.; Wilkowski, K.; Marzilli, L.G.;
    Kistenmacher, T.J. Inorg. Chem. 1981, 20, 1835.

7. Gellert, R.W.; Fischer, B.E.; Bau, R. J. Amer. Chem. Soc.
    1980, 102, 7812.

8. Faggiani, R.; Lock, C.J.L.; Lippert, B. J. Amer. Chem. Soc.
    1980, 102, 5418.

9. Harder, H.C. Chem.-Biol. Interactions 1975, 10, 27.

10. Lippert, B.; Lock, C.J.L.; Speranzini, R.A. Inorg. Chem.
    1981, 20, 808.

11. Britten, J.; Lippert, B.; Lock, C.J.L. Manuscript in
    preparation.

12. Guschlbauer, W. "Nucleic Acid Structure" Springer-Verlag.
    New York 1976 p. 35.

13. Macquet, J.-P.; Butour, J.-L.; Biochimie, 1978, 60, 901.

14. Lippard, S.J. in "Inorganic Chemistry in Biology and
    Medicine", Martell, A.E. Ed.; ACS Symposium Series
    No. 140, 1980.

15. Rosenberg, B. Biochimie 1978, 60, 859.

16. Sleiten, E.; Apeland, A. Acta Crystallogr. 1975, B31, 2019.

17. Heitner, H.I.; Lippard, S.J. Inorg. Chem. 1974, 13, 815.

18. Szalda, D.; Kistenmacher, T.J.; Marzilli, L.G. J. Amer. Chem. Soc. 1976, 98, 8371-7.

19. Faggiani, R.; Lippert, B.; Lock, C.J.L.; Speranzini, R.A. Inorg. Chem. In press.

20. Lock, C.J.L.; Pollock, R.J.; Rosenberg, B.; Turner, G. Inorg. Chem. 1981, 20, 804.

21. Lock, C.J.L.; Speranzini, R.A.; Powell, J. Can. J. Chem. 1976, 54, 53.

22. Barton, J.K.; Szalda, D.J.; Rabinowitz, H.N.; Waszczack, J.V.; Lippard, S.J. J. Amer. Chem. Soc. 1979, 101, 1434.

23. Chu, G.Y.H.; Mansy, S.; Duncan, R.E.; Tobias, R.S. J. Amer. Chem. Soc. 1978, 100, 593.

24. Lee, P.A.; Citrin, P.H.; Eisenberger, P.; Kincaid, B.M. Rev. Mod. Phys. 1981, 53, 769.

25. Citrin, P.H.; Eisenberger, P.; Kincaid, B.M. Phys. Rev. Lett. 1976, 36, 1346.

26. Hitchcock, A.P.; Lock, C.J.L.; Pratt, W.M.C. Inorg. Chim. Acta, 1982, 66, L45.

27. Faggiani, R.; Lippert, B.; Lock, C.J.L. Inorg. Chem. 1982. In press.

28. Srivastava, R.C.; Froehlich, J.; Eichhorn, G.L. Biochimie, 1978, 60, 879.

29. Marzilli, L.G.; Chalilpoyil, P.; Chiang, C.C.; Kistenmacher, T.J. J. Amer. Chem. Soc. 1980, 102, 2480.

30. Faggiani, R.; Lippert, B.; Lock, C.J.L. Submitted to Inorg. Chem.

RECEIVED October 14, 1982

INORGANIC CHEMISTRY RELATED TO PLATINUM ANTITUMOR DRUGS

Hydrolytic Equilibria and N7 Versus N1 Binding in Purine Nucleosides of *cis*-Diamminedichloroplatinum(II)

Palladium(II) as a Guide to Platinum(II) Reactions at Equilibrium

R. BRUCE MARTIN

University of Virginia, Department of Chemistry, Charlottesville, VA 22901

Antitumor Pt(II) amines are usually administered as cis dichloro complexes. This form persists in human blood plasma with its high 103 mM Cl^- content. The net zero charge on the complex fosters its passage through cell walls. Within many cells the Cl^- concentration is much lower, only ~4 mM. Substitution of Cl^- by H_2O then occurs. Depending upon pH deprotonation may also yield hydroxo containing complexes. In neutral solutions of low Cl^- content the chloro-hydroxo complex predominates but aquo-hydroxo, chloro-chloro, aquo-chloro, and hydroxo-hydroxo complexes also appear. Of the three leaving groups H_2O is by far the best, followed by Cl^- and OH^-, which is inert. Most likely the aquo complexes react with cell constituents. At sufficient Pt(II) concentrations complexes with hydroxo bridges form at the expense of a water ligand, reducing the Pt(II) complex reactivity. Dihydroxo bridges were first observed on analogous Pd(II) complexes in solution and found to form more slowly with Pt(II).

In purine nucleosides metal ion binding may occur at either N(7) or N(1). In guanosine and inosine the ratio of binding at N(1) to N(7) is pH dependent. At pH 7 the stability order for dienPd(II) binding at the common 5'-nucleotides is G7>I7>I1>G1>U3>T3>C3>A1>A7. This series represents a considerable promotion of guanosine and inosine N(7) stabilities over that found for H^+ and CH_3Hg^+. Pt(II) appears to favor N(7) to N(1) even more than Pd(II). Even when binding at N(1) is favored, Pt(II) may become kinetically fixed at N(7) in the 6-oxopurines. Of the several common nucleoside binding sites both thermodynamic and kinetic factors favor Pt(II) binding at guanosine N(7).

0097-6156/83/0209-0231$06.00/0

Cis $(NH_3)_2PtCl_2$ and other Pt(II) complexes react only slowly
with the nucleic bases. The slowness may be essential to their
efficacy as tumor inhibitors, for it provides integrity and
neutrality during circulation and passage into cells. Equilibrium constants for association of cis $(NH_3)_2Pt(II)$ complexes
with nucleic bases remain unknown. It has been argued that
published constants fail to reflect systems at equilibrium (1).
The aqueous chemistry of Pt(II) relevant to biological molecules
has received review (2).

As an indicator of equilibrium tendencies and constants for
Pt(II) complexes, we have employed analogous Pd(II) complexes.
Both metal ions form diamagnetic, planar complexes and prefer
nitrogen to oxygen donor atoms. They exhibit similar effective
ionic radii of 0.60 Å for Pt(II) and 0.64 Å for Pd(II) (3).
However, complexes of dienPd(II) react about 10^5 times faster
than those of dienPt(II) (4). At the same time Pd(II) exchanges
slowly among nucleic base ligand sites so that in ^1H NMR spectra
individual ligand resonances appear for each kind of Pd(II)
binding site. Because of its convenient rate of attainment of
equilibrium concentrations, as well as its diamagnetism and slow
rate of exchange on the NMR time scale, Pd(II) offers one of
the most attractive metal ions for investigation of its complexes.

This article deals with two separate aspects of Pt(II)
binding to nucleic bases. The first section describes the complexes present in aqueous solutions containing cis $(NH_3)_2Pt(II)$
over a range of pH in media of high and low chloride ion content.
The second section considers aspects of the N(1) versus N(7)
dichotomy for binding at purine nucleosides. To elucidate the
binding of Pt(II) at equilibrium, both sections rely on research performed on analogous Pd(II) complexes.

Solution Properties of cis $(NH_3)_2Pt(II)$ Complexes

Antitumor Pt(II) complexes exist in human blood plasma in
an ambient chloride ion concentration of 103 mM. A much lower
value of only ~4 mM Cl^- occurs within many cells. Equilibrium
and rate constants have been reported for substitution of Cl^- by
H_2O in cis $(NH_3)_2PtCl_2$. The successive equilibrium constants
for formation of aquo and cis diaquo complexes are 3.3 and 0.4 mM,
respectively (5). Similar values are found for enPtCl₂ (6). The
above values are used herein as prototypes for cis Pt(II) amines.

The complex cis $(NH_3)_2Pt(H_2O)_2^{2+}$ undergoes two deprotonations to give first the aquo-hydroxo, and finally the dihydroxo
complexes. From the titration data furnished by Jensen (7) at
20°, I calculate from a non-linear least squares program of pH
versus equiv base, $pK_1 = 5.5$ and $pK_2 = 7.1$. These values come
out slightly lower than those calculated by Jensen. However,
the newly calculated values are identical to those reported by
the Russian school for solutions at 25° with 0.1 - 0.3 M
$NaNO_3$ (8).

The acidity constant for water deprotonation in cis $(NH_3)_2Pt(Cl)(H_2O)$ is unknown and needs to be estimated. For three examples (9) I note that the pK_a value for deprotonation from an aquo-chloro complex is about the average of the successive pK_1 and pK_2 values from the corresponding diaquo complex. Thus from the average of the pK_1 and pK_2 values in the preceding paragraph I estimate for cis $(NH_3)_2Pt(Cl)(H_2O)$ that $pK_a = 6.3$. This values is identical to that reached in reference 9 by a similar argument.

Combination of the above equilibrium constant values with the ambient Cl^- concentrations yields the Pt(II) complex distribution curves shown in Figures 1-3.

Figure 1 shows mole fraction Pt(II) versus pH for cis $(NH_3)_2PtX,Y$ in the presence of 103 mM Cl^-, as occurs in blood plasma. From low pH to pH 7.8 the cis $(NH_3)_2PtCl_2$ complex predominates. From $7.8 < pH < 8.7$ the cis $(NH_3)_2Pt(Cl)(OH)$ complex dominates. At pH > 8.7 the dihydroxo complex becomes predominant.

Figure 2 shows a similar plot but in the presence of only 4 mM Cl^-, as might occur within a cell. The distribution curves vary more than at the higher chloride concentration. At low pH the dichloro and aquo-chloro complexes appear in comparable amounts and account for most of the Pt(II). In neutral solutions the chloro-hydroxo complex becomes dominant and accounts for about 38% of the Pt(II), while the aquo-hydroxo complex accounts for about 24%. At pH $\geq$ 7.3 the dihydroxo complex becomes increasingly predominant.

Figure 3 shows mole fraction Pt(II) versus mM chloride concentration at pH 7.0. The predominant complexes present are strongly dependent upon chloride concentration at low concentrations. At zero chloride concentration the aquo-hydroxo and hydroxo-hydroxo complexes account for >98% of the Pt(II); the aquo-aquo complex occurs at less than 2%. All three complexes decrease in amount as Cl^- is added. Mole fractions of the chloro-hydroxo and chloro-aquo complexes peak at 9 mM Cl^-. Above 17 mM Cl^- the chloro-chloro complex predominates. This complex also predominates in clinical formulations containing 0.15 M NaCl.

From the second order rate constants for substitution by pyridine in dienPt(II) complexes (4,10), I estimate the relative leaving group abilities of H_2O to Cl^- to be 70 to 1. Bound hydroxide ion appears inert and apparently undergoes substitution only after conversion to water in a rapid protonic equilibria.

Distribution curves in Figures 1-3 representing complexes with the good leaving group H_2O appear as solid curves. Complexes with only the poor leaving groups Cl^- and OH^- are shown as dashed curves. At 103 mM Cl^- in Figure 1 only traces of complexes contain the good water leaving group. Under conditions such as occurs in plasma, the Pt(II) complexes remain relatively inert. At the intracellular 4 mM Cl^- shown in

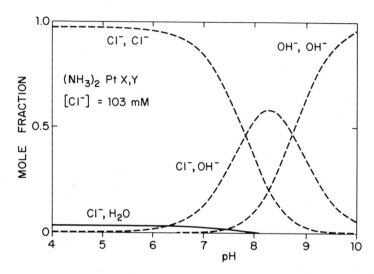

Figure 1.   Mole fraction of Pt(II) vs. pH for cis-(NH₃)₂Pt(II) complexes in presence of 103 mM ambient Cl⁻. Solid curve represents complex with a water ligand. The mole fractions of the diaquohydroxo and aquohydroxo complexes never exceed 0.015.

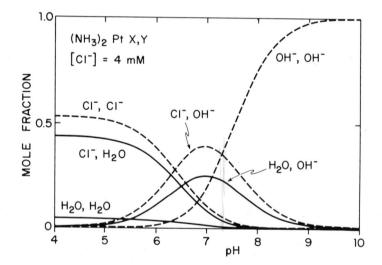

Figure 2.   Mole fraction of Pt(II) vs. pH for cis-(NH₃)₂Pt(II) complexes in presence of 3.5 mM ambient Cl⁻. Solid curves represent complexes with a water ligand. Polymerization of the aquohydroxo complex to give hydroxo-bridged dimers and trimers is not considered.

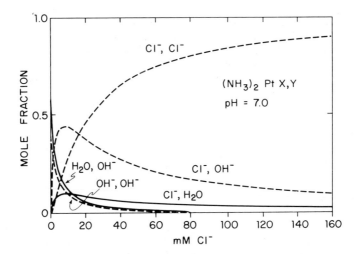

Figure 3.   Mole fraction of Pt(II) vs. [Cl⁻] for cis-*(NH₃)₂Pt(II) complexes at pH 7.0. Solid curves represent complexes with a water ligand.*

Figure 2 the solid curves indicate appreciable mole fractions of
complexes with good water leaving groups from pH 4-8. In neutral
solutions about 33% of the Pt(II) complexes contain good water
leaving groups at 4 mM Cl^- while only about 3% do so at 103 mM
Cl^-. When equilibrium is attained, a much greater fraction of
Pt(II) complexes contain good water leaving groups within cells
than in the plasma.

Combination of the rate and distribution results at pH 7
indicates that the Pt(II) complexes within a cell are about 7
times more reactive than those in the plasma. Aquo complexes
are almost the only reactive species within a cell and the major
reactive species in the plasma. Due to their general predominance, cis dichloro complexes provide about 1/3 of the reactivity in the plasma.

Upon titration of 10 mM $enPd(OH_2)_2$ with standard base an
endpoint is reached at pH 7.5 after addition of one equiv base.
We discovered, however, that the reversible titration curve
flattens on the pH axis and cannot be fitted with an equilibrium
expression for a simple deprotonation (11). We succeeded in
fitting the titration curve to a combination deprotonation and
dimerization process that yields a binuclear, dihydroxo bridged
dimer. For this reaction the overall equilibrium constant was
found to be $K_d = 10^{-8.3}$ M.

$$enPd(OH_2)_2{}^{2+} \rightleftarrows 2\ H_3O^+ + (en)Pd\underset{\underset{H}{O}}{\overset{\overset{H}{O}}{\diagup\diagdown}}Pd(en)^{2+}$$

For the corresponding Pt(II) complex, $enPt(OH_2)_2{}^{2+}$, an
endpoint is reached after addition of two equivs base. The
dimerization proceeds slowly, and it is possible to resolve
the titration curve obtained at 23° with 0.2 M KNO_3 into two
successive deprotonations (11) with $pK_1 = 5.8$ for formation of
the aquo-hydroxo complex and $pK_2 = 7.6$ for formation of the
dihydroxo complex. If only one equiv base is added to
$enPt(OH_2)_2{}^{2+}$ and the solution containing predominantly the aquo-
hydroxo complex is allowed to stand, no titrable groups remain (11). Thus dimerization does occur, but more slowly than
with the corresponding Pd(II) complex.

Presence of binuclear, dihydroxo bridged Pd(II) and Pt(II)
complexes in solution receives support from crystal structure
determinations of cis diamine Pt(II) complexes (12,13). Trinuclear complexes with three Pt(II) and three hydroxo bridges
also occur in crystals (14,15).

Reducing the concentration of $enPd(OH_2)_2$ to 1 mM makes it
possible to resolve the previous reaction into component deprotonation and dimerization steps.

$$enPd(OH_2)_2^{2+} \overset{K_1}{\rightleftarrows} H^+ + enPd(H_2O)(OH)^+$$

$$2\ enPd(H_2O)(OH)^+ \overset{K_D}{\rightleftarrows} 2\ H_2O + (en)Pd \underset{\underset{H}{O}}{\overset{\overset{H}{O}}{\diamondsuit}} Pd(en)^{2+}$$

Consistent with the crystal structure results we also write a reaction for formation of trinuclear, trihydroxo bridged trimer.

$$3\ enPd(H_2O)(OH)^+ \overset{K_T}{\rightleftarrows} 3\ H_2O + trimer^{3+}$$

A new non-linear least squares analysis of pH vs. equiv base from the 1976 titration data at 23° with 0.2 M KNO_3 (11) yields $pK_1 = 6.2$, $\log K_D = 3.7$ (M^{-1}), and $\log K_T = 6.5$ (M^{-2}). At total Pd(II) concentrations greater than 0.2 mM more Pd(II) occurs as dihydroxo bridged dimer than as the aquo-hydroxo complex.

It is possible to make an approximate comparison of the trimerization and dimerization constants of enPd(II) with those for cis $(NH_3)_2Pt(II)$. From the constants given above in the enPd(II) system, $K_T = 9K_D^{3/2}$. From the pair of points for dimer (0.60) and trimer (0.40) Pt(II) mole fractions at the end of Figure 7 in reference (16) I calculate that $K_T = 4K_D^{3/2}$. (If the system is not at equilibrium, the numerical 4 factor should be greater.) The comparison suggests that the two metal ion systems have comparable tendencies to form hydroxo bridged dimers and trimers.

The distribution curves in Figure 2 are incomplete in neutral solutions where the aquo-hydroxo complex polymerizes to yield hydroxo bridged dimer and trimer. The extent of the dimerization depends upon the total Pt(II) concentration, and the dimerization equilibrium constant is unknown. If the value for $enPd(H_2O)(OH)^+$ of $K_D = 10^{3.7}$ is taken as representative, at all concentrations greater than 0.2 mM more Pt(II) occurs as dimer than as the aquo-hydroxo complex. The dihydroxo bridged dimer is expected to be virtually inert to substitution. Because it is less strained, the hydroxo bridged trimer promises to be even more inert than the dimer. Thus the reactivity of Pt(II) complexes in neutral solutions in the presence of a low Cl^- background drops markedly at greater than 0.1 mM total Pt(II) concentrations. Concentrations greater than 0.1 mM total Pt(II) are unlikely within a cell, but they are common in many in vitro experiments.

Efforts to use cis $(NH_3)_2Pt(H_2O)_2{}^{2+}$ and other cis diaquo complexes to provide greater reactivity than the cis dichloro complexes may be self-defeating under some circumstances. In neutral solutions with a low Cl⁻ background, substantial fractions of inert hydroxo bridged dimer and trimer form depending upon the total Pt(II) concentration. Dimer and trimer formation occurs via the aquo-hydroxo monomer which occurs in maximum concentration in neutral solutions. The rate of monomer disappearance exhibits a maximum in neutral solutions ([16]). At concentrations greater than 0.1 mM total Pt(II), the rate of inert dihydroxo bridged dimer formation may exceed that of water substitution by another ligand. Thus conclusions based on the ratio of reactive Pt(II) complex to other ligands such as nucleic bases may have to be reconsidered. This conclusion appears especially relevant to reaction of supposed cis diaquo Pt(II) complexes with helical nucleic acids, where the secondary structure slows further the rate of complex formation with the ligand. An otherwise inexplicable report that cis $(NH_3)_2Pt(H_2O)_2{}^{2+}$ reacts more slowly at pH 7 with DNA than does cis $(NH_3)_2PtCl_2$ ([17]), is probably due to formation of inert hydroxo complexes and hydroxo bridged dimers and trimers.

A dimer with a single hydroxo bridge forms with $dienPd(H_2O)^{2+}$. The irregular nature of the titration curve had been noted ([11]). A recent non-linear least squares analysis resolved the titration curve obtained in 0.5 M KNO_3 and 21° into a deprotonation with $pK_a = 7.74 \pm 0.01$ and a dimerization reaction ([18]). We can reformulate the dimerization reaction as

$$dienPd(H_2O)^{2+} + dienPd(OH)^{+} \overset{K_6}{\underset{\leftarrow}{\rightarrow}} (dien)Pd-OH-Pd(dien) + H_2O$$

and from the constants already given in reference [18] calculate $K_6 = 132$ M^{-1}. At pH 7.74 the concentrations of the two reactants at the left appear in equal concentrations, and at 60 mM Pd(II) is divided evenly between the two sides of the reaction. Higher total Pd(II) concentrations favor the dimer. The analogous compound $dienPt(H_2O)^{2+}$ exhibits a regular titration curve with $pK_a = 6.13$ at 25° in 0.1 M $NaClO_4$ ([19]). The slow dimerization reaction permits easy evaluation of the acidity constant. The dimerization reaction in $dienPt(H_2O)^{2+}$ awaits study.

Hydroxo groups on Pt(II) complexes might also react as nucleophiles. Though it is $10^{9.2}$ times less basic than unbound hydroxide, the hydroxide bound to $dienPtOH^+$ is only 450 times less reactive in promoting hydrolysis of p-nitrophenylacetate ([11]). Metal ion bound hydroxide of greatly decreased basicity but only modestly reduced nucleophilicity occurs commonly with metal ions and provides a relatively high concentration of potent hydroxide nucleophiles in neutral and even acidic solutions ([20]).

N(1) versus N(7) Dichotomy in Purine Nucleosides (21)

When substituted at N(9) as in nucleosides and derivatives, the purine bases offer two potential metal ion binding sites. In neutral solutions of adenosine both N(1) and N(7) deprotonate while with the 6-oxopurines inosine and guanosine only N(7) deprotonates. N(1)H deprotonations occur with pK_a values of 3.6, 8.7, and 9.2 in adenosine, inosine, and guanosine, respectively (21). The relative extent of metal ion binding to N(7) and N(1) in neutral solutions of inosine and guanosine depends on pH.

Despite reports on studies of many metal ions, the N(7)/N(1) metal ion binding ratios at equilibrium in purine nucleosides are known quantitatively for only two cases, owing to an early study on CH_3Hg^+ (22) and a more recent one on dienPd(II) (18). The intrinsic N(1)/N(7) metal ion binding ratios of CH_3Hg^+ approach more closely those of the proton than do the binding ratios of dienPd(II), which exhibit a strong bias toward the less basic N(7) (18).

This research seeks to clarify the intrinsic N(1)/N(7) binding ratios for cis diamine Pt(II). Owing to the difficulty of attaining and judging attainment of equilibrium with Pt(II) (1), we performed experiments with Pd(II). The enPd(II) binds at both N(1) and N(7) to produce extensive polymer formation (23). We find no evidence for any N(7)-O(6) chelation of enPd(II) in 6-oxopurines. With only a single site for substitution, $dienPdH_2O^{2+}$ avoids the complexities offered by $enPd(H_2O)_2^{2+}$ and provides an intrinsic measure of Pd(II) binding at individual nucleic base sites. Studies with tridentate dipeptides instead of dien chelated about Pd(II) yield similar results (24,25).

A comprehensive investigation of $dienPdH_2O^{2+}$ binding to nucleosides and 5-nucleotides has been reported (18); this description will highlight only a few points. From the separate peaks in ^{1}H NMR spectra it is possible to follow the chemical shifts of each kind of dienPd(II) complex as a function of pH. Figure 4 shows a plot of H(8) chemical shift versus pH for several species in a solution of 5'-GMP and dienPd(II). Upon protonation of the phosphate group, (designated by Hp) the H(8) chemical shift moves upfield, reversing the usual direction. For inosine and adenosine and their 5'-nucleotides, the H(2) chemical shift has also been identified over a wide pH range (18). Chemical shift data such as that shown in Figure 4 allow a calculation of acidity constants for deprotonations from free ligand and complexes.

Comparison of areas under individual peaks in the ^{1}H NMR spectrum of dienPd(II)-nucleoside and nucleotide complexes permits evaluation of equilibrium stability constants for complex formation. Figure 5 shows the species distribution in a nearly equimolar solution of dienPd(II) and 5'-GMP and Figure 6 does the same for 5'-AMP. The difference between the distributions in Figure 5 and 6 results largely from the different absolute

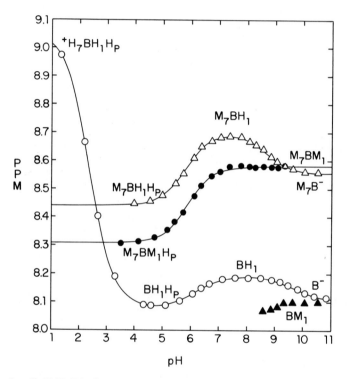

Figure 4.   5'-GMP H8 chemical shift vs. pH for several species. The ppm scale is downfield from DDS. (Reproduced from Ref. 18. Copyright 1981, American Chemical Society.)

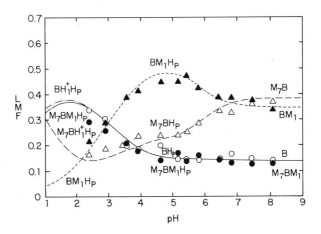

Figure 5.   Species distribution of 5'-GMP binding by dienPd²⁺ presented as ligand mole fraction (LMF) vs. pH at 0.10 M dienPd²⁺ and 0.11 M GMP. Individual points are calculated from ¹H-NMR intensities. Curves are derived from equilibrium constants given in Ref. 18. (Reproduced from Ref. 18. Copyright 1981, American Chemical Society.)

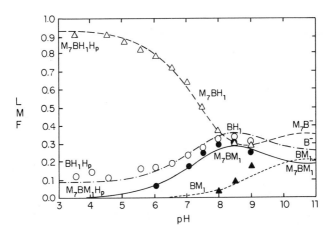

Figure 6.   Species distribution of 5'-AMP binding by dienPd²⁺ presented as ligand mole fraction (LMF) vs. pH with both total Pd(II) and total AMP at 0.10 M. Individual points are calculated from ¹H-NMR intensities. Curves are derived from equilibrium constants given in Ref. 18. (Reproduced from Ref. 18. Copyright 1981, American Chemical Society.)

basicities of N(1); the two 5'-nucleotides possess a similar intrinsic Pd(II) N(7)/N(1) binding ratio of ~1.4. This ratio differs radically from that for the proton, which amounts to $10^{4.6}$ for 5'-GMP and $10^{2.7}$ for 5'-AMP (18). Thus the extent of dienPd(II) binding to N(7) of GMP and guanosine greatly exceeds what might be expected from N(7) basicity.

In neutral solutions our results show that the dienPd(II) complex distribution favors M_7BH_1 for 5'-GMP and BM_1 for inosine and adenosine while for 5'-IMP and 5'-AMP both N(7) and N(1) complexed species occur in comparable amounts (18). Presence of the 5'-phosphate group favors formation of the N(7) complexes. The stability order of decreasing dienPd(II) binding strengths at the common 5'-nucleotides at pH 7 is G7>I7>I1>G1>U3>T3>C3>A1>A7 (18). Thus of the common nucleosides, N(7) of a guanine base provides the strongest dienPd(II) binding site in neutral solutions.

How do the intrinsic N(1)/N(7) binding ratios for dienPt(II) compare with those now known for dienPd(II)? Because it is difficult to achieve equilibrium with Pt(II) complexes of the N(1) protonated 6-oxopurines, we approached equilibrium with an equimolar solution of $dienPtH_2O^{2+}$ and 5'-AMP at pH 5.1 (26). The solution sat for two months, during which time it was heated at $50°$ for 13 days. Leveling off in the slow growth of the ^1H NMR peaks due to the BM_1 complex suggests that equilibrium may have been obtained. The last ratio of M_7BHp to BM_1Hp complexes is 1.9 (26). This value is 4.4 times greater than that found for dienPd(II) to AMP (18). If we generalize the result for AMP to the other nucleic bases, we conclude that Pt(II) favors N(7) over N(1) binding to an even greater extent than Pd(II). Thus the N(7) binding site of guanosine already atop the stability order for Pd(II) becomes relatively stronger for Pt(II) compared to sites on the other bases. We conclude that the predominant Pt(II) binding site in nucleosides and nucleotides is N(7) of guanosine.

During a study of the H(8) promoted exchange by Pt(II) bound to N(7) in purines, we noted at pH 5-6 a migration of dienPt(II) from inosine N(7) to N(1) (27). First $dienPtH_2O^+$ reacts at N(7).

$$M + BH_1 \rightarrow M_7BH_1$$

The metal ion at N(7) promotes the acidity of the proton at N(1) by up to 2 log units (18).

$$M_7BH_1 \rightarrow H^+ + M_7B^-$$

The greater fraction of N(1) deprotonated species with M_7BH_1 than with BH_1 provides a facile pathway for metal ion coordination at N(1) at lower pH than occurs with unbound ligand

$$M + M_7B^- \rightarrow M_7BM_1$$

Our experiments with equimolar inosine and $dienPtH_2O^{2+}$ produced a complete reaction to give M_7BH_1, followed by appearance of the binuclear complex M_7BM_1 and reappearance of free ligand BH_1. Finally the metal ion bound at N(7) may be released.

$$M_7BM_1 \rightarrow M + BM_1$$

Even with dienPd(II) and inosine the overall transfer of metal ion from N(7) to N(1) is slow (18).

With N(1) protonated nucleic bases, metal ion coordination at N(1) occurs via the binuclear M_7BM_1 complex because of the greater acidity of M_7BH_1 compared to BH_1. For all five ligands studied with dienPd(II), the greater fraction of N(1) deprotonated species when the ligand is metalated at N(7) more than offsets the decrease in stability for metal ion binding at N(1) in M_7B compared to B. (K_{71}/K_{a7B} vs. K_1/K_{aB} in reference 18). The above mechanism provides the main pathway for metal ion coordination at N(1) in acidic and neutral solutions of inosine, guanosine, and derivatives containing comparable amounts of metal ion.

Pt(II) does displace the basic N(3) proton from uridine ($pK_a = 9.2$); the stability constant for dienPt(II) binding to uridine has been estimated as at least 10 times greater than that for dienPd(II) (28). For dienPd(II) and uridine in H_2O the stability constant is $\log K = 8.1$ (29). Since dienPt(II) yields a greater adenosine N(7)/N(1) stability constant ratio than dienPd(II), the stability constant for Pt(II) at N(7) of purines should be about 50-100 times greater than that for Pd(II). Displacement of the N(1) proton of guanosine and inosine and derivatives by Pt(II) is diverted by prior coordination and kinetic fixation at N(7). Of the several common nucleoside binding sites, both equilibrium and kinetic factors favor Pt(II) binding at guanosine N(7). Reactions of Pd(II) compounds with nucleic bases serve as a thermodynamic reference for reactions of analogous Pt(II) compounds at equilibrium. Large differences between reaction products of analogous Pd(II) and Pt(II) compounds may be attributed to introduction of kinetic effects in the latter.

Acknowledgments

This research was supported by a research grant from the National Science Foundation.

Literature Cited

1. Vestues, P.; Martin, R.B. J. Am. Chem. Soc. 1981, 103, 806.
2. Howe-Grant, M.E.; Lippard, S.J. Metal Ions Biol. Syst. 1980, 11, 63.
3. Shannon, R.D. Acta Crystallogr. 1976, A32, 751.
4. Basolo, F.; Gray, H.B.; Pearson, R.G. J. Am. Chem. Soc. 1960, 82, 4200.
5. Reishus, J.W.; Martin, Jr., D.S. J. Am. Chem. Soc. 1961, 83, 2457.
6. Coley, R.F.; Martin, Jr., D.S. Inorg. Chim. Acta 1973, 7, 573.
7. Jensen, K.A. Z. Anorg. Allg. Chem. 1939, 242, 87.
8. Grinberg, A.A.; Stetsenko, A.I.; Mitkinova, N.D.; Tikhonova, L.S. Russ. J. Inorg. Chem. 1971, 16, 137.
9. LeRoy, A.F. Cancer Treat. Rep. 1979, 63, 231.
10. Gray, H.B.; Olcott, R.J. Inorg. Chem. 1962, 1, 481.
11. Lim, M.C.; Martin, R.B. J. Inorg. Nucl. Chem. 1976, 38, 1911.
12. Faggiani, R.; Lippert, B.; Lock, C.J.L.; Rosenberg, B. J. Am. Chem. Soc. 1977, 99, 777.
13. Lippert, B.; Lock, C.J.L., Rosenberg, B.; Zvagulis, M. Inorg. Chem. 1978, 17, 2971.
14. Faggiani, R.; Lippert, B.; Lock, C.J.L.; Rosenberg, B. Inorg. Chem. 1977, 16, 1192.
15. Faggiani, R.; Lippert, B.; Lock, C.J.L.; Rosenberg, B. Inorg. Chem. 1978, 17, 1941.
16. Rosenberg, B. Biochimie 1978, 60, 859.
17. Mansy, .S.; Chu, G.Y.H.; Duncan, R.E.; Tobias, R.S. J. Am. Chem. Soc. 1978, 100, 607.
18. Scheller, K.; Scheller-Krattiger, V.; Martin, R.B. J. Am. Chem. Soc. 1981, 103, 6833.
19. Alcock, R.M.; Hartley, F.R.; Rogers, D.E. J. Chem. Soc. Dalton 1973, 1070.
20. Martin, R.B. J. Inorg. Nucl. Chem. 1976, 38, 511.
21. Martin, R.B.; Mariam, Y.H. Metal Ions Biol. Syst. 1979, 8, 57.
22. Simpson, R.B. J. Am. Chem. Soc. 1964, 86, 2059.
23. Sovago, I.; Martin, R.B. Inorg. Chem. 1980, 19, 2868.
24. Vestues, P.I.; Martin, R.B. Inorg. Chim. Acta 1981, 55, 99.
25. Scheller-Krattiger, V.; Scheller, K.H.; Martin, R.B. Inorg. Chim. Acta 1982, 59, 281.
26. Kim, S-H.; Martin, R.B. 1981, unpublished results.
27. Noszal, B.; Scheller-Krattiger, V.; Martin, R.B. J. Am. Chem. Soc. 1982, 104, 1078.
28. Lim, M.C.; Martin, R.B. J. Inorg. Nucl. Chem. 1976, 38, 1915.
29. Lim, M.C. J. Inorg. Nucl. Chem. 1981, 43, 221.

RECEIVED October 4, 1982

Extended X-Ray Absorption Fine Structure (EXAFS) Spectroscopic Analysis of 6-Mercaptopurine Riboside Complexes of Platinum(II) and Palladium(II)

MICHAEL A. BRUCK, HANS-JÜRGEN KORTE, and ROBERT BAU—
University of Southern California, Department of Chemistry,
Los Angeles, CA 90089

NICK HADJILIADIS—University of Ioannina, Department of Chemistry,
Domboli 31, Ioannina, Greece

BOON-KENG TEO—Bell Laboratories, Murray Hill, NJ 07974

EXAFS evidence is presented to support the existence of N(7)-S(6) chelates in the structures of Pt(6—mercaptopurineriboside)$_2$, Pt(2—amino—6—mercaptopurineriboside)$_2$, Pd(6—mercaptopurineriboside)$_2$ and Pd(2—amino—6—mercaptopurineriboside)$_2$. Relevant bond distances are as follows: for Pt(6—mercaptopurine riboside)$_2$, Pt—N = 2.02(2)Å, Pt—S = 2.31(1)Å; for Pt(2—amino—6—mercaptopurineriboside)$_2$, Pt—N = 2.02(2)Å, Pt—S = 2.31(1)Å.

The possible existence of an N(7)-O(6) chelate from guanine to platinum remains one of the most actively-debated issues among researchers studying the mode of action of anti-tumor platinum drugs (1-13). Even though many compounds have been prepared which are believed to contain such chelates (3-7), there are as yet no reported crystal structure determinations which unambiguously prove the existence of this mode (14-17). In contrast, the related question of an N(7)-S(6) chelate involving the sulfur analog of guanine, 6-mercaptopurine, is much less controversial: there is general agreement that such chelates are readily formed. Crystal structures have been reported showing the existence of such chelates in complexes of Cu(II) (18), Cd(II) (19), and, most notably, Pd(II) (20,21).

The syntheses of several Pt complexes with 6-mercaptopurines have been reported (22,23). Spectroscopic evidence, conductivity measurements and chemical analyses suggest that these compounds have the formula Pt(6—mercaptopurine)$_2$ with the N(7)-S(6) chelate binding mode. Since Pd complexes are often considered to be good structural models for Pt complexes, the known existence of an N(7)-S(6) chelate in Pd(6—mercapto—9—benzylpurine)$_2$ (20,21) provided further support for the chelate model in analogous Pt complexes. In the absence of an X-ray crystallographic determination, we report here the determination of the structure in the vicinity of the Pt atom for Pt(6—mercaptopurine riboside)$_2$ [Pt(6—MPR)$_2$] and Pt(2—amino—6—mercaptopurine riboside)$_2$ [Pt(2—A—6—MPR)$_2$], using Extended X-ray Aborption Fine Structure (EXAFS) spectroscopy. The EXAFS technique (24-34) allows an accurate determination of interatomic distances between an X-ray absorbing atom and its near-neighbors as well as the coordination numbers.

The abbreviations for ligands used in this paper are shown in Figure 1. It should be noted that for the complexes described in this paper, the ligands become deprotonated at the N(1) position when complexed to a metal and hence acquire a formal charge of −1.

<u>Experimental Section</u>

The compounds studied in this work are cis—Pt(NH$_3$)$_2$Cl$_2$ (A), Pt(2—A—6—MPR)$_2$ (B), Pt(6—MPR)$_2$ (C), Pd(6—MPR)$_2$ (D), Pd(2—A—6—MPR)$_2$ (E), and Pd(Guo)$_2$Cl$_2$ (F). Compounds A and D were used as models and compound F was used as a check for the model compound approach used in this study. The synthesis and characterization of the Pt-6-mercaptopurineribosides has been previously reported (23). The Pd complexes were prepared in an analogous manner. Cis—Pt(NH$_3$)$_2$Cl$_2$ (35) and Pd(Guo)$_2$Cl$_2$ (7) were prepared according to literature methods. The EXAFS experiments were conducted on the C2 beam-line at the Cornell High Energy Synchrotron Source (CHESS) (37). The synchrotron radiation was monochromated by a channel-cut silicon <220> crystal.

Samples were prepared by first grinding the solids into homogenous fine powders and then pressing the powder into a pellet (cross-section of pellet: 3mm × 19mm; cross-section of synchrotron beam: ∼ 1mm × 14mm). For some samples it was necessary to dilute the powder with boron nitride. The sample concentration and the pellet thickness were adjusted such that the change in μX across the absorption-edge was approximately equal to one (where μ is the linear absorption coefficient and X is the pellet thickness).

All data were collected in the transmission mode using gas-filled ionization chambers to measure the X-ray intensity before (I$_o$) and after (I) the sample. For the Pt samples, the Pt L$_{III}$-edge absorption spectra (E$_o$ ∼ 11560 eV) were collected using N$_2$ in both ion chambers. For Pd samples, the Pd K-edge spectra (E$_o$ ∼ 24350 eV) were collected using N$_2$ in the I$_o$ chamber and Ar in the I chamber.

Each spectrum was measured at a series of discrete energy values, starting at a point approximately 100 eV below the absorption edge and continuing up in energy to a point approximately 900 eV above the absorption edge. The actual increments were in steps of constant k and therefore ranged from 2 to 9 eV from the beginning to the end of a scan. The average dwell time per data point was about 1 sec., the actual time per data point was varied so that a constant count was obtained for I$_o$. Plots of the raw data in the form ln (I$_o$/I) vs. E are shown in Figure 2.

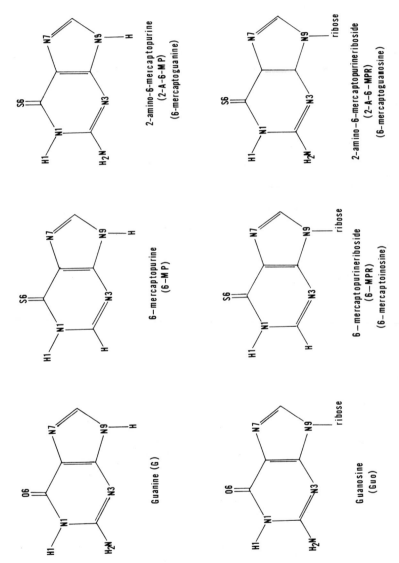

Figure 1.   Schematic of the ligand structures referenced within text and the abbreviations used.

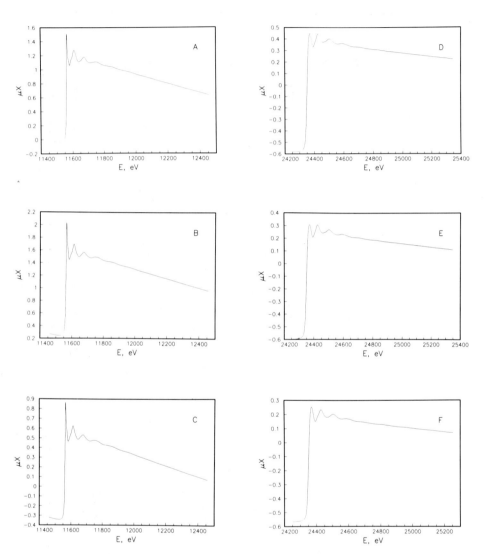

Figure 2.   X-Ray absorption spectra, μx vs. E, eV. Key: A, cis-Pt(NH₃)₂Cl₂; B, Pt(2-A-6-MPR)₂; C, Pt(6-MPR)₂; D, Pd(6-MPR)₂; E, Pd(2-A-6-MPR)₂; and F, Pd(Guo)₂Cl₂.

Data Reduction

The raw data were processed as described in the literature (28,29,38,39). The procedure involves (a) transformation of the absorption data from energy space into momentum or k-space according to the equation,

$$k = \left[(2m/\hbar^2)(E-E_o)\right]^{1/2} \tag{1}$$

followed by (b) background subtraction using a cubic spline, (c) k^3-weighting, (d) normalization of the edge-jump, and (e) corrections for the fall-off in absorption cross-section according to Victoreen's equation (40). The resultant $k^3X(k)$ vs. k plots are shown as solid curves in Figure 3.

Fourier transforms of the k-space data are depicted as solid curves in Figure 4. To obtain the actual distances, r, a phase-shift factor must be added to the apparent distance, r', in the Fourier transform. This phase-shift may be estimated from model compounds. However, more accurate values for r can be obtained from curve-fitting as described below.

For the purposes of this study, the first two major maxima in the Fourier transform, corresponding to the M-N (M=Pt or Pd) and M-S or M-Cl distances, were Fourier filtered and back-transformed into k-space. The filtering windows are shown as dashed curves in Figure 4 and the back-transformed, filtered data in k-space are shown as dashed curves in Figure 3.

A non-linear least-squares minimization technique was used to fit the filtered spectrum with a semi-empirical expression for the EXAFS as follows:

$$k^3\chi(k) = B_1F_1(k_1)k_1^2(1/r_1^2) \sin\left[2k_1r_1 + \phi_1(k_1)\right] \exp\left[-2\sigma_1^2k_1^2\right]$$

$$+ B_2F_2(k_2)k_2^2(1/r_2^2) \sin\left[2k_2r_2 + \phi_2(k_2)\right] \exp\left[-2\sigma_2^2k_2^2\right] \tag{2}$$

Subscript 1 refers to M-N parameters and subscript 2 refers to M-S or M-Cl parameters. The functions $F_j(k_j)$ and $\phi_j(k_j)$ used in this study are the theoretically calculated amplitude and phase functions for the jth back-scatterer (41). Four parameters are least-squares refined for each term: the scale factor, B; the Debye-Waller thermal parameter, σ; the interatomic distance, r; and the energy threshold, ΔE_o.

A set of best-fit values (denoted by subscript bf) were obtain by curve-fitting the filtered k-space data. Plots of the filtered data (solid curve) and associated best-fit values (dashed curve) are shown in Figure 5. These results, which are based upon theory, and hence totally independent of "model" compounds, are listed in the left-hand portion of Table I, under the heading "BFBT results" (best-fit based upon theory).

The Pd-N distances are between 1.97Å and 2.04Å for the compounds studied. The Pt-N distances range from 2.04Å to 2.06Å. The Pd-S and Pt-S BFBT distances, as well as the Pd-Cl and Pt-Cl distances, are all around 2.33Å. These distances are within the ranges of expected values. For comparison, the average value for the Pt-Cl distance in cis − $Pt(NH_3)_2Cl_2$ is 2.331Å. However, the coordination numbers (N) were not well determined by the BFBT technique.

In order to improve the accuracy of the BFBT results, as well as to determine reliable coordination numbers, a newly developed fine adjustment procedure (42) was applied to the best-fit results (FABM: fine adjustment based upon model). This technique helps to alleviate parameter correlation problems and provides a simple graphical technique to distinguish a good "model" from a "bad" model. A "good" model has been operationally defined as one which has parameters and parameter correlation

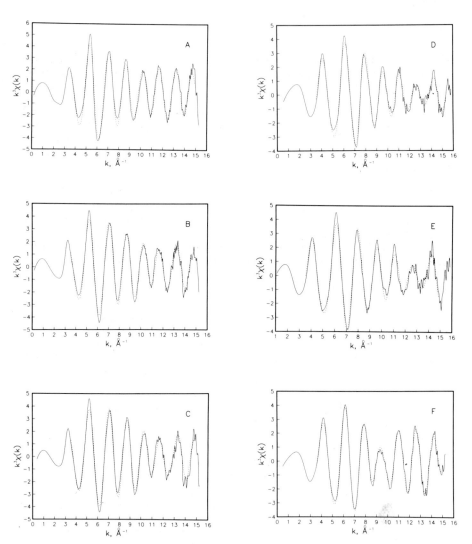

Figure 3. Background-subtracted (solid curve) and Fourier-filtered (dashed curve) EXAFS data {k³χ(k), [Å⁻³] vs. k, [Å⁻¹]}. Key: A, cis-Pt(NH₃)₂Cl₂; B, Pt(2-A-6-MPR)₂; C, Pt(6-MPR)₂; D, Pd(6-MPR)₂; E, Pd(2-A-6-MPR)₂; and F, Pd(Guo)₂Cl₂.

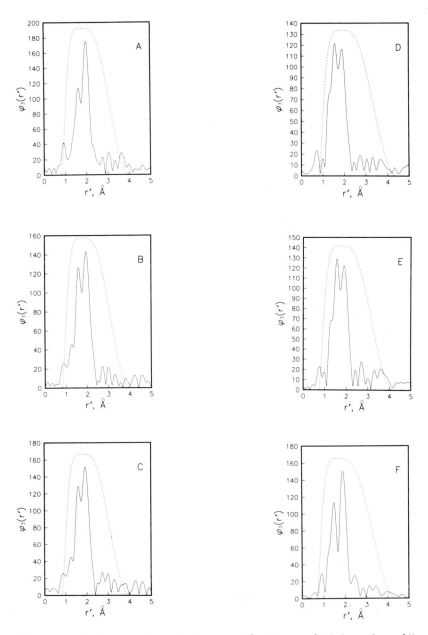

Figure 4. Fourier transforms (solid curves) [φ₃(r) vs. r, Å (before phase shift correction)] of the background-subtracted EXAFS spectra in Figure 3 and Fourier-filtering windows (dashed curves). Key: A, cis-Pt(NH₃)₂Cl₂; B, Pt(2-A-6-MPR)₂; C, Pt(6-MPR)₂; D, Pd(6-MPR)₂; E, Pd(2-A-6-MPR)₂; and F, Pd(Guo)₂Cl₂.

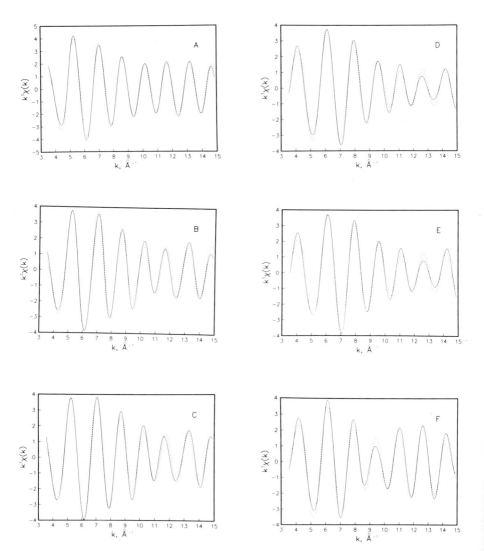

Figure 5.   Fourier-filtered EXAFS spectra, $k^3\chi(k)$ vs. k, (solid curve) and BFBT nonlinear least-squares curve fit (dashed curve). Key: A, cis-Pt(NH₃)₂Cl₂; B, Pt(2-A-6-MPR)₂; C, Pt(6-MPR)₂; D, Pd(6-MPR)₂; E, Pd(2-A-6-MPR)₂; and F, Pd-(Guo)₂Cl₂.

TABLE I. Results of the EXAFS Analysis

Compound	Term	r,Å	BFBT Results E_0^P,eV	ΔE_0^P,eV	r,Å	σ,Å	FABM Results r,Å	N
(A) cis-Pt(NH₃)₂Cl₂	Pt-N	2.000[a]	11560.3	9.60	2.06(3)	0.075(12)	2.000[c]	2.0[c]
	Pt-Cl	2.331[a]	11560.3	17.11	2.34(1)	0.032(20)	2.331[c]	2.0[c]
(B) Pt(2-A-6-MPR)₂	Pt-N	-	11560.8	5.25	2.04(3)	0.063(48)	2.02(2)	2.0(5)
	Pt-S	-	11560.8	19.77	2.33(2)	0.040(14)	2.31(1)	1.9(6)
(C) Pt(6-MPR)₂	Pt-N	-	11560.8	4.62	2.04(4)	0.058(48)	2.02(2)	1.9(4)
	Pt-S	-	11560.8	18.13	2.32(1)	0.040(16)	2.31(1)	2.0(7)
(D) Pd(6-MPR)₂	Pd-N	2.064[b]	24349.0	-10.36	2.03(4)	0.057(48)	2.064[c]	2.0[c]
	Pd-S	2.308[b]	24349.0	12.39	2.33(2)	0.055(26)	2.308[c]	2.0[c]
(E) Pd(2-A-6-MPR)₂	Pd-N	-	24350.0	-10.75	2.04(5)	0.059(50)	2.08(4)	2.2(19)
	Pd-S	-	24350.0	12.49	2.33(2)	0.047(20)	2.31(2)	2.1(13)
(F) Pd(Guo)₂Cl₂	Pd-N	-	24350.0	-15.56	1.97(5)	0.025(32)	2.02(4)	1.9(14)
	Pd-Cl	-	24350	12.18	2.33(2)	0.051(20)	2.31(2)	2.1(13)

a) Reference 57

b) Assuming that Pd-N and Pd-S distances in Pd(6-mercaptopurineriboside)₂ (Compound D) are the same as those in Pd(6-mercapto-9-benzylpurine)₂ (reference 20).

c) Known from model compounds. (refs. 20,57).

d) Calculated with $\sigma_{Pt-N}^* = 0.075$Å and $\sigma_{Pt-X}^* = 0.032$Å from the model compound A.

e) Calculated with $\sigma_{Pd-N}^* = 0.057$Å and $\sigma_{Pd-X}^* = 0.055$Å from the model compound D.

behavior similar to that of the unknown. This procedure is described in detail elsewhere (42), and details of our results are given in the Appendix.

The final results of the EXAFS analysis (FABM results) are summarized in the right-hand portion of Table I. The FABM values for all M-N distances in this study are between 2.00Å and 2.08Å. All of the values are reasonable, though they do show a wider range than the BFBT results. The range for M-S and M-Cl distances is 2.31Å to 2.33Å. The FABM values for coordination numbers, N, fall within ±10% of the expected values of 2 nitrogen and 2 chlorine or sulfur atoms per metal.

<u>Discussion</u>

Transition metal complexes of 6-mercaptopurines have been characterized with three binding modes: N-only, S(6)-only and [N(7)-S(6)] chelation. Two additional binding modes, the [N(1)-S(6)] chelate and the [N(3)-N(9)] chelate, have also been proposed, but not characterized.

S(6)-only binding has been shown crystallographically to occur in the complexes Hg(6−MP)$_2$Cl$_2$ (43), and [Cu(6−MP)Cl$_2$]$_2$ (44,45,46); and also is believed to exist (based upon IR evidence) in W(CO)$_5$(6−MP) (47,48). Nitrogen-only binding has been implied from ESR studies on iron-nitrosyl/mercaptopurine complexes (49).

The N(7)-S(6) chelation mode appears to be the dominant mode of bonding in metal complexes of 6-mercaptopurines. It has been crystallographically shown to exist in [Cu(9−methyl−6−mercaptopurine)Cl$_2$] (18), [Cd(6−mercaptopurine)(H$_2$O)Cl$_2$]$_2$ (19), and Pd(9−benzyl−6−mercaptopurine)$_2$ (20,21); and also indicated in some tungsten and iron complexes (47,48,49).

Various other spectroscopic studies have been reported on metal-mercaptopurine complexes (50-56). In these studies, however the specific binding sites are not discussed. These studies have included the metals Ag, Au, Pd, Pt, Pb, Zn, Ni, Co, Cu, Cd, Mg, Ca, Be, Al, Cr, and U.

Spectroscopic evidence (23) indicates that Pt(6−MPR)$_2$ and Pt(2−A−6−MPR)$_2$ have the [N(7)-S(6)] chelate structure. A comparison of the Fourier-transformed spectra for the Pt and Pd complexes of 6-MPR in this study (Figure 4) shows that they all contain two distinguishable peaks. The assignment of these peaks to Pt-N and Pt-S back-scatterings, in increasing distance, was subsequently supported by curve-fitting.

In this paper we have left unresolved the actual geometrical configuration (i.e., <u>cis</u> or <u>trans</u>) of the Pt and Pd mercaptopurine complexes. The original paper by Grinberg and co-workers (22), which favored a <u>trans</u> configuration, cited the strong <u>trans</u>-influence of sulfur as being a factor that would support a <u>trans</u>-geometry. This argument was also cited by Hadjiliadis and Theophanides (23,36), who presented infra-red evidence consistent with the <u>trans</u>-configuration in their platinum/mercaptopurine complexes. On the other hand, the crystal structure of Pd(6−mercapto−9−benzylpurine)$_2$ by Heitner and Lippard (20,21) unambiguously shows the <u>cis</u> configuration and these authors argued that the <u>cis</u> geometry allows maximum π-backbonding to sulfur (in other words, that a soft ligand like sulfur prefers to be opposite a hard ligand like nitrogen). Our present EXAFS data do not allow us to distinguish the <u>cis</u> and <u>trans</u> isomers.

Finally, we should point out that the existence of N(7)-S(6) chelates to platinum does not mean that N(7)-O(6) chelates to platinum are also present in the corresponding platinum-purine complexes. In fact, Heitner and Lippard have pointed out that the steric requirements for a [N−C−C−S−M] five-membered ring are significantly different from those for a [N-C-C-O-M] five-member ring, so that the existence of the former does not necessarily imply the existence of the latter.

Conclusion

The purpose of these experiments was to determine the binding mode of 6-mercaptopurineriboside to platinum using EXAFS spectroscopy. The Pt-EXAFS data presented here establish the presence of two nitrogen and two sulfur atoms at normal bonding distances from the platinum in Pt(6—mercaptopurineriboside)$_2$ and Pt(2—amino—6—mercaptopurine—riboside)$_2$. For Pt(6—MPR)$_2$ and Pt(2—NH$_2$—6—MPR)$_2$, we find Pt—N = 2.02(2)Å, Pt—S = 2.31(1)Å. The results from the Pt complexes in conjunction with the Pd-EXAFS, also presented here, [of Pd(6—MPR)$_2$ and Pd(2—A—6—MPR)$_2$ which are chemical analogs of the known N(7)-S(6) chelate Pd(9—benzyl—6—mercaptopurine)$_2$ (20,21)], define the binding mode in the Pt-complexes of this study to be of the [N(7)-S(6)]-chelate type.

Acknowledgments

This research was supported by NIH Grant #CA-17367 to R.B., and NATO Grant #1809 awarded jointly to R.B. and N.H. We thank the administrative and technical staff of the Cornell High Energy Synchrotron Source (CHESS) for their enthusiastic assistance. We would like to thank Dr. Douglas M. Ho for helpful discussions. Finally, we would like to express our gratitude for the technical and computer software assistance provided to us by M. R. Antonio (M.S.U.) and V. Bakirtzis (Bell Labs).

Literature Cited

1. Rosenberg, B. *J. Clin. Hematol. Oncol.* 1977, *7*, 817.
2. Goodgame, D. M. L.; Jeeves, I.; Phillips, F. L.; Skapski, A. C. *Biochim. Biophys. Acta* 1975, *378*, 153.
3. Millard, M. M.; Macquet, J. P.; Theophanides, T. *Biochim. Biophys. Acta* 1975, *402*, 166.
4. Dehand, J.; Jordanov, J. *J. Chem. Soc., Chem. Commun.* 1976, 598.
5. Macquet, J. P.; Theophanides, T. *Bioinorg. Chem.* 1975, *5*, 59.
6. Pneumatikakis, G.; Hadjiliadis, N.; Theophanides, T. *Inorg. Chim. Acta* 1977, *22*, L1.
7. Pneumatikakis, G.; Hadjiliadis, N.; Theophanides, T. *Inorg. Chem.* 1978, *17*, 915.
8. Chu, G. Y. H.; Tobias, R. S. *J. Am. Chem. Soc.* 1976, *98*, 2641.
9. Chu, G. Y. H.; Mansy, S.; Duncan, R. E.; Tobias, R. S. *J. Am. Chem. Soc.* 1978, *100*, 593.
10. Kelman, A. D.; Peresie, H. J.; Stone, P. J. *J. Clin. Hematol. Oncol.* 1977, *7*, 440.
11. Sletten, E. *J. Chem. Soc., Chem. Commun.* 1971, 558.
12. Kuntz, G. P. P.; Kotowycz, G. *Biochemistry* 1975, *14*, 4144.
13. Martin, R. B.; Mariam, Y. H. "Metal Ions in Biological Systems"; Sigel, H., Ed.; Marcel Dekker: New York, 1979; Vol. 8, Chapter 2.
14. Hodgson, D. J. *Prog. Inorg. Chem.* 1977, *23*, 211.
15. Swaminathan, V.; Sundaralingam, M. *C.R.C. Crit. Rev. Biochem.* 1979, *6*, 245.

16. Gellert, R. W.; Bau, R. "Metal Ions in Biological Systems"; Sigel, H., Ed.; Marcel Dekker: New York, 1979; Vol. 8, Chapter 1.
17. de Castro, B.; Kistenmacher, T. J.; Marzilli, L. G. *"Agents and Actions"*; in press.
18. Sletten, E.; Apeland, A. *Acta Cryst.* 1975, *B31*, 2019.
19. Griffith, E. A. H.; Amma, E. L. *J. Chem. Soc., Chem. Commun.* 1979, 1013.
20. Heitner, H. I.; Lippard, S. J. *Inorg. Chem.* 1974, *13*, 815.
21. Heitner, H. I.; Lippard, S. J.; Sunshine, H. R. *J. Am. Chem. Soc.* 1972, *94*, 8936.
22. Grinberg, A. A.; Varshavskii, Yu. S.; Gel'fman, M. I.; Kiseleva, N. V.; Smolenskaya, D. B. *Russ. J. Inorg. Chem.* 1968, *13*, 422.
23. Hadjiliadis, N.; Theophanides, T. *Inorg. Chim. Acta* 1975, *15*, 167.
24. Stern, E. A. *Contemporary Physics* 1978, *19*, 289.
25. Lee, P. A.; Citrin, P. H.; Eisenberger, P.; Kincaid, B. M. *Rev. Mod. Phys.* 1981, *53*, 769.
26. Eisenberger, P.; Kincaid, B. M. *Science* 1978, *200*, 1441.
27. Sandstrom, D. R.; Lytle, F. W. *Annu. Rev. Phys. Chem.* 1979, *30*, 215.
28. Teo, B. K. *Acc. Chem. Res.* 1980, *13*, 412.
29. Teo, B. K. "EXAFS Spectroscopy: Techniques and Applications"; Teo, B. K., Joy, D. C., Eds.; Plenum Press: New York, 1981; pp. 13-58.
30. Shulman, R. G.; Eisenberger, P.; Kincaid, B. M. *Annu. Rev. Biophys. Bioeng.* 1978, *7*, 559.
31. Cramer, S. P.; Hodgson, K. O. *Prog. Inorg. Chem.* 1979, *25*, 1.
32. Doniach, S.; Eisenberger, P.; Hodgson, K. O. "Synchrotron Radiation Research"; Winich, H., Doniach, S., Eds.; Plenum Press: New York, 1980; pp. 425-458.
33. Chan, S. I.; Gamble, R. C. *Methods in Enzymol.* 1978, *54*, (Part E), 323.
34. Powers, L. S. *Biochim. Biophys. Acta Rev.: Bioenerg.* in press.
35. Dhara, S. C. *Indian J. Chem.* 1970, *8*, 193.
36. Hadjiliadis, N.; Theophanides, T. *Can. J. Spectry.* 1977, *22*, 51.
37. Batterman, B. W.; Ashcroft, N. W. *Science* 1979, *206*, 157.
38. Teo, B. K.; Shulman, R. G.; Brown, G. S.; Meixner, A. E. *J. Am. Chem. Soc.* 1979, *101*, 5624.
39. Teo, B. K.; Eisenberger, P.; Kincaid, B. M. *J. Am. Chem. Soc.* 1977, *100*, 1735.
40. "International Tables for X-Ray Crystallography"; Macgillavry, C. H., Rieck, G. D., Lonsdale, K., Eds.; Kynoch Press: Birmingham, England, 1968; Vol. III, pp. 161, 171-173.
41. Teo, B. K.; Lee, P. A. *J. Am. Chem. Soc.* 1979, *101*, 2815.
42. Teo, B. K.; Antonio, M. R.; Averill, B. A. submitted for publication.
43. Lavertue, P.; Hubert, J.; Beauchamp, A. L. *Inorg. Chem.* 1976, *15*, 322.
44. Caira, M. R.; Nassimbeni, L. R. *Acta Cryst.* 1975, *B31*, 1339.
45. Pope, L.; Laing, M.; Caira, M. R.; Nassimbeni, L. R. *Acta Cryst.* 1976, *B32*, 612.
46. Shoemaker, A. L.; Singh, P.; Hodgson, D. J. *Acta Cryst.* 1976, *B32*, 979.
47. Kottmair, N.; Beck, W. *Inorg. Chim. Acta* 1979, *34*, 137.
48. Beck, W.; Kottmair, N. *Chem. Ber.* 1976, *109*, 970.
49. Basosi, R.; Gaggelli, E.; Tiezzi, E.; Valensin, G. *J. Am. Chem. Soc., Perkin II* 1975, 423.
50. Cheney, G. E.; Freiser, H.; Fernando, Q. *J. Am. Chem. Soc.* 1959, *81*, 2611.
51. Grinberg, A. A.; Kustova, N. A.; Gel'fman, M. I. *Russ. J. Inorg. Chem.* 1968, *13*, 1230.
52. Behrens, N. B.; Goodgame, D. M. L. *Inorg. Chim. Acta* 1980, *46*, 45.

53. Ghosh, A. K.; Chatterjee, S. *J. Inorg. Nucl. Chem.* 1964, *26*, 1459.
54. Taqui Khan, M. M.; Krishnamoorthy, C. R. *J. Inorg. Nucl. Chem.* 1973, *35*, 1285.
55. Nayan, R.; Dey, A. R. *J. Indian Chem. Soc.* 1973, *50*, 98.
56. Ghose, R.; Ghose, A. K.; Dey, A. K. *J. Indian Chem. Soc.* 1980, *57*, 929.
57. Milburn, G. H. W.; Truter, M. R. *J. Chem. Soc. (A)* 1966, 1609.

RECEIVED October 4, 1982

Appendix: the FABM technique as applied to the title compounds.

The structurally known compound cis—$Pt(NH_3)_2Cl_2$ (57) was chosen as the Pt model compound for use in the fine adjustment based on model (FABM) technique (for a full discussion of the method, see ref. 42). Pd(9-ribose-6-mercaptopurine) (23) was used as the Pd-model, assuming the average values for the Pd-N and Pd-S distances from Pd(9—benzyl—6—mercaptopurine)$_2$ (20,21).

The choice of a model compound with two nitrogen and two chlorine neighbors (hereafter designated as Pt—N_2Cl_2) [i.e., cis—$Pt(NH_3)_2Cl_2$; compound A] for an unknown with two nitrogen and two sulfur (Pt-N_2S_2) neighbors is not unreasonable. Small differences in atomic number are not distinguishable using EXAFS. To demonstrate this point, the cis—$Pt(NH_3)_2Cl_2$ data was fit using the theory for (Pt-N,S) and then again with (Pt-N,Cl) theory. The resulting best-fit values are shown in Table II. Note that the σ and r values are very similar.

Correlations between the parameters B_j and σ_j and $\Delta E_{0_j}^p$ and r_j within each term can affect the accuracy of the best-fit results. An even worse problem for the present system is that the phase and amplitude functions for the two types of neighbors (nitrogen and sulfur or chlorine) are not sufficiently different to prevent "trade offs" between the two terms. Both of these problems can be circumvented by the FABM method.

To explore and characterize the B_j vs. σ_j correlation, a series of fits are made for each absorber-backscatterer pair. For these fits the parameter σ_j is fixed at various values in the vicinity of the best fit value, σ_{bf}. While least-squares refining the parameters r_j, $\Delta E_{0_j}^p$, B_j, and B_i the parameters σ_i, r_i and $\Delta E_{0_i}^p$ are held at their best-fit values, here i and j denote two different terms. The B_j values are then plotted against σ_j to give a graphical representation of the correlation. This correlation is fit with a quadratic least-squares curve (goodness-of-fit R $\geq$ 0.998). The correlation of $\Delta E_{0_j}^p$ and r_j is probed in a similar manner. A series of fits is performed by fixing r_j at values around its best-fit value and allowing $\Delta E_{0_j}^p$, σ_j, B_j and B_i to refine while holding $\Delta E_{0_i}^p$, σ_i and r_i at their best-fit values. The $\Delta E_{0_j}^p$ values are then plotted against $\Delta r_j = r_j - (r_{bf})_j$. The plots of $\Delta E_{0_j}^p$ vs. Δr_j generally exhibit linear behavior. However, if a compound shows significant deviation from linearity, a quadratic term is added to reflect the curvature. In either case R $\geq$ 0.998.

TABLE II.   Comparison of an (N,Cl) Fit with an (N,S) Fit

Parameter	$Pt(NH_3)_2Cl_2$ (N,Cl fit)	$Pt(NH_3)_2Cl_2$ (N,S fit)
B_1	1.136	0.994
σ_1	0.0753	0.0727
r_1	2.059	2.050
B_2	0.693	0.775
σ_2	0.0365	0.0335
r_2	2.337	2.344
ΔE_{o_1}	0.20	-1.24
ΔE_{o_2}	7.71	8.10

The correlation curves for the platinum and palladium compounds are plotted in Figure 6 and Figure 7 respectively: (a) ΔE_o^p vs. Δr plots for M-N; (b) ΔE_o^p vs. Δr plots for M-X; (c) B vs. σ plots for M-N; (d) B vs. σ plots for M-X (M=Pt or Pd; X=Cl or S). The regression coefficients corresponding to the curves are tabulated in Table III. The fact that the curvatures and slopes of the curves within each figure are quite similar is a strong indication that we have chosen reasonable model compounds for our unknown systems.

The FABM procedure makes use of these curves as described below. The results are collected into Table IV with the best-fit values and relevant intermediate variables. The B values and σ values are now related as $B_j = b_o + b_1 \sigma_j + b_2 \sigma_j^2$. The $\Delta E_{o_j}^p$ values are related to the r_j values by $\Delta E_{o_j}^p = a_o + a_1(\Delta r_j) + a_2(\Delta r_j)^2$ and $\Delta r_j = r_j - r_{bf}$.

The distance correction Δr_j is determined for each term of each unknown from the *characteristic* $\Delta E_{o_j}^*$. The $\Delta E_{o_j}^*$ is obtained using a Δr_m for the model compound calculated as $\Delta r_m = r_{cryst} - r_{bf}$. At Δr_m, ΔE_o^* is found using the ΔE_o^p vs. Δr correlation curve of the model compound. The values of Δr_m and ΔE_o^* thus determined are:

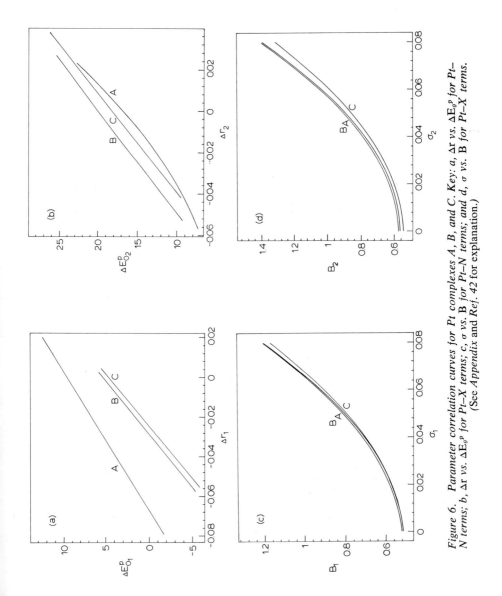

Figure 6. Parameter correlation curves for Pt complexes A, B, and C. Key: a, Δr vs. ΔE_0^p for Pt–N terms; b, Δr vs. ΔE_0^p for Pt–X terms; c, σ vs. B for Pt–X terms; and d, σ vs. B for Pt–X terms. (See Appendix and Ref. 42 for explanation.)

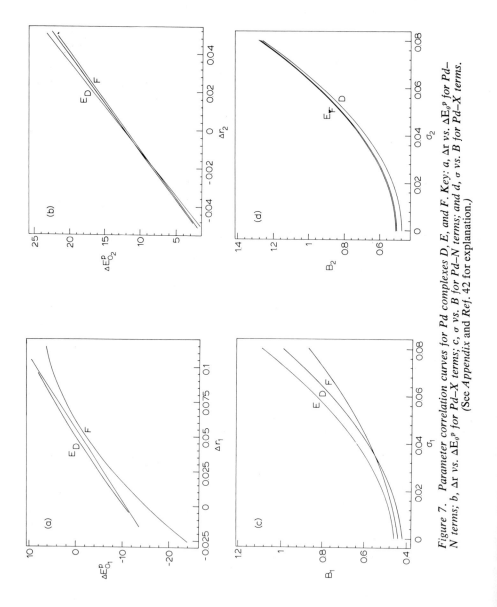

Figure 7. Parameter correlation curves for Pd complexes D, E, and F. Key: a, Δr vs. ΔE_0^p for Pd–N terms; b, Δr vs. ΔE_0^p for Pd–X terms; c, σ vs. B for Pd–N terms; and d, σ vs. B for Pd–X terms. (See Appendix and Ref. 42 for explanation.)

TABLE III   Least-Squares Regression Coefficients

Compound	Term	a_0	a_1	a_2	b_0	b_1	b_2
(A) $Pt(NH_3)_2Cl_2$	PtN	9.585	143.187	---	0.515	0.767	98.696
	PtCl	16.733	229.349	1126.518	0.563	0.055	129.196
(B) $Pt(2-A-6-MPR)_2$	PtN	5.263	185.393	---	0.522	1.070	93.536
	PtS	19.914	201.866	---	0.542	0.523	114.464
(C) $Pt(6-MPR)_2$	PtN	4.617	189.777	---	0.515	0.955	90.518
	PtS	18.258	210.133	---	0.574	0.315	126.000
(D) $Pd(6-MPR)_2$	PdN	-10.348	224.389	-334.344	0.421	0.973	76.786
	PdS	12.40	200.934	---	0.476	0.152	122.018
(E) $Pd(2-A-6-MPR)_2$	PdN	-10.651	193.634	---	0.459	0.852	88.857
	PdS	12.49	217.974	---	0.510	0.082	120.089
(F) $Pd(Guo)_2Cl_2$	PdN	-15.094	314.474	-1110.490	0.440	1.421	49.054
	PdCl	12.104	198.006	---	0.506	0.491	114.714

$\Delta r_{m(Pt-N)} = -0.059$, $\Delta E_{o(Pt-N)}^* = 1.14$; $\Delta r_{m(Pt-X)} = -0.0062$, $\Delta E_{o(Pt-X)} = 15.35$; $\Delta r_{m(Pd-N)} = 0.0384$, $\Delta E_{o(Pd-N)}^* = -.2.22$; $\Delta r_{m(Pd-X)} = -0.0205$, $\Delta E_{o(Pd-X)}^* = 8.28$.

The correction, Δr, for each bond-type is then determined from the ΔE_o^p vs. Δr curve of the unknown at ΔE_o^*. In this way the ΔE_o^* from the model is transferred to the unknown and a small adjustment, Δr, is determined and applied to r_{bf} ($r_{FABM} = r_{bf} + \Delta r$). The final distances are given in Table I and repeated in Table IV, along with the starting values and intermediate results.

To determine the coordination numbers, the best-fit Debye-Waller factors $\sigma_{Pt-N}^* = 0.075Å$; $\sigma_{Pt-X}^* = 0.032Å$; $\sigma_{Pd-N}^* = 0.057Å$ and $\sigma_{Pd-X}^* = 0.055Å$; (where X indicates S or Cl) of the models (A and D) were transferred to the corresponding terms of the unknowns (B, C and E, F).

For each type of bond, the B values of the model compounds, B_m, and the unknowns, B_m, are determined from the B vs. σ correlation curves (subscripts m and u refer to model and unknown respectively). The B_m values of the model compounds ((A) $B_{Pt-N} = 1.132$, $B_{Pt-X} = 0.694$; (D) $B_{Pd-N} = 0.722$, $B_{Pd-X} = 0.848$) are used to determine a amplitude reduction factor, S^*. Which is just a proportionality factor such that $S^* = B_m/N_m$ where N_m is the known coordination number of the model.

The coordination numbers for the unknowns, N_u, are then calculated as $N_u = B_u/S^*$. The final values of the unknown coordination numbers are listed in Table I and also in Table IV with the values of intermediate variables B_m, S^* and B_u.

TABLE IV Summary of the FABM Method

| | | Parameters Used for Calculating FABM Distances[a] | | | | | Parameters Used for Calculating FABM Coordination Numbers[b] | | | | |
		Δr (Å)	ΔE_0^* (eV)	$\Delta r +$ (Å)	$r_{bf} =$ (Å)	r_{FABM} (Å)	σ^* (Å)	B_m (B_M/N_M)	S^* (B_M/N_M)	B_u	N_u (B_u/S^*)
(A) cis–Pt(NH₃)₂Cl₂	Pt-N	-0.059	1.14	-0.059	2.059	2.000	0.075	1.132	0.566	-	2.00
	Pt-Cl	-0.006	15.35	-0.006	2.337	2.331	0.032	0.694	0.347	-	2.00
(B) Pt(2–A–6–MPR)₂	Pt-N	-	-	-0.022	2.037	2.015	-	-	-	1.133	2.00
	Pt-S	-	-	-0.023	2.333	2.310	-	-	-	0.673	1.94
(C) Pt(6–MPR)₂	Pt-N	-	-	-0.018	2.035	2.017	-	-	-	1.100	1.94
	Pt-S	-	-	-0.014	2.322	2.308	-	-	-	0.710	2.05
(D) Pd(6–MPR)₂	Pd-N	0.038	-2.22	0.038	2.025	2.063	0.057	0.722	0.361	-	2.00
	Pd-S	-0.021	8.28	-0.021	2.329	2.308	0.055	0.848	0.424	-	2.00
(E) Pd(2–A–6–MPR)₂	Pd-N	-	-	0.044	2.036	2.079	-	-	-	0.791	2.19
	Pd-S	-	-	-0.019	2.330	2.301	-	-	-	0.872	2.06
(F) Pd(Guo)₂Cl₂	Pd-N	-	-	0.050	1.966	2.016	-	-	-	0.677	1.88
	Pd-Cl	-	-	-0.019	2.331	2.312	-	-	-	0.847	2.06

a) $\Delta E_0 = a_0 + a_1 \Delta r + a_2 \Delta r^2$ where a_0, a_1, a_2 are given in Table III.

b) $B = b_0 + b_1 \sigma + b_2 \sigma^2$ where b_0, b_1, b_2 are given in Table III.

PLATINUM DRUG DEVELOPMENT AND ANALYSIS

Synthesis and Biological Studies of a New Class of Antitumor Platinum Complexes

DAVID B. BROWN, ABDUL R. KHOKHAR, MILES P. HACKER, JOHN J. McCORMACK, and ROBERT A. NEWMAN

University of Vermont and the Vermont Regional Cancer Center, Departments of Chemistry and Pharmacology, Burlington, VT 05405

A series of platinum complexes having the general formula $LPtCl_3$, where L is a ligand bearing a formal positive charge, have been prepared and have been demonstrated to exhibit significant antitumor activity. Complexes with this formulation satisfy the generally accepted criteria for structural features required in an antitumor-active platinum complex, but are expected to possess kinetic advantages when compared to the prototype antitumor platinum complex, cis-dichlorodiamineplatinum (II). Complexes have been prepared where L is a monoprotonated diamine and also where L is a protonated amino-olefin. All complexes have been examined for cytotoxicity against L1210 leukemia in cell culture, and selected compounds have been tested for antitumor activity in vivo (L1210 leukemia in BDF_1 mice). One compound, where L is protonated 3-aminoquinuclidine, has significant in vivo activity, with T/C approaching 150%.

More than a decade has elapsed since Rosenberg first reported (1) the antitumor activity of cis-dichlorodiamineplatinum(II), DDP. It would be fortuitous indeed if the first platinum complex reported proved to be the most effective compound of its type. Furthermore, although DDP is one of the most effective antitumor drugs available, its use is accompanied by severe nausea and a range of toxic effects (2). These factors, combined with the rather limited range of clinical activity for DDP, have led to the search for new antitumor platinum compounds having either increased efficacy or decreased toxicity, or both.

A vast number of platinum compounds have now been screened for antitumor activity, and the results of these investigations have led to a set of empirical guidelines for the minimum structural features required for activity. Although they may be stated in various forms, the key structure-activity relationships (3) are:

0097-6156/83/0209-0265$06.00/0

1. The complex must have a pair of <u>cis</u>-anionic ligands (the
    leaving groups), as the <u>trans</u> analogs are invariably much
    less active.
2. The anionic ligands must be moderately hard Lewis bases,
    such as chloride ions or oxygen donors.
3. The Pt complexes must be water soluble, but must also be
    capable of entering the cell intact. For all practical
    purposes, this limits compounds to those bearing no net
    charge.
4. The identity of the neutral ligands (the amines) is
    crucial to activity in that there is suggestion that only
    complexes of primary (and possibly secondary) amines are
    effective oncolytic agents.

Compliance with these guidelines means that virtually all
compounds which have been examined have had the general structure
I.

$$
\begin{array}{c}
(Y) \\
| \\
A \diagdown \quad \diagup X \\
\quad Pt \\
A \diagup \quad \diagdown X \\
| \\
(Y)
\end{array}
$$

I

In I, X is an anionic ligand, typically chloride, and A is an
amine (or A_2 a chelating diamine.) Oxidation to the frequently
more soluble platinum (IV) analogs requires the incorporation of
two additional anionic ligands, Y.
    The general fate of DDP analogs in the body seems clear
(equation 1). It is thought that DDP enters the cell intact.

$$
\begin{array}{c}
A \diagdown \quad \diagup Cl \\
\quad Pt \\
A \diagup \quad \diagdown Cl
\end{array}
\;\underset{H_2O}{\overset{}{\rightleftharpoons}}\;
\left[
\begin{array}{c}
A \diagdown \quad \diagup OH_2 \\
\quad Pt \\
A \diagup \quad \diagdown OH_2
\end{array}
\right]^{+2}
\;\underset{(\longleftarrow)}{\overset{DNA}{\longrightarrow}}\;
A_2\,Pt/DNA\;Complex
$$

$?$

In the cell, an area of low chloride ion concentration, equilibrium favors loss of the anionic ligands with the formation of
various hydrated derivatives. It is these very reactive complexes, with their labile aquo ligands, which coordinate to DNA
and lead to the observed cytotoxicity. Excepting considerations
of solubility, the broad structure/activity observations of the
past decade are probably a reflection of variations in only the
end of this process. In particular, variations in the amine
identity are likely to have only minor effects on the kinetics

and thermodynamics of the hydrolysis equilibrium. The amine identity will however have a significant effect (due to steric factors, hydrogen bonding, etc.) on the thermodynamics of platinum binding to DNA, and hence on oncolytic activity.

In principle, it should be possible to vary the activity of platinum complexes not only by altering the thermodynamics of platinum binding to DNA, but also by altering the rate at which the equilibrium of equation 1 is attained. The kinetics of this hydrolysis reaction will be dictated by the trans-effect, that is, by the ability of the ligand lying trans to the chloride to increase the rate of the chloride ion substitution reactions. Amines lie low in the trans-effect series, and consequently the hydrolysis of a chloride ion lying trans to an amine is a rather sluggish reaction. Our work centers on efforts to improve antitumor activity by varying the substituents on platinum in such a fashion that the rate of the hydrolysis reaction in equation (1) is enhanced. We have chosen to do this by replacing one of the amines by a ligand lying higher in the trans-effect series. Practical considerations generally restrict the choice of ligand to anionic species, and we have focused on the use of the chloride ion. Replacement of a neutral amine by an anionic chloride would lead to a net negative charge on the complex. In order to maintain overall complex neutrality (which is presumably necessary for cellular penetration), the remaining amine must be replaced by a ligand bearing a formal positive charge. This leads to a complex having the general formula II:

$$\left[\ \overset{\oplus}{L}\underset{\underset{Cl}{|}}{\overset{\overset{Cl}{|}}{Pt}}Cl\ \right]^{0}$$

II

Such complexes can in fact, as well as in principle, exhibit significant antitumor activity. We report here the synthesis, characterization, and antitumor activity of two broad classes of complex having structure II, those where the positively charged ligand is a monoprotonated (or monoalkylated) diamine and those where it is a monoprotonated amino-olefin.

Complexes of Protonated Diamines

Prior to our work, there had been few reports of platinum complexes bearing monoprotonated (or monoalkylated) diamines as ligands. To our knowledge, only three complexes having this structure have been characterized. Terzis (4) prepared and determined the crystal structure of trichloro(9-methyladeninium)

platinum(II), Maresca, et al. (5) prepared trichloro(tetra-
methylethylenediammonium)platinum(II), and Adeyemo, et al. (6)
prepared trichloro(4-amino-2,6-dimethylpyridine)platinum(II). We
have found a large number of such complexes can be prepared using
the two general reactions outlined below.

$$N\sim N \quad + \quad K_2PtCl_4 \quad + \quad HCl \quad\longrightarrow$$

$$\overset{+}{HN}\sim N \longrightarrow Pt \longrightarrow Cl$$

$$N\sim N \cdot 2HCl \quad + \quad K_2PtCl_4 \quad + \quad NaOH$$

Under these preparative conditions, a large number of alternative
products (e.g., $(N\sim N)_2PtCl_2$, $(N\sim \overset{+}{N}H)_2PtCl_4$, etc.) are plausible,
and indeed in certain cases were found. For the compounds re-
ported here, the combination of C, H, N, and Cl microanalytical
data was adequate to demonstrate unequivocally a ratio of 3Cl/
diamine/Pt.

Although this is supportive of the coordination sphere of
platinum being $PtCl_3N$, it is a more difficult problem to determine
which of the two nitrogen sites of the diamine is coordinated to
platinum and, consequently, which nitrogen site is protonated. It
is probable that the specific isomeric form which is produced is a
consequence of some complex interplay of both kinetic and thermodynamic factors. In particular, its identity will depend upon the
Lewis basicity of each nitrogen donor site toward the Lewis acid
platinum in the form $PtCl_3^-$. Since knowledge of that Lewis basicity does not exist, we have no predictive ability.

In the case of the compound derived from 3-aminoquinuclidine
(trichloro(3-aminoquinuclidinium)platinum(II), or QTP) we have
tried to resolve the structural question by examination of infrared spectra in the N-H stretching region. Comparisons of spectra
for 3-aminoquinuclidine, its mono- and di-protonated hydrochlor-
ides, and QTP suggest that in the platinum complex it is the $-NH_2$
group which is protonated. Specifically, a broad and intense band
at ca 2800 cm^{-1} which can be assigned to the protonated tertiary
amine group in the mono- and di-hydrochloride is absent from QTP.
Infrared spectra thus suggest structure III for QTP.

$$H_3N$$

$$N \longrightarrow Pt \longrightarrow Cl$$

III

Biological Studies of Protonated Diamine Complexes

All of the compounds we have prepared have been evaluated as inhibitors of the growth of murine leukemic cells (L1210) and a DDP-resistant subline (L1210/DDP) in vitro. We have chosen a 50% inhibitory dose (ID_{50}) of 10 μg/ml as our upper-limit criterion for a significant level of activity. Compounds that satisfy the criterion are evaluated further for their ability to prolong the life span of mice inoculated with L1210 cells. Although we have prepared a large number of complexes having the general formulation II, most exhibit relatively little activity against L1210 in the cell culture screen (Table I gives selected ID_{50} values).

Table I.   Compounds $(L^+)PtCl_3$ Which Satisfy the Criterion for Activity in Cell Culture Studies

L	ID_{50}, μg/ml	
	L1210	L1210/DDP
	9	>10
	2	5
	4.2	>10
	10	>10
	>10*	5*
	4*	5*

*Solubilized in DMSO.

The most interesting compound in terms of biological activity is QTP, the compound with 3-aminoquinuclidine as the ligand, especially in view of its ability to produce roughly equivalent inhibition of the growth of both L1210 and L1210/DDP cells. QTP is, unfortunately, very poorly soluble in water. In an attempt to find water-soluble analogs of QTP, several derivatives were prepared by the routes outlined below:

$$LPtCl_3 + Ag_2SO_4 \longrightarrow LPtCl(SO_4) \cdot H_2O + 2AgCl$$

$$LPtCl_3 + 2H_2O_2 \longrightarrow LPt^{IV}Cl_3(OH)_2 + 2H_2O$$

$$LPtCl_3 + H_2O_2 + 2HCl \longrightarrow LPt^{IV}Cl_5 + 2H_2O$$

$$LPtCl(SO_4) + Ba\,CH_2(COO)_2 \longrightarrow LPtCl\,CH_2(COO)_2 + BaSO_4$$

These compounds, several having enhanced aqueous solubility, were evaluated for in vitro activity. Each of the compounds (Table II) has activity against DDP-sensitive L1210 cells comparable to that of QTP, but is less effective against L1210 cells resistant to DDP.

Table II.   Activity of 3-Aminoquinuclidinium Derivatives Against L1210 Cells In Vitro

Compound	ID_{50} ($\mu g/ml$)	
	L1210/0	L1210/DDP
$LPtCl_3$	2	5
$LPtCl_5$	4.4	>10
$LPtCl_3(OH)_2$	4.5	>10
$LPtCl_3(SO_4)$	4.6	>10
$LPtCl(CH_2(COO)_2)$	2.7	–

To evaluate the activity of compounds against L1210 in vivo, the following procedure was employed. L1210 cells (1 x 10^6 suspended in 0.1 ml of physiological saline solution) were inoculated intraperitoneally (i.p.) into BDF$_1$ mice (20-22 gm) and drug treatment (i.p.) was initiated 24 hours later. Animals that received no drug treatment died between 7 and 9 days after inoculation of L1210 cells (mean survival time ~8.5 days). Results express the ratio of the mean survival time of treated animals to the mean survival time of control animals (%T/C).

Studies in our laboratory reveal that QTP has significant antileukemic activity. For example, when given as a single dose (10 mg/kg; day 1) the compound gave a T/C value of 125% and the %T/C value was increased somewhat (to 138) when a more intensive schedule of administration was employed (5 mg/kg; days 1, 2, 5, 6, 9). Our results were confirmed by independent studies carried out under the auspices of the Developmental Therapeutics Program, National Cancer Institute (Table III).

The water soluble malonato derivative of QTP exhibited limited in vivo activity. Thus, at a single dose (day 1) of 50 mg/kg the compound gave a %T/C value of 126%. We also evaluated the soluble sulfato derivative of QTP in vivo but found it to be more toxic than QTP and to be ineffective against murine leukemia at a non-toxic dose (5 mg/kg). The biological activity of QTP is not shared by the ligand per se since 3-aminoquinuclidine hydrochloride was found to exhibit no cytotoxicity in vitro under conditions in which the complex was quite active.

The activity of QTP in the experimental leukemia system prompted us to carry out toxicological studies on this complex. When administered as a single i.p. injection, QTP caused no immediate signs of toxicity but within 48 hours mice became lethargic, developed piloerection and displayed signs of tetany. The toxic effects progressed until paralysis of the hind limbs was observed. Deaths occurred 3 to 8 days following treatment. Gross necropsy revealed signs of renal toxicity including pale renal cortex, friability and exaggerated corticomedullary border. Other grossly observable signs of toxicity were sharply reduced spleen size and distention of small intestine. The calculated LD_{10}, LD_{50} and LD_{90} values were 22, 42 and 83 mg/kg respectively.

These studies of the biological activity of QTP indicate that complexes of the type LPtCl$_3$ represent a new class of antitumor platinum coordination compounds. We are currently engaged in studies of the preparation and evaluation of new examples of this class of compound that may be more effective and less toxic than QTP.

Complexes of Protonated Amino-Olefins

Although monoprotonated diamines are a convenient choice for the positively charged ligand in structure II, other ligands L^+ may be considered. We have consequently examined complexes where

Table III.   Activity of Trichloro(3-Aminoquinuclidinium)
Platinum(II) Against L1210 Cells In Vivo[a]

	Dose (mg/kg)	Schedule	%T/C
1.[b]	5	1	123
	10	1	125
	50	1	Toxic
	5	1,2,5,6,9	138
2.[c]	2.50	1,5,9	126
	5	1,5,9	120
	10	1,5,9	130
	20	1,5,9	133
3.	2.5	1,5,9	119
	5	1,5,9	122
	10	1,5,9	139
	20	1,5,9	140
	40	1,5,9	148

a.)   Because of the low solubility of this compound, data
from different laboratories may not be directly comparable due to different sonification/suspension/
solubilization procedures.

b.)   Data obtained at the University of Vermont.

c.)   Experiments 2 and 3 represent data obtained from the
NCI utilizing two different screening contractors.

the ligand L^+ is a protonated amino-olefin. In particular, we have prepared a series of compounds having structure IV, in which a substituted allyl amine is coordinated to platinum through the

IV

olefinic π-system. This structure possesses the kinetic advantages discussed above for all compounds of type II, but in addition the third chloride is highly activated toward substitution because of the large trans-effect of the coordinated olefin.

Several compounds analogous to IV have been reported, and X-ray crystallographic studies have established that in each case the coordination environment at platinum is similar to that in Zeise's salt, e.g., square-planar platinum coordination by three chlorides and the olefin π-system (7). We have prepared complexes having structure IV by the direct reaction of the N-substituted allyl amine with potassium tetrachloroplatinite in acidic aqueous solution. Analytical data establish the formulation, and infrared spectra demonstrate that the olefin is coordinated to platinum. The structure is retained in dimethylformamide solution, as demonstrated by extensive nmr measurements.

Biological Studies of Amino-Olefin Complexes

The compounds prepared in this study have been evaluated as inhibitors of L1210 growth using the cell culture screen. Using our criterion for a significant cytotoxicity, many of the compounds having structure IV are found to be active in vitro (Table IV). Several trends are apparent from these data. First, most of the protonated amino-olefin complexes have comparable cytotoxicity (the exceptions will be discussed shortly). Furthermore, most are approximately equitoxic to the sensitive and resistant cell lines. This suggests that there may be a significant difference in the mechanism of action of these compounds compared to DDP, since in DDP and many of its analogs there is a ca 20-fold difference in activity toward these cell lines. The three protonated amino-olefin compounds with large values of ID_{50} are equivalent, and distinct from the other complexes, in that they are derived from tertiary amines. For simple DDP analogs there is significant evidence that complexes of primary, and possibly secondary, amines are much more active than complexes of tertiary amines (8). This trend seems to be repeated here, but in this case the amine is not coordinated to platinum. Consequently, substitution at the amine would not be expected to have any

Table IV. Cell Culture Activity for Protonated and
Neutral Complexes of Allylamines

Allyl Amine, L	Protonated Ligand Complex, $(LH^+)PtCl_3$			Neutral Ligand Complex, $LPtCl_2$	
	Compound No.	ID_{50} (µg/ml)		Compound No.	ID_{50}
		L1210	L1210/DDP		L1210
	1a	3.0	5.0	1b	5
	2a	>10			
	3a	2.5	4.0	3b	>10
	4a	6	4.3	4b	7
	5a	8	27	5b	>10
	6a	>10			
	7a	>10			

significant effect upon activity. The observation that the effect persists here should be accounted for in any discussion of the origin of the effect of the amine substitution upon antitumor activity.

In the absence of protonation, the neutral amino-olefin is, in principle, capable of coordination as a chelate ligand, utilzing both the olefin π-system and the nitrogen lone pair. This would produce a neutral complex of type V, which should also be activated toward the substitution reaction of equation (1), and,

$$
\begin{array}{c}
\text{Cl} \\
| \\
||\text{---Pt---Cl} \\
| \\
\text{N---} \\
| \\
\text{V}
\end{array}
$$

consequently, have potential as an antitumor agent, Yellow solids having the composition (amino-olefin)$PtCl_2$ can be prepared by neutralization of the (protonated amino-olefin)$PtCl_3$ complexes with aqueous hydroxide, followed by extraction into chloroform. Alternatively, at least in certain cases, identical materials can be prepared by the direct reaction of the amino-olefin with aqueous K_2PtCl_4. Once formed, these compounds are only poorly soluble in solvents which do not cause decomposition, and this fact has made their characterization elusive. Denning and Venanzi (9) have reported complexes of this form with N-ethylallylamine and N-octylallylamine, which they formulate as polymeric and dimeric, respectively. Apparently, a monomeric chelate complex having Structure V cannot be formed because of the steric problems inherent in the formation of the 4½-membered chelate ring. Based on their low solubility, we believe that the complexes we have prepared have oligomeric structures as well. Infrared spectra do, however, demonstrate conclusively that both the amine and the olefin are coordinated to platinum.

Although the neutral ligand complexes corresponding to each of the protonated ligand complexes could not be prepared, biological data is available for four such complexes. In general, cell culture activity is comparable for both the protonated ligand and neutral ligand complexes. Although this may be fortuitous, it is also possible that under biological conditions the two types of compound are interconvertible. Since the neutral ligand complexes are typically prepared by deprotonation of the protonated ligand complexes, it is conceivable that this deprotonation reaction occurs at physiological pH.

As representative samples, the complexes (protonated N-ethylallylamine)$PtCl_3$ and (N-ethylallylamine)$PtCl_2$ have been given a preliminary screening for antitumor activity *in vivo*. The complexes were administered intraperitoneally to mice with L1210

Leukemia. At the dosages used, neither compound exhibited significant antitumor activity at less than toxic dose.

None of these compounds are particularly water soluble. Consequently, we considered that the poor in vivo activity might reflect poor water solubility, rather than inherent molecular inactivity. In order to test this hypothesis, we prepared the sulfate derivative of (protonated allylamine)$PtCl_3$ by reaction 4.

$$H_3\overset{+}{N} \diagup\!\!\!\diagdown \| - PtCl_3 + Ag_2SO_4 \quad H_3\overset{+}{N} \diagup\!\!\!\diagdown \| - PtCl(SO_4) + 2AgCl$$

This sulfate complex is readily water soluble but, like its insoluble chloride analogs, appears to be inactive in vivo.

We are forced to conclude that although these compounds are indeed cytotoxic, they do not have significant antitumor effects at acceptable levels of host toxicity.

Conclusion

No single compound among those reported here exhibits the combination of increased activity, decreased toxicity and desirable physical properties which would provide for a likely clinical improvement over cis-dichlorodiamineplatinum(II). Nonetheless, this work demonstrates clearly that activity is not restricted to simple analogs of DDP, but may be found as well in significantly different structural classes. In particular, at least one compound having a structure $(L^+)PtCl_3$-trichloroquinuclidiniumplatinum(II)--has exhibited activity comparable to that of DDP.

Acknowledgment: This work was sponsored by the National Cancer Institute through grants 24543 and 22435.

Literature Cited

1. Rosenberg, B.; Van Camp, L; Trosko, J.E.; Mansour, V.H. Nature 1969, 222, 385-386.
2. Schaeppi, U.; Hoyman, L.A.; Fleischman, R.W.; Rosenkrantz, H.; Ilievski, V.; Phelan, R.; Cooney, D.; Davis, R.D. Toxicol-Appl. Pharmacol. 1973, 25, 230.
3. Rosenberg, B. "Cisplatin: Current Status and New Developments"; A.W. Prestayko, S.T. Crooke, and S.K. Carter, eds. Academic Press, Inc., 1980, pp. 9-20.
4. Terzis, A. Inorg. Chem., 1976, 15, 793.
5. Maresca, L.; Natile, G.; Rizzardi, G. Inorg. Chim. Acta, 1980, 38, 137.

6. Adeyemo, A.; Teklu, Y.; Williams, T. Inorg. Chim. Acta, 1981, 51, 19.
7. Mura, P.; Spagna, R.; Zambonelli, L. J. Organometal. Chem. 1977, 142, 403.
8. Roberts, J.J. "Metal Ions in Genetic Information Transfer"; Vol.'3, G.L. Eichlorn and L.G. Marzilli, eds., 273–332 (1981).
9. Denning, R.G.; Venanzi, L.M. J. Chem. Soc. 1963, 3241.

RECEIVED October 13, 1982

Chemical and Biological Activity of Metal Complexes Containing Dimethyl Sulfoxide

NICHOLAS FARRELL[1]

Simon Fraser University, Department of Chemistry,
Burnaby, British Columbia V5A 1S6 Canada

The requirement for inert amine-type ligands in the coordination sphere is a major feature of the structure-activity relationships so far delineated for antineoplastic complexes such as cis-[$PtCl_2(NH_3)_2$]. In the ensuing study of the biological activity of other heavy metal complexes, much emphasis has therefore been placed on amine complexes which are structurally analogous to the original platinum species. There are few systematic studies using other ligands or mixed ligand systems. This contribution summarises the biological and related chemical activity of complexes containing dimethylsulfoxide (DMSO).

The scope of the article requires, first, a brief summary of the nature of DMSO as a ligand in coordination compounds. The discussion is then divided into simple complexes containing DMSO as the only donor ligand and the recently-developed mixed amine-sulfoxide complexes, where DMSO plays the role of the leaving group.

Nature of DMSO as a Ligand

The alkyl sulfoxides of general formula, R_2SO, are examples of ambidentate ligands which may bind to metal ions through either the sulfur or oxygen donor atom, the canonical forms being represented by:

[1] Current address: Departamento de Quimica, Universidade Federal de Minas Gerais, Belo Horizonte MG 30.000, Brazil

$$\underset{R}{\overset{R}{\diagdown}}S^- \equiv O^+ \longleftrightarrow \underset{R}{\overset{R}{\diagdown}}S=O \longleftrightarrow \underset{R}{\overset{R}{\diagdown}}{}^+S-O^-$$

Complexes for most d-block elements have been prepared and a
recent review (1) updating that of Reynolds (2), summarises
these.   Considerations of the hard and soft properties of the
donor atoms allow us to predict that, in general, sulfoxides
should bind via oxygen to the hard first-row transition metals and
via sulfur to soft metals, such as those of Group VIII.   Both
steric and electronic effects have been shown to dictate the
choice of donor atom and these effects may be summarized: -

Steric Effects.   These may be manifested by the sulfoxide,
other ligands in the coordination sphere and the central metal
ion.

effect of sulfoxide ligand

Whereas $[PdCl_2(DMSO)_2]$ and $[PdCl_2(MBSO)_2]$ (MBSO = 3-methyl-
butylsulfoxide) have both sulfoxides bound through sulfur, the
sterically more demanding MBSO ligand results in a trans configuration.   Similarly, $[Pd(DMSO)_4]^{2+}$ has been shown to have two
sulfur-bound trans to two oxygen-bound sulfoxides, while
$[Pd(MBSO)_4]^{2+}$ results in a complex with all oxygen-bound ligands (3).

other ligands

This is demonstrated in complexes of the type
$[M(dppe)(DMSO)Cl](A)$ and $[Pd(dppe)(DMSO)_2](A)_2$ (dppe = 1,2(di-
phenylphosphino)ethane, M = Pd,Pt, A = non-coordinating anion)
(4).   Bonding through sulfur is disfavoured because of interaction of the methyl groups with the phenyl groups of the bulky
phosphine ligand and, thus, bonding via the sterically-unrestrict-
ed oxygen is preferred.

size of central metal ion

The effect of the metal ion may be gauged by comparison of
trans-$[FeCl_2(DMSO)_4]^+$, all oxygen-bound (5), and cis-
$[RuCl_2(DMSO)_4]$, with three sulfur and one oxygen-bound ligand
(5).   Within the same row, the $[RuCl_3(DMSO)_3]^-$ anion contains
three sulfur-bound sulfoxides in the fac configuration (7), whereas, in the isoelectronic $[RhCl_3(DMSO)_3]$, the smaller size of the
Rh(III) allows for only two S-bonded ligands (8,9), although minor
amounts of linkage and geometric isomers have been observed in
solution (10).

Electronic Effects.   A graphic demonstration of how purely-
electronic effects control the mode of coordination of the
sulfoxide ligand is demonstrated in DMSO adducts of rhodium carboxylates, $[Rh_2(O_2CR)_4(DMSO)_2]$ (11,12).   The dimeric structure of
the rhodium carboxylates with bridging carboxylate groups has been
confirmed (3) and these readily add donor ligands L in the axial

positions. Where R = CH$_3$ or C$_2$H$_5$ sulfur coordination in DMSO occurs but, upon the replacement of alkyl by CF$_3$ groups, the highly-electronegative CF$_3$ substituents force preference of oxygen-atom bonding.

Solvent Effects

The steric and electronic effects illustrated are not the unique determining factors of binding sites in sulfoxide complexes and, as noted, linkage and geometric isomers may exist in solution. A further relevant effect is that of solvent.

The X-ray crystal structure of [Ru(DMSO)$_6$](BF$_4$)$_2$ shows three sulfur-bound <u>fac</u> to three oxygen-bound ligands (14), confirming the structure proposed from ^{1}H N.M.R. studies in CD$_2$Cl$_2$. However, in D$_2$O, the ^{1}H N.M.R. measurements show <u>four</u> S-bound ligands and two free DMSO molecules arising from substitution of the easily-displaced O-bound sulfoxides by solvent:

$$[Ru(DM\underline{S}O)_4(DMS\underline{O})_2]^{2+} \rightarrow [Ru(DM\underline{S}O)_4(H_2O)_2]^{2+} \quad (1)$$

Thus, an aqueous medium favours S-bonding and that this is a general characteristic was confirmed in the case of platinum. The [Pt(DMSO)$_4$]$^{2+}$ cation is considered to have two S- and two O-bound ligands in a <u>cis</u> arrangement, as judged by I.R. and ^{1}H N.M.R. studies (3), and analogy with the Pd analog whose structure is now known (15). In D$_2$O, only a trace of O-bonded or free DMSO is observed, indicating that the predominant species in aqueous solution contains all S-bound sulfoxides, the only example so far of a totally S-bound homoleptic sulfoxide complex. A rationale for this behaviour may be found by considering that S-bound species will allow for continued H-bonding interaction with H$_2$O and, indeed, that the H-bonding in aqueous solution may reduce the metal-affinity of the oxygen atom.

A further feature of the solution chemistry observed in these systems is their solvolysis behaviour. The O-bound sulfoxides are easily displaced by solvent molecules; hydrolysis products are immediately formed in water or even in wet non-aqueous solvents. Recently, slower hydrolysis of the sulfur-bound ligand has also been observed (16). The ^{1}H N.M.R. spectrum of [Ru(DMSO)$_6$]$^{2+}$ in D$_2$O shows a three-line pattern at 6.51, 6.58 and 6.62τ and a singlet a 7.4τ, with an intensity ratio of 2:1. Upon raising the temperature, the ratio varies until, at 82°C, the observed integration is 1:1, the basic three-line pattern for the methyl resonances of the S-bound ligands being unaltered. The spectrum is not reversed upon cooling to room temperature. The data are readily explained:

$$[Ru(DM\underline{S}O)_4(DMS\underline{O})_4]^{2+} \xrightarrow{R.T.} \begin{array}{c} [Ru(DM\underline{S}O)_4(H_2O)_2]^{2+} \\ [Ru(DM\underline{S}O)_3(H_2O)_3]^{2+} \end{array} \xrightarrow{82°C}$$

A further, unusual base labilisation was observed at 32° in 2% OD^-/D_2O, where only two 1:1 singlets at 6.8τ and 7.4τ are found. Thus, both temperature and basicity may labilise the S-bound ligand.

For the $[Pt(DMSO)_4]^{2+}$ cation, similar behaviour is also shown; slow hydrolysis of one S-bound ligand after 24 h at 32°C being observed or, upon heating, to 82°C. The interconversions may be summarised:

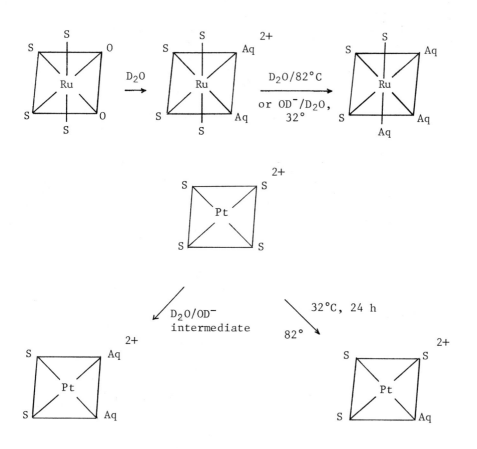

Thus, a picture emerges of sulfoxide complexes in aqueous solution, where initial fast hydrolysis of O-bound ligand occurs, followed by a slow displacement of S-bound groups, the exact species formed being under investigation. (At time of writing, a complex corresponding to $[Pt_2(DMSO)_6](BF_4)_4$ has been isolated from the hydrolysis of the monomeric species.) That this behaviour is not restricted to homoleptic complexes is evidenced by results on the more labile Rh and Pd systems. Thus, $[PdCl_2(DMSO)_2]$ in D_2O immediately shows 1:1 singlets at 6.45 and 7.4τ and a solution of mer-$[RhCl_3(DMSO)_3]$ shows initial loss of the unique O-bound ligand, followed by loss of one S-bound sulfoxide within hours:

$$\text{trans-}PdCl_2(DMSO)_2 \xrightarrow{\text{imm.}} [PdCl_2(DMSO)]_2 + 2DMSO \qquad (2)$$

$$[RhCl_3(\underline{DMSO})_2(DMSO)] \xrightarrow{\text{imm.}} [RhCl_3(\underline{DMSO})_2(H_2O)] \xrightarrow{t, R.T.}$$
$$[RhCl_3(\underline{DMSO})(H_2O)_2] \qquad (3)$$

Displacement of S-bound sulfoxide has been observed in non-aqueous solvents for these metals (17,18).

Kinetic and Thermodynamic Studies

The kinetic cis and trans effects and the thermodynamic cis and trans influences of DMSO in platinum coordination chemistry have been extensively investigated.

From the study of acid hydrolysis of the complex $K[PtCl_3(DMSO)]$, formed readily by the reaction of one equivalent of DMSO with K_2PtCl_4 in water, Elding (19) concluded that the cis and trans influences were of the magnitude of C_2H_4, a point made by Kukushkin in comparison of the DMSO complex with Zeise's salt, $K[Pt(C_2H_4)Cl_3]$ (20). These influences are small compared to the kinetic effects which are in the order:

trans efffect $C_2H_4 > DMSO > Cl^- > NH_3 > H_2O$
$\qquad\qquad\qquad (10^{11} : 2 \times 10^6 : 330 : 200 : 1)$

cis effect $DMSO > H_2O \approx NH_3 > Cl^- > C_2H_4$
$\qquad\qquad\quad (5 \quad : \quad 1 \quad : \quad 1 \quad : 0.4 : 0.05)$

Thus, DMSO is considered to have an intermediate trans effect and a relatively large cis effect, compared to other ligands. The approximate order of magnitude difference in the cis effects of DMSO and NH_3 has also been confirmed in the following system (21):

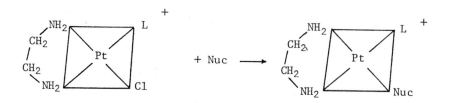

$$L = DMSO, NH_3; \quad Nuc = NH_3, N_2H_4, X^-, SC(NH_2)_2$$

This relevant finding is attributed to the greater nucleophilic discrimination factor of DMSO in its complex, whereas the trans effect is attributed to transition-state stabilisation arising from the π-acceptor properties of the ligand, S-bound DMSO being considered a better σ-donor and π-acceptor than ethylene (22).

The lability of S-bound DMSO was studied by measuring the kinetics of ligand replacement in $[Pt(dien)L]^{2+}$ (dien = 1,5-diamino-3-aza-pentane; L = DMSO, H_2O). The H_2O ligand is approximately three orders of magnitude more labile than DMSO and a lability sequence, derived by compilation of the data from the reaction:

$$[Pt(dien)L]^{n+} + SC(NH_2)_2 \rightarrow [Pt(dien)SC(NH_2)_2]^{2+} + L \text{ (or } L^-) \quad (4)$$

(n = 1,2) was suggested (23):

$$H_2O > I^- > Br > Cl > DMSO \approx SCN^- > N_3^- > NO_2^-$$

Biological Activity of Metal-Dimethylsulfoxide Complexes

The most comprehensively studied complex is cis-$[RuCl_2(DMSO)_4]$. In a series of studies comparing its biological activity with that of cis-$[PtCl_2(NH_3)_2]$, the ruthenium species was shown to produce filamentous growth in E. coli and induce λ prophage (24). It is mutagenic (25) and has in vivo anti-tumour activity (26).

The comparisons with the platinum complex showed that, at 10 μg/mL, filamentous growth was an order of magnitude less for $[RuCl_2(DMSO)_4]$, whereas, at 100 μg/mL, 100% filamentation was found, the platinum complex inhibiting growth at this concentration. Both complexes are mutagenic for uvr B and uvr$^+$ strains of T. thypimurium carrying the His G46 missense mutation, specific for base pair substitution mutagens. However, some differences in response were noted, which may reflect a difference in mode of action at the DNA level.

The similarity in activity is also demonstrated by inhibition of the in vitro blastogenic response of human peripheral lymphocytes, stimulated by mixed culture of phytohaemaglutinin (PHA) (27).

These studies culminated in a comparison of the anti-tumour activity of the complexes. The ruthenium compound was shown to be active at doses of 400 mg/kg. The animal numbers involved are, however, small and it would be unwise to extrapolate further. The dose levels possible for $[RuCl_2(DMSO)_4]$ are noteworthy and indicate a high LD_{50} for this complex.

These findings prompted us to undertake a survey of the biological activity of the other M-DMSO complexes (28). The method used was cytotoxic assay, using Raji Burkitt lymphoma cells and L 5178Y cells. These particular assay results, in general, correlate well with observed in vivo anti-tumour activity and cis-$[PtCl_2(NH_3)_2]$ was used for comparison.

The results for the Pt and Ru complexes are shown in Figures 1 and 2. For the L 5178Y case, the approximate order of magnitude difference in activity between cis-$[RuCl_2(DMSO)_4]$ and cis-$[PtCl_2(NH_3)_2]$ was confirmed from counts after 24 h. Using Raji Burkitt lymphoma cells, at 24 and 48 h, some differences were noted. Increased time did not improve cell kill for the ruthenium complex, a fact which may be attributed to inherent lack of cytotoxicity or a failure to enter the cells in the first place. Similar behaviour was found for $[Ru(DMSO)_6]^{2+}$, $[RhCl_3(DMSO)_3]$, $[RhCl(DMSO)_5]^{2+}$ and $[Pt(DMSO)_4]^{2+}$ (cationic species as their BF_4^- salts), none of the complexes being more active than the original ruthenium species and the complexes do not appear to be promising candidates for anti-tumour activity. A rhodium complex mer-$[RhCl_3(DMSO)py_2]$ has been reported as having remarkable activity in vitro against P388 leukemia and KB carcinoma. The role of DMSO in the complex is not obvious but the similarity in structure to the bacteriostatic series (30) $[RhA_4Cl_2]Cl$ (A = aromatic heterocyclic; e.g., pyridine) should be noted.

Interaction of Metal-DMSO Complexes with Nucleic Acids and Nucleic Acid Bases

Apart from the understanding of the mechanism of anti-tumour action of cis-$[PtCl_2(NH_3)_2]$, a major interest in the area of nucleic acid-metal ion interactions is the possibility of sequence determination, using specific binding of metal complexes.

The specific interaction of K_2PtCl_4 with DNA bases was first reported in 1967 (31). The necessity for a monofunctional agent to dominate side reactions, such as cross-linking, prompted the use of $[PtCl_3(DMSO)]^-$ utilising the trans influence of the sulfoxide ligand. Reaction conditions with DNA and RNA were found, in which the complex could be used as a differential staining agent

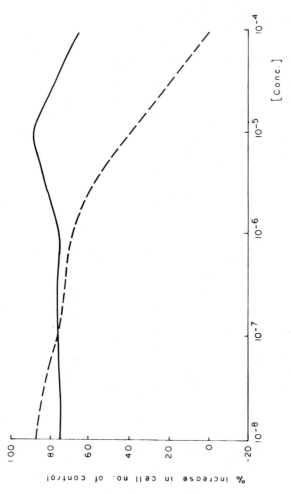

Figure 1. Cytotoxic assay of L5178Y cells. Key: ——, cis-RuCl₂(DMSO)₄; and — — —, cis-PtCl₂-(NH₃)₂.

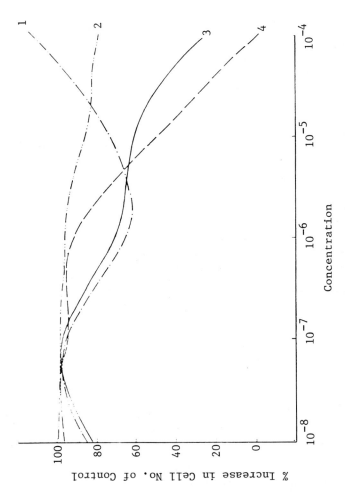

Figure 2. Cytotoxic assay of Raji Burkitt lymphoma cells. Key: 1, cis-RuCl₂(DMSO)₄ (24 h); 2, cis-RuCl₂(Me₂SO)₄ (48 h); 3, cis-PtCl₂(NH₃)₂ (24 h); and 4, cis-PtCl₂(NH₃)₂ (48 h).

for adenine and guanine residues in both polynucleotides (32).
The reactions found are worthy of note in that binding to both pyrimidine and purine bases bases was found, the differential staining being made possible by binding of two platinum atoms per adenine residue at both pH 6.0 and pH 7.5, while at the lower pH one
platinum and at high pH two platinum atoms were bound to guanine,
albeit in a much slower reaction.

Neither this complex nor its neutral analogue,
cis-[PtCl$_2$(DMSO)$_2$], are active against tumours and this fact has
prompted studies with simple bases in attempts to explore the difference between the amine and sulfoxide ligand. Both complexes
react with a variety of purines and pyrimidines, the anionic complex reacting more readily. A generalized scheme may be written:

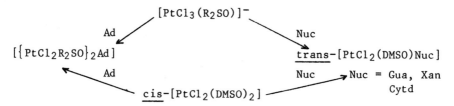

The binding of two Pt atoms per adenine moiety via an N$_1$, N$_7$ dimer
was confirmed by an X-ray crystal structure determination of
[{PtCl$_2$(DIPSO)}$_2$(9-MeAde)] (33) and by ^{1}H N.M.R. observations of
the reaction between cis-[PtCl$_2$(DMSO)$_2$] and adenosine (34). The
other binding sites are summarized in Table I, along with relevant
studies on the octahedral ruthenium and rhodium systems.

The anti-tumour activity of cis-[RuCl$_2$(DMSO)$_4$] prompted us
to study the reactivity of this complex with simple bases (35).
An interesting difference emerges between the octahedral and
square-planar cases; for adenine or adenosine only monodentate
binding via N$_7$ is found for both Ru and its Rh analogue (Table
I), with a further distinct preference for adenine over guanine
binding. Hydrogen-bonding interactions between the exocyclic
groups of purine and pyrimidine bases and ligand atoms may
dictate specificity and binding sites in metal complex-base interactions (36). By analogy with the factors delineated, H-bonding
between the exocyclic 6-NH$_2$ group of adenine and the DMSO oxygen
atoms or chlorine atoms (both H-bond acceptors) in the octahedral
sphere may dictate specificity, these interactions being minimised
in a square-planar complex upon removal of the axial ligands.

These interpretations await definitive structural confirmation. Certainly, DMSO as ligand in the ruthenium complexes dic-
tates a different behaviour than that observed by Clark and
Taube in their study of the [Ru(NH$_3$)$_5$Cl]$^{2+}$ system (7). Further,
depending on the structure, displacement of chloride and both S-
and O-bound sulfoxide has been observed in these reactions with
the simple nucleic acid bases.

Table I

Reaction Products and Binding Sites of M-DMSO Complexes

with Nucleobases

Complex	Base	Product	Binding Site	Reference
cis-[PtCl$_2$(DMS)$_2$]	Adenosine	trans-[[PtCl$_2$(DMSO)]$_2$Ado]	N$_1$, N$_7$	34
[PtCl$_3$(DIPSO)]$^-$	9-Me Adenie	trans-[[PtCl$_2$(DIPSO)]$_2$ 9-Me Ade]	N$_1$, N$_7$	39
cis-[PtCl$_2$(DMSO)$_2$]	Guanosine	trans-[PtCl$_2$(DMSO)Gua]	N$_7$	38
cis-[PtCl$_2$(DMSO)$_2$]	Xanthosine	trans-[PtCl$_2$(DMSO)Xan]	N$_7$	38
[PtCl$_3$(DMSO)]$^-$	Inosine	trans-[PtCl$_2$(DMSO)Ino]	N$_7$	38
cis-[PtCl$_2$(DMSO)$_2$]	Cytidine	trans-[PtCl$_2$(DMSO)Cytd]	N$_3$	40
[PtCl$_3$(DIPSO)]$^-$	1-Me Cytosine	trans-[PtCl$_2$(DIPSO)(1-Me Cyt)]	N$_3$	33
cis-[RuCl$_2$(DMSO)$_4$]	Adenine	cis-[Ru(DMSO)$_4$(Ade)$_2$]Cl$_2$	N$_7$	34, 35
fac-[RuCl$_3$(DMSO)$_3$]$^-$	Adenine	cis-[RuCl$_2$(Ade)(DMSO)$_3$]	N$_7$	34, 35
mer-[RhCl$_3$(DMSO)$_3$]	Adenosine	mer-[RhCl$_3$(Ado)(DMSO)$_2$]	N$_7$	34, 35

Chemical and Biological Activity of cis-[Pt(amine)$_2$(DMSO)$_2$](A)$_2$

A major obstacle to the more widespread clinical use of cis-[PtCl$_2$(NH$_3$)$_2$] is its low solubility and high toxicity. Many "second-generation" analogues have substantially improved toxicities but solubility still remains a handicap.

A novel approach to this problem suggested itself from our work on hydrolysis of S-bound sulfoxide. The unique properties of DMSO in its pharmacological actions, such as membrane transport and membrane penetration, are well known (41) and the water-solubilising properties in its metal complexes was readily apparent from the good aqueous solubility of the M-DMSO species. Further, the lability seemed qualitatively of the order of halide (a point confirmed quantitatively during the course of these experiments (23)) and these observations prompted us to probe the following structure-activity relationship:

$$\underline{cis}\text{-[PtCl}_2\text{(amine)}_2] \xrightarrow{H_2O} [Pt(H_2O)_2\text{(amine)}_2]^{2+}$$
$$\underline{cis}\text{-[Pt(DMSO)}_2\text{(amine)}_2]^{2+} \xrightarrow{H_2O} [Pt(H_2O)_2\text{(amine)}_2]$$

to study the solubility of these latter species and especially if hydrolysis of DMSO would occur. Clearly, the paramount requirement is for a S-bonded ligand. Further, weak non-coordinating anions, to avoid formation of chloro species, are deemed necessary.

The results obtained to date will be illustrated using complexes of 1,2-diaminocyclohexane (dac). Addition of this chelating diamine to a methanolic solution of [Pt(DMSO)$_4$]$^{2+}$ readily gives, upon reduction to half-volume and addition of ether, the [Pt(dac)(DMSO)$_2$]$^{2+}$ cation with both DMSO ligands bound through sulfur (42) (ν(NH) = 3280, 3220 cm^{-1}; ν(SO) = 1150, 1070 cm^{-1}; τ{(CH$_3$)$_2$SO} = 6.4τ in D$_2$O; ^{3}J(Pt-H) = 26.0 Hz). The formation of this cation was confirmed by reaction of [PtCl$_2$(dac)] with two equivalents of a silver salt in DMSO and by reaction of cis-[PtCl$_2$(DMSO)$_2$] with two equivalents of a silver salt in methanol, followed by addition of a methanolic solution of the diamine. The [Pt(DMSO)$_4$]$^{2+}$ reaction is, however, the cleanest and is easily extendable to other amines for a range of counter-anions:

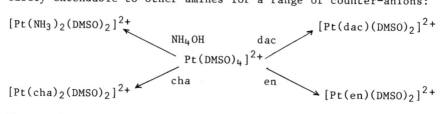

The complexes are all remarkably soluble in water and, because the aqueous medium is avoided in their preparation, are easily obtained as pure crystalline solids. Toxicity studies show an LD$_{50}$ significantly greater than the parent dichloro derivatives. The solubility and LD$_{50}$ values for some complexes of 1,2-diaminocyclohexane are shown in Table II.

Table II. Solubility and Toxicity of [Pt(1,2-dac)X$_2$]

X	Solubility (mg/mL)	LD$_{50}$ (mg/kg ip)	Reference
Cl	<0.5	28	42
SO$_4$ (=X$_2$)	10	22.5	43
malonato	<0.5	36.0	43
4'carboxyphthalato	<0.1 25 (1.5% NaHCO$_3$)	76.5	43
DMSO (BF$_4$)	>200	140	42

Of the complexes shown, three (sulfato, malonato and carboxylphthalato) are deemed to be promising candidates for full clinical use as anti-tumour agents (44), partly because of their low incidence of renal toxicity (the limiting side-effect of the original cis-[PtCl$_2$(NH$_3$)$_2$]) and because of their activity against cis-platin-resistant tumours (45). Only the malonato derivative presents a higher LD$_{50}$ than the DMSO complex; the solubility is, however, 10^2-10^3 times less.

The remarkable solubility of these mixed amine-sulfoxide cations is a general property. Thus, for the NH$_3$ derivative (counter-anion NO$_3^-$), solubilities of 75-100 mg/mL are easily obtainable. This is particularly useful in the case of the alicyclic amines developed by Tobe (46). The complex cis-[PtCl$_2$(cha)$_2$] has one of the highest therapeutic indices of any of the platinum complexes but is one of the most insoluble of all derivatives. The complex [Pt(cha)$_2$(DMSO)$_2$](NO$_3$)$_2$ has an aqueous solubility of ≈5 mg/mL which now compares favourably with cis-[PtCl$_2$(NH$_3$)$_2$] (1 mg/mL).

The behaviour of the [Pt(amine)$_2$(DMSO)$_2$] species in aqueous solution parallels that of [Pt(DMSO)$_4$]$^{2+}$. Slow dissociation (18 h, 25°C) of one DMSO ligand occurs. Similar dissociation occurs upon heating to 82°C, also verified for cis-[Pt(NH$_3$)$_2$(DMSO)$_2$](NO$_3$)$_2$. Thus, the kinetic inertness of the amine ligands, and perhaps the mutual cis effects of the DMSO ligands, favour DMSO hydrolysis, even though this S-bonded ligand would be considered to have a greater trans-influence. It is especially interesting to note that use of DMSO as a solvent for cis-[PtCl$_2$(NH$_3$)$_2$] results in a complex mixture (47), whereas incorporation of DMSO in a well-defined molecular species greatly

enhances the water-solubility of the Pt(amine)$_2$ moiety which remains intact even upon initial hydrolysis. The
[Pt(amine)$_2$(DMSO)$_2$]$^{2+}$ cations may be considered to be molecular
slow-release systems.

In the quest for improved analogues of cis-[PtCl$_2$(NH$_3$)$_2$],
the major considerations in the choice of suitable analogs are
solubility, toxicity and activity. Results are not yet available
on anti-tumour tests of this series; however, results have been
obtained on other systems and, indeed, the general activity of
1,2-dac complexes (44) bodes well in this particular case.

Platinum-Metal Complexes in Parasitic Diseases

In a parallel study, we have investigated the activity of
metal complexes in parasitic diseases and, especially, trypanosomiasis, responsible for sleeping sickness in man. Of the parasitic diseases, this does not now present a major problem,
compared to malaria, filariasis and schistosomiasis, but the pre-
valence of the disease has increased in latter years due to dramatic changes in the political and economic climate in the tropical
areas (48). A number of platinum derivatives has been found to be
active in vitro and in vivo against T. rhodesiense and the platinum complexes, as a family, may be considered active trypanocides
(49). The in vitro results of selected complexes (Table III)
shows that the DMSO and chloro derivatives of the Pt(dac) complex
show essentially the same activity.

Table III. Biological Activity of Trypanocidal Platinum Complexes

Complex	Trypanocidal titre* in vitro			LD$_{50}$ (mg/kg) (single intraperitone-aldose; mice)
	Motility	Abolition of infectivity Total	Partial	
cis-[PtCl$_2$(NH$_3$)$_2$]·	3	<3	5	13
[PtCl$_2$(dac)]	3	3	5	28 (17.5-44.8)
[Pt(dac)(DMSO)$_2$](BF$_4$)$_2$	3	3	5	140 (107-183)

*   Titre = log$_{10}$[molarity]$^{-1}$ (i.e., 3 = mM). Values <3 have no
       significance.

A representative trypanocide (Ethidium bromide) gives values of 4,
4 and 5.

The similarity of the metabolism of African typanosomes to
that of some tumour cells has prompted the correlation between

anti-trypanosomal and anti-tumour properties of drugs and, indeed, a good correspondence exists (51,52). These results place the platinum complexes in this category, also demonstrated by Steck et al. (63) for cis-[PtCl$_2$(NH$_3$)$_2$], a further demonstration of their general pharmacological utility. The advantages of trypanosomes as tumour cell models and biochemical probes has been emphasised (54,55) and should not be under-emphasised in the case of heavy metal complexes. Indeed, ruthenium complexes, such as [RuCl(NH$_3$)$_5$]$^{2+}$ and Ruthenium Red, also show activity with roughly the order of magnitude difference observed in tumour systems (56). A series of complexes is now being tested further under the auspices of the World Health Organisation.

Interaction of [Pt(amine)$_2$(DMSO)$_2$]$^{2+}$ with Nucleic Acid Bases

Despite the extensive data accumulated on the anti-tumour activity of Pt-amine complexes, few model studies with simple bases and dinucleotides have been reported with amines, other than NH$_3$ and ethylene-diamine. The complexes cis-[Pt(amine)$_2$(DMSO)$_2$]$^{2+}$ readily react with bases such as guanosine, displacing a DMSO molecule. Thus, the series is useful for studying the generality of intra-ligand H-bonding interactions delineated in earlier studies but for a much wider range of amines.

Summary

Dimethylsulfoxide, as a ligand, has been shown to possess many of the properties desirable for metal-based chemotherapeutic agents. Complexes containing DMSO, in place of amine, do not generally exhibit much activity but consideration of DMSO as a leaving group and substitution for Cl in the cis-[Pt(amine)$_2$X$_2$] unit results in more water-soluble, less toxic derivatives. Activity has been demonstrated in trypanosomiasis for a series of complexes. In chemical studies, DMSO, as a ligand, may be displaced by nucleobases, the products and binding sites being dictated by the nature of the starting complex.

Legend of Symbols

DMSO =   dimethylsulfoxide
DIPSO =   diisopropylsulfoxide
DMSO or S =   S-bound sulfoxide in a metal complex
DMSO or O =   O-bound sulfoxide
dac =   1,2-diaminocyclohexane (as a mixture of isomers)
en. =   1,2-diaminoethane
cha =   cyclohexylamine
Ad =   substituted adenine

Acknowledgments

I thank Johnson-Matthey and Co. Ltd. for a loan of precious metal salts. The financial support of CNPq, Brasil and Simon Fraser University is acknowledged. Collaboration with Prof J. Williamson on the trypanocidic properties of platinum complexes is especially acknowledged as is that of Prof. J.M. Goldie for the crytotoxicity studies.

Literature Cited

1. Davies, J.A. Adv. Inorg Radiochem. 1981, 24, 116.
2. Reynolds, W.L. Prog. Inorg. Chem. 1970, 12, 1.
3. Price, J.H.; Williamson, H.N.; Schramm, R.F.; Wayland, B.B. Inorg. Chem. 1972, 11, 1280.
4. Davies, J.A.; Hartley, F.R.; Murray, S.G. J. Chem. Soc., Dalton Trans. 1979, 1705.
5. Bennet, M.J.; Cotton, F.A.; Weaver, D.L. Nature (London) 1966, 212, 280.
6. Mercer, A.; Trotter, J. J. Chem. Soc., Dalton Trans. 1975, 2480.
7. James, B.R.; McMillan, R.S.; Mercer, A.; Trotter, J. J. Chem. Soc., Dalton Trans. 1975, 1006.
8. Sokol, V.I.; Rubtsova, N.D.; Gribenyuk, A.Yu. J. Struct. Chem. (Engl. Transl.) 1974, 15, 296.
9. James, B.R.; Morris, R.H. Can. J. Chem. 1980, 58, 399.
10. Barnes, J.R.; Goggin, P.L.; Goodfellow, R.J. J. Chem. Res. 1979, (S) 118; M 1610.
11. Cotton, F.A.; Felthouse, T.R. Inorg. Chem. 1980, 19, 323.
12. Cotton, F.A.; Felthouse, T.R. Inorg. Chem. 1980, 19, 2347.
13. Porai-Koshits, M.A.; Artsyshkina, A.S. Dokl. Akad. Nauk. USSR 1961, 146, 1102.
14. Davies, A.R.; Einstein, F.W.B.; Farrell, N.P.; James, B.R.; McMillan, R.S. Inorg. Chem. 1978, 17, 1965.
15. Johnson, B.F.G.; Prega, J.; Raithby, P.R. Acta Cryst. 1981, B37, 953.
16. Farrell, N.; de Oliveira, N.G. Inorg Chim. Acta 1980, 44, L255.
17. Kitching, W.; Moore, C.J.; Doddrell, D. Inorg. Chem. 1970, 8, 541.
18. Jones, F.N.; Parshall, G.W. J. Am. Chem. Soc. 1965, 87, 5356.
19. Elding, L.I.; Gröning Ö. Inorg. Chem. 1978, 17, 1872.
20. Kukushkin, Yu.N. Inorg. Chim. Acta 1974, 9, 117.
21. Bonicento, M.; Cattalini, L.; Marangoni, G.; Michelon, G.; Schwab, A.P; Tobe, M.L. Inorg. Chem. 1980, 19, 1743.
22. Braddock, P.D.; Romeo, R.; Tobe, M.L. Inorg. Chem. 1974, 13, 1170.
23. Romeo, R.; Cusumano, M. Inorg. Chim. Acta 1981, 49, 167.

24. Monti-Bragadin, C.; Ramani, L.; Samer, L.: Mestroni, G.; Zassinorich, G. Antimicr. Ag. Chemother. 1975, 7, 825.
25. Monti-Bragadin, C.; Tamaro, M.; Banti, E. Chem.-Biol. Interactions 1975, 11, 469.
26. Giraldi, T.; Sava, G.; Bertoli, G.; Mestion, G.; Zassinovich, G. Cancer Research 1977, 37, 2662.
27. Klugmann, F.B.; Pari, B.; Castellani, G. Pharmacol. Res. Comm. 1977, 9, 149.
28. Farrell, N.; Goldie, J.M. unpublished results.
29. Colamarino, P.; Orioli, P. J. Chem. Soc. Dalton Trans 1979, 845.
30. Bromfield, R.J.; Dainty, R.H.; Gillard, R.D.; Heaton, B.T. Nature (London), 1969, 223, 735.
31. Ulanov, B.P.; Malaysheva, L.F.; Moshkovskii, Yu.Sh. Biofizika 1967, 12, 326.
32. Whiting, R.F.; Ottensmeyer, F.B. Biochim. Biophys. Acta 1977, 434, 334.
33. Lock, C.J.L.; Speranzini, R.A; Powell, J. Can. J. Chem. 1976, 54, 53.
34. Farrell, N. J. Chem. Soc. chem. Comm. 1980, 1014.
35. Farrell, N.; de Oliveira, N.G. Inorg. Chim. Acta 1982, 66, L61.
36. Marzilli, L.G.; Kistemacher, T.J. Acc. Chem. Res. 1977, 10, 146.
37. Clarke, M.J. J. Am. Chem. Soc. 1978, 100, 5068 and references therein.
38. Kong, P.C.; Iyamuremye, D.; Rochon, F.B. Bioinorg. Chem. 1976, 6, 83.
39. Lock, C.J.; Speranzini, R.A.; Turner, G.; Powell, J. J. Am. Chem. Soc. 1976, 98, 7865.
40. Melanson, R.; Rochon, R.B. Inorg. Chem. 1978, 17, 679.
41. "Dimethyl Sulfoxide: Vol. I, Basic Concepts of DMSO" (Jacob, S.W.; Rosenbaum, E.E.; Wood, D.C., Eds), Marcel Dekker, New York, 1971.
42. Farrell, N. J. Chem. Soc. Chem. Comm 1982, 331.
43. Schurig, J.E.; Bradner, W.T.; Huftalen, J.B.; Doyle, G.J.; Gylys, G.A. "Cisplatin, Curent Status and New Developments", Academic Press, New York, 1980, P. 227.
44. Cleare, M.J.; Hydes, P.C.; Hepburn, D.R.; Malerbi, B.W. ibid; P. 149.
45. Burchenal, J.H. Biochimie 1978, 60, 915.
46. Connors, T.A.; Jones, M.; Ross, W.C.J.; Braddock, P.D.; Khokhar, A.R.; Tobe, M.L. Chem.-Biol. Interactions 1972, 5, 415.
47. Kerrison, J.S.; Sadler, P.J. J. Chem. Soc. Chem. Comm. 1977, 861.
48. Van der Bossche, H. Nature (London) 1978, 273. 626.

49. Farrell, N.; Vargas, M.D.; McLaren, D.J.; Williamson, J.
    Abstract A19, International Conference on the Chemistry of
    the Platinum Group Metals, Bristol, England, July, 1981;
    manuscript in preparation.
50. Williamson, J.; Scott-Finnigan, T.J. Trans. Roy. Soc. Trop.
    Med. Hyg. 1975, 69, 1.
51. Williamson, J. "The African Trypanosomiases"; Mulligan,
    H.W., Ed., Allen and Urwin, London, 1970, P. 125.
52. K.E. Kinnamon, E.A. Steck and D.S. Rane, J. Natl. Cancer
    Institute, 1980, 64, 391.
53. K.E. Kinnamon, E.A. Steck and D.S. Rane, Antimicr. Agents
    Chemother., 1979, 15, 157.
54. Williamson, J. Trop. Dis. Bull. 1976, 73, 531.
55. Newton, B.A. "Biochemistry of Parasites and Host-Parasite
    Relationships", (Van der Bossche, H., Ed.), North-Holland,
    Amsterdam, 1976, P. 459.
56. M.J. Clarke in "Metal Ions in Biological Systems", Vol. II,
    ed. H. Sigel, Dekker, New York, 1980, P. 231.

RECEIVED October 4, 1982

Determination and Location of Platinum Metals in Biological Samples by Neutron Activation and Microprobe Analyses

M. E. FARAGO and P. J. PARSONS

Bedford College, Chemistry Department, Regent's Park, London NW1 4NS England

Instrumental Neutron Activation Analysis (INAA) was
applied to the determination of the platinum metals
as part of a study of their uptake, accumulation and
toxicity in plants. Long irradiations are described
for iridium, osmium and ruthenium determinations in
specially grown plant materials. An interference in
the determination of platinum in plant matrices by
this method is reported also. Short irradiations,
utilising thermal and epithermal fluxes are
investigated for rhodium and palladium determinations,
with further studies using cyclic activation analysis.
Water hyacinths (*Eichhornia crassipes* MART Solms)
were grown in nutrient solutions containing platinum
as $PtCl_6^{2-}$. The roots were examined using electron
microscopes equipped with X-ray microanalysis
facilities. Platinum deposits were detected and
located within the cortical layers of the root.

Several studies have demonstrated already the effects of the
platinum group metals on plants and that the metals can be taken
up into the tissues either from soil or from solution in hydroponic experiments (1-5). The principal aims of this study are
summarised:

(1) to investigate whether aquatic plants, such as the water
    hyacinth, *Eichhornia crassipes*, are able to assimilate
    soluble complexes of the platinum group metals from a
    nutrient solution;

(2) to develop sensitive methods of analysis for the platinum
    metals in bio-materials;

(3) to characterise the sites of storage and the mode of chemical
    binding of the metals within the tissues;

(4) to examine the biological effects of platinum group metals
    on the plants.

In this paper we report on the results of an investigation
into the use of (a) Instrumental Neutron Activation Analysis (INAA)
for the determination of platinum group metals in plants, and

(b) Electron Microscopy with X-ray Microprobe Analysis for the
location of platinum deposits in plant roots.

Analytical Techniques

A wide range of techniques is available for the quantitative
determination of the platinum group metals (Table I). However,
there is no NBS Biological Standard Reference material containing
certified levels of the platinum group metals for the comparison
of analytical techniques. For this reason, plant materials were
specially prepared, each of which contained one of the platinum
group metals. The free floating aquatic plant, water hyacinth
(*Eichhornia crassipes* MART Solms) was grown in half strength
nutrient solution containing one of the platinum group metals as
a soluble complex. Each metal was supplied at two concentrations,
designated as 'H1' and 'LO'.

After two week's growth, the plants were harvested, washed,
dried and homogenised. In this way a number of representative
samples were obtained.

Non-destructive methods such as INAA or PIXE remove the need
to oxidise organic matter prior to metal determination. In some
cases it is preferable to 'ash' before analysis, since this
concentrates the metals of interest and may remove an interfering
matrix. In other cases dry ashing can concentrate an interfering
element.

Other methods in Table I have been investigated and will be
reported elsewhere (6). For INAA in this work standards were
prepared by spiking Bowen's kale with platinum metals.

Neutron Activation Analysis

The use of activation methods for the analysis of biological
material has been reviewed by Bowen (7). In Instrumental Neutron
Activation Analysis, the dried sample is placed in the core of a
nuclear reactor where it is bombarded with neutrons. Many of the
elements present in the sample undergo nuclear reactions of which
the most common are the (n, γ) type. The products of these
reactions are radioactive and decay with the emission of gamma
photons of characteristic energy.

Although determination of the platinum metals by this method
is well documented (8-10), those concerning biological materials
are few (11,12). The irradiation time in the reactor is set
according to the half-life, $t_{\frac{1}{2}}$, of the daughter product (Figure 1)
and the various characteristics for the reaction being monitored,
i.e. thermal neutron cross section, isotope abundance and type of
backgrounds. (Table II). In this work the platinum metals can be
divided into the long irradiations: Pt, Ir, Ru, Os: and the short
irradiations: Rh, Pd.

Table I. Modern Methods for the Analysis of Biological Materials

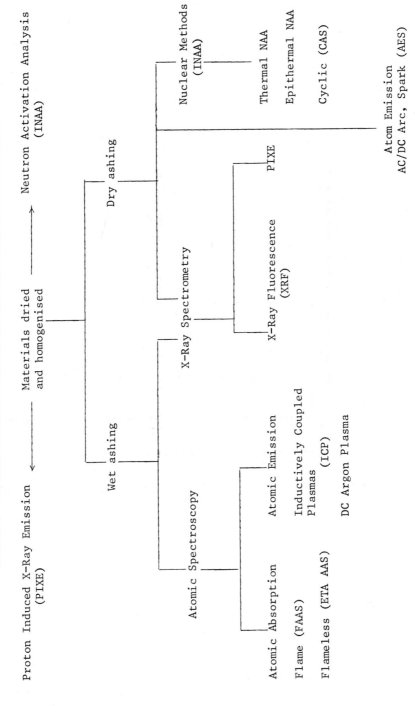

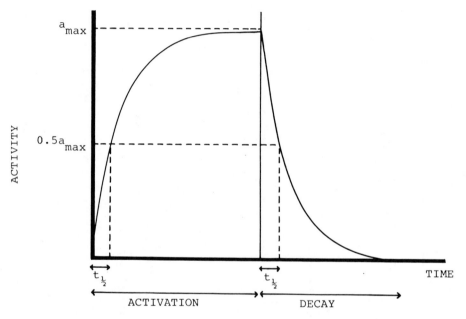

Figure 1. A typical plot of radioactivity vs. time showing both activation and decay.

Table II.   Nuclear Data for the Platinum Group Metals

Element	Nuclide	Isotopic Abundance %	Nuclear Reaction Utilised	Thermal Neutron Cross Section σ (barns)	Activated Isotope			
					Nuclide	Half Life	Decay Mode	γ keV
Pd	^{108}Pd	26.7	^{108}Pd (n,γ) ^{109m}Pd	0.2	^{109m}Pd	4.69 m	IT	188.9
	^{106}Pd	27.3	^{106}Pd (n,γ) ^{107m}Pd	0.013	^{107m}Pd	21.3 s	IT	215.0
Rh	^{103}Rh	100.0	^{103}Rh (n,γ) ^{104m}Rh	11	^{104m}Rh	4.34 m	IT	51.4
			^{103}Rh (n,γ) ^{104}Rh	139	^{104}Rh	42.3 s		555.8
Ir	^{191}Ir	38.5	^{191}Ir (n,γ) ^{192}Ir	300	^{192}Ir	74.4 d	$β^-$ EC	316.5 468.1
Os	^{190}Os	26.4	^{190}Os (n,γ) ^{191}Os	3.9	^{191}Os	14.6 d	$β^-$	129.4
Ru	^{102}Ru	31.6	^{102}Ru (n,γ) ^{103}Ru	1.4	^{103}Ru	38.9 d	$β^-$	497.0
Pt	^{198}Pt	7.2	^{198}Pt (n,γ) ^{199}Pt	4	^{199}Pt	30.8 m	$β^-$	(47.960)
			^{199}Pt $\xrightarrow{β^-}$ ^{199}Au		^{199}Au	3.15 d	$β^-$	158.37 208.20

Long Irradiations

Table III gives the conditions, data and reactions for the long irradiations of iridium, osmium and ruthenium. Samples and standards were irradiated in the University of London Reactor under a maximum thermal neutron flux of 1.4×10^{12} n cm^{-2} s^{-1}. The samples were counted using a lithium drifted germanium detector (Ortec Inc) linked to a computer based gamma ray spectrometer (Nuclear Data Inc. 6620 Multichannel Analyser). A general Neutron Activation Package written in FORTRAN IV was employed to run a peak search and calculate PGM concentrations in the plant samples. The irradiation of platinum is a special case 'and details are given in Table IV. Various nuclides emit γ-rays of similar energy, and in INAA these become a serious interference in the determination of platinum in biological samples.

Table III.   Neutron Activation Analysis : Long Irradiations

Ir, Os and Ru   Irradiated for 1 week; allowed to decay over
                  2-3 days and counted for 30 m (long lived
                  radioactive products)

$$^{191}Ir \xrightarrow{\quad (n, \gamma) \quad} {}^{192}Ir \xrightarrow[t_{\frac{1}{2}} = 74\,d]{\gamma\ 316\,keV,\ \ 406\,keV} {}^{192}Pt$$

37.3%   stable

$$^{102}Ru \xrightarrow{\quad (n, \gamma) \quad} {}^{103}Ru \xrightarrow[t_{\frac{1}{2}} = 39.8\,d]{\gamma\ 497\,keV} {}^{103}_{m}Rh$$

31.6%

$$^{190}Os \xrightarrow{\quad (n, \gamma) \quad} {}^{191}Os \xrightarrow[t_{\frac{1}{2}} = 14.6\,d]{\gamma\ 129\,keV} {}^{191}_{m}Ir$$

26.4%

Short Irradiations

Both rhodium and palladium undergo (n, γ) reactions which result in short lived decay products. Short irradiations and short counting times are thus required. In biological samples some matrix elements give rise to a background of short lived decay products. These are not a serious problem with long irradiations, where long cooling periods can reduce their activity, but with short lived products they produce an unfavourable back-ground. Various refinements of Instrumental Neutron Activation Analysis can be used to reduce this interference in the determination of short lived nuclides.

Table IV. Determination of Platinum by Neutron Activation

$$^{198}Pt \xrightarrow{(n, \gamma)} {}^{199}Pt \xrightarrow{\beta^-} {}^{199}Au$$

7.21% $\qquad$ $t_{\frac{1}{2}} = 30$ m $\qquad$ γ 158.37 keV, 208.20 keV

$$t_{\frac{1}{2}} = 3.15 \text{ d}$$

(Long irradiation) $\qquad$ ^{198}Au

Interferences:

Nuclide	$t_{\frac{1}{2}}$	keV
$^{117}_{m}Sn$	14.0 d	158.40
^{47}Sc	3.43 d	159.40 (via $^{47}Ti(n,p)$ ^{47}Sc)
$^{117}_{m}In$	1.9 h	158.40
$^{199}_{m}Hg$	42 m	158.30
^{177}Lu	6.74 d	208.20

Epithermal Irradiation

Figure 2 gives the general features of a reactor neutron spectrum. Most of the available neutrons from fission are thermal, with fewer in the epithermal region, and even fewer in the fast region. In thermal neutron activation analysis, the whole reactor spectrum contributes to the activation process. Some nuclides have a neutron spectrum which is suited to resonance absorbance in the epithermal region. By screening out thermal neutrons, activation of the matrix is reduced relative to the nuclide of interest. Such a flux is possible under a cadmium filter. In this study epithermal irradiations were carried out under a neutron flux of 0.5 x 10^{12} n cm^{-2} s^{-1}. The samples were then transferred by a fast pneumatic system to a Ge(Li) detector situated close to the reactor. Gamma spectra were accumulated using a Laben 8000 MCA of 4096 channels. Peak areas and thus concentrations were calculated using Covell's method (13).

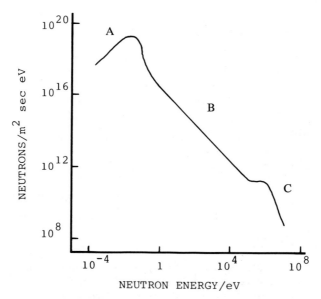

Figure 2.   The general features of a reactor neutron spectrum. Key: A, thermal region; B, epithermal region; and C, fast region.

Cyclic Activation Analysis

Cyclic activation analysis is a recent improvement in NAA in which optimum use is made of the experimental time available for the counting of short lived isotopes. The signal to noise ratio for the radionuclide of interest is enhanced if the sample is irradiated for a short period of time, allowed to decay, and then counted for a short period of time; the sample is then re-irradiated and the process repeated for 'n' cycles. Figure 3 gives the variation in isotope activity with time and cycle number. The principles and applications of cyclic activation analysis have been reviewed by Spyrou (14). Cyclic activation was carried out using the CAS system of the University of London Reactor where a thermal flux of 1.3×10^{12} n cm^{-2} s^{-1} is obtainable. Epithermal fluxes in the region are available with CAS also. In this study the CAS programme involved five cycles, each of 60 s epithermal irradiation, 1 s decay and followed by 60 s counting using a Ge(Li) detector coupled to a Laben 8000 MCA of 4096 channels. Table 5 gives the results of the investigation of the determination of rhodium and palladium by various refinements of INAA, and Table VI compares the determination of platinum metals in plants by INAA and various techniques.

Table V.   Short Irradiation of Plant Material containing either Rhodium or Palladium

Sample	Nuclide	γ, keV	Method	Metal Concentration (μg/g dry wt)
Rh LO	^{104}Rh	555.8	A	5.25 ($\pm$0.54)
Rh LO	^{104}Rh	555.8	C	4.43 ($\pm$0.14)
Rh LO	$^{104}_{m}$Rh	51.4	C	5.24 ($\pm$0.03)
Pd LO	$^{109}_{m}$Pd	188.8	B	4.13 ($\pm$1.43)
Pd LO	$^{109}_{m}$Pd	188.8	C	4.62 ($\pm$1.26)

Key: Method A = Single Thermal Irradiation

              B = Single Epithermal Irradiation

              C = Cyclic Activation Epithermal

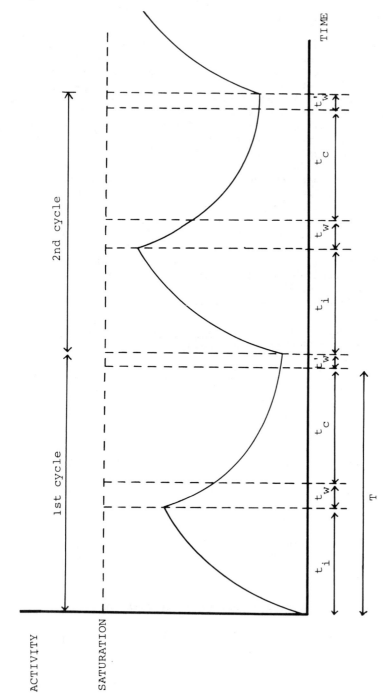

*Figure 3.   Cyclic activation analysis. Variation of induced activity with time and cycle number.
Key: T, cycle period; t_i, time of irradiation; t_w, time between end of irradiation and start of count;
t_c, time of counting; and t_w', time between end of counting and start of irradiation. The detected
radiations at each counting period are summed to give a cumulative detector response, D_c, over
the total experimental time. D_c is maximized when $t_w = t_w'$ and $t_i = t_c = T/2$ (See reference 17
for details).*

Table VI.   A Comparison between INAA and other
            Determination Methods

Sample	Plant Grown in a solution of:	INAA	PIXE	ETA AAS	DC Arc
Rh LO	$Na_3[RhCl_6]$	4.43(±0.14)	3.8	4.22	8
Pd LO	$[Pd(NH_3)_2Cl_2]$	4.62(±1.26)	5.6	3.40	1
Ir LO	$Na_3[IrCl_6]$	1.28(±0.02)	nd	nd	nd
Os LO	$Na_2[OsCl_6]$	1.79(±0.07)	nd	–	–
Ru LO	$(NH_4)_3[RuCl_6]$	nd	1.1	nd	0.5
Pt LO	$(NH_4)_2[PtCl_6]$	?	5.6	14.7	8

Electron Microscopy with X-ray Microanalysis

When a specimen is examined with an electron microscope, it is
bombarded with a beam of high velocity electrons. As the beams
of electrons bombards the specimen many events take place, some
electrons are absorbed by the specimen, some pass through, some
are deflected or scattered. If one of the inner electrons is
removed by the electron beam, then an electron falls from a
higher energy shell into the hole to stabilise the atom. When
this happens energy is emitted as X-rays. Each element has its
own characteristic X-ray spectrum.

Energy Dispersive Analysis

The recent development of solid state detectors has enabled
highly efficient X-ray analysis to be carried out by energy
dispersive methods. The detector unit consists of a silicon-
lithium doped crystal cooled to liquid nitrogen temperature.
X-rays of all energies are processed by a microcomputer
simultaneously and the energy spectrum is displayed on a CRT
screen.

Wavelength Dispersive Analysis

This method of analysis uses a rotating crystal to diffract
the X-rays. The crystal is preset to a particular angle
corresponding to the diffraction of specific X-ray wavelengths.
All other wavelengths are eliminated from the detector; the
result is much better spectral resolution and lower detection

limits, when compared with the energy dispersive systems. The latter has the advantage of a rapid multi-element determination. With the wavelength dispersive system, the location of individual elements may be mapped, either on the surface of a sample or in a tissue section (15).

The roots of water hyacinth treated with 10 µg cm^{-3} of Pt applied as $(NH_4)_2[PtCl_6]$ were investigated using scanning electron microscopy (SEM). The specimens were prepared for investigation by conventional methods; fixed in glutaraldehyde, and dehydrated in alcohol. The cut specimens were dried and mounted on aluminium stubs, then sputter coated with either carbon or a metal. Energy dispersive analysis (EDXA) of a typical root surface of a treated plant was performed, the results are presented in Figure 4. EDXA of a similar section of a control root grown in nutrient solution without platinum added was also performed. The spectra of both samples show Al from the stubs. The control sample shows a high concentration of Ca, and small amounts of P and S. The platinum-treated root shows Ca also, but a distinctly large peak at the platinum Mα position, 2.05 keV is seen; this completely masks the P and S lines seen in the control sample. The platinum line at 9.44 keV (Lα) can also be seen.

A section of root was studied using wavelength dispersive analysis. The distribution of Pt, as studied using both the Mα and Lα lines show that the platinum is concentrated in the cortical layers of the root, with very little passing into the vascular system.

Discussion

INAA of rhodium and palladium by the epithermal cyclic activation method is very satisfactory. Osmium and iridium appear to be satisfactorily determined by the long irradiation method. However, the most interesting element, platinum, appears to suffer from an interference which is still under investigation.

Determination on the Pt LO sample for platinum using various techniques are given in Table VI for INAA, the figure for the dried plant sample was unusually high (~ 44 ppm Pt), and no agreement was obtained between the 158 keV peak and 208 keV peak.

Control water hyacinths, grown under the same controlled hydroponic conditions, but without platinum added were irradiated under similar conditions. A large photopeak at 158 keV resulted, whereas the 208 keV peak was not visible. Thus some interfering nuclide with a photopeak around 158 keV is present even in the control material. The interfering elements are under further investigation. This interference seems to be present both in animal and in plant tissue. LeRoy (16) has compared the results of the analysis of canine heart, liver and muscle by both electrothermal atomisation atomic absorption spectroscopy (ETA AAS) and INAA. It was found that the results for Pt using INAA

were higher in all cases. At present it appears that results of
the analysis of biological tissue for platinum by INAA must be
treated with caution.

Scanning electron microscope studies (SEM) have shown that the
energy dispersive system (EDXA) is successful in detecting high
concentrations ($\sim$ 10,000 ppm Pt) of platinum in biological
tissues, both the Mα and Lα lines being visible. The wavelength
dispersive system can be used successfully to map platinum
located in biological samples when local concentrations are high
enough.

This work has also given an indication of the relative
toxicity of the platinum metals towards the water hyacinth, these
are shown in Table VII.

Table VII. Relative Toxicity of the Platinum Group Metals
to the Water Hyacinth (*Eichhornia crassipes*)

(Applied at a concentration of 10 mg dm^{-3})

Pt: $cis[Pt(NH_3)_2Cl_2] \approx [PtCl_4]^{2-} > trans[Pt(NH_3)_2Cl_2] \gg [PtCl_6]^{2-}$

Pd: $cis[Pd(NH_3)_2Cl_2] > [PdCl_4]^{2-}$

Ru: $[Ru(phen)_3]^{2+} > [RuCl_6]^{3-}$

PGM's: $Pd^{II} \approx Pt^{II} > Ru^{III} > Os^{IV} \approx Ir^{III} \approx Pt^{IV} \gg Rh^{III}$

It can be seen that as far as Pt is concerned, Pt(II) is
far more toxic than Pt(IV). Rh(III) is relatively non-toxic
compared with the other platinum metals. In fact low
concentrations of Rh(III) appear to have a tonic effect (5). At
low concentrations this metals is not phytotoxic to corn and
tomato (5). The growth of Kentucky bluegrass is stimulated by
small amounts of palladium(II) chloride, whereas at higher
concentrations it is phytotoxic (3). We have found that the
effect of $K_2[PtCl_4]$ on the grass *Setaria verticillata* (L) P. Beauv.
is very similar, low levels stimulate growth and higher levels
are phytotoxic. (Figure 5). We have found also that platinum
and rhodium complexes stimulate vegetative reproduction in the
water hyacinth (17). Thus in the case of higher plants, the
bi-phasic reaction, stimulation at low levels and phytotoxicity
at high levels, has been demonstrated for compounds of platinum,
palladium and rhodium.

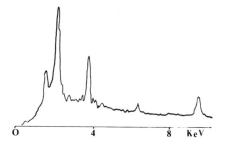

Figure 4.   Energy dispersive x-ray analysis (EDXA) of water hyacinth root treated with $(NH_4)_2[PtCl_6]$. This method gives the x-ray lines of all elements in the whole field of the microscope (X625). Conditions: Pt, $M\alpha = 2.05$ keV, $L\alpha = 9.44$ keV; and Ca, $K\alpha = 3.69$ keV.

Figure 5.   Effects of platinum on a grass species compared with control. Key: B, 0.5 ppm of $K_2[PtCl_4]$; and C, 2.5 ppm of $K_2[PtCl_4]$.

Acknowledgments

We thank Johnson Matthey Research Centre for the loan of platinum group metals and for provision of EDXA and microprobe facilities. We thank Miss M. Minski, University of London Reactor Centre, Ascot, for co-operation and helpful discussions. P.J.P. thanks SERC for the award for a studentship.

Literature Cited

1. Brenchley, W.E. *Ann. App. Biol.* 1934, *21*, 389.
2. Hamner, C.H. *Bot. Gaz.* 1942, *104*, 161.
3. Sarwar, M.; Thirbert, R.J.; Benedict, W.G. *Can. J. Plant Sci.* 1970, *50*, 91.
4. Pallas, J.E.; Jones, J.B. *Plant and Soil*, 1978, *50*, 207.
5. Farago, M.E.; Mullen, W.A.; Payne, J.B. *Inorg. Chim. Acta*, 1979, *34*, 151.
6. Farago, M.E.; Parsons, P.J. *Analyst*, in the press, 1982.
7. Bowen, H.J.M. *CRC Crit. Revs. Amalyt. Chem.* Dec. 1980, 127.
8. Caramella-Crespi, V.; Pisani, U.; Ganzerli-Valentini, M.T.; Meloni, S.; Maxia, V. *J. Radioanalyt. Chem.* 1974, *23*.
9. Nadkarni, R.A.; Morrison, G.H. *J. Radioanalyt. Chem.* 1977, *38*, 435.
10. Parry, S.J. *Analyst*, 1980, *105*, 1157.
11. Farago, M.E.; Parsons, P.J. *Royal Society of Chemistry Inorganic Biochemistry Discussion Group Meeting*, London, December 1980.
12. Valente, I.M.; Minski, M.J.; Peterson, P.J.; personal communication 1981.
13. Covell, D.F. *Anal. Chem.* 1959, *31*, 1785.
14. Spyrou, N.M. *J. Radioanalyt. Chem.* 1981, *61*, 211.
15. Lauchli, A.; Spurr, A.R.; Epstein, E. *Plant Physiol.* 1971, *48*, 118.
16. LeRoy, A.F.; Whehling, M.L.; Sponseller, H.L.; Friaf, W.S.; Solomon, R.E.; Dedrick, R.L.; Litterst, C.L.; Gram, T.E.; Guarino, A.M.; Becker, D.A. *Biochem. Med.* 1977, *18*, 194.
17. Parsons, P.J. Ph.D. Thesis, University of London, 1982.

RECEIVED October 29, 1982

NONPLATINUM ANTICANCER AGENTS

Tumor Inhibition by Metallocene Dihalides of Early Transition Metals

Chemical and Biological Aspects

H. KÖPF

Technische Universität Berlin, Institut für Anorganische und Analytische Chemie, 1 Berlin 12, Federal Republic of Germany

P. KÖPF-MAIER

Freie Universität Berlin, Institut für Anatomie, 1 Berlin 33, Federal Republic of Germany

Metallocene dihalides, $(\eta^5-C_5H_5)_2MX_2$, represent the first organometallic antitumor agents. Their antitumor activity has been established in vitro and in vivo, e.g. against the Ehrlich ascites tumor, the lymphoid leukemia L1210, or the lymphocytic leukemia P388. Considering the structure-activity relation three statements can be made: (i) There exists a strong dependence of the cytostatic activity of the metallocene dichlorides $(C_5H_5)_2MCl_2$ upon the central metal atom M. (ii) Within the titanocene dihalide system $(C_5H_5)_2TiX_2$ the Cl ligands can be replaced by other halide or pseudohalide ligands without reduction of the tumor-inhibiting potency. (iii) Chemical modification of the cyclopentadienyl rings, e.g. mono- or 1,1'-disubstitution with organic residues, leads to a diminution of the cytostatic activity in dependence on the degree of substitution. With regard to the mechanism of action of the metallocene dihalides, precursor incorporation studies indicate an attack within the nucleic acid metabolism. This is confirmed by cytokinetic and by microanalytical (electron energy loss-spectroscopic) investigations as well as by the light-microscopic and ultrastructural alteration patterns of treated tumor cells.

The development of the inorganic compound cis-diamminedichloroplatinum(II) (DDP) to a potent antitumor drug during the last twelve years, leading to a valuable enrichment of the therapeutic arsenal of cytostatic drugs (1, 2), has strongly stimulated the search for other metal-containing tumor-inhibiting species. Thus, the antitumor activity of certain representatives of the metallocene dihalides was detected three years ago (3). Since then, the cytostatic behavior of the metallocene dihalides has been demonstrated at the experimental stage against various animal tumor systems as well as against in vitro cultured cells.

The metallocene dihalides represent the first example of a group of o r g a n o m e t a l l i c compounds which exhibit cancerostatic properties by their own. Both containing a cis-dihalometal moiety, the metallocene dihalides are, in contrast to the tumor-inhibiting inorganic noble metal complexes of the planar L_2MX_2 type, tetrahedrally coordinated and are characterized by early transition metals featuring as the central atoms M and η^5-cyclopentadienyl rings as the ligands L.

Structure-Activity Relation

To study the structure-activity relation of the metallocene dihalides, the influence of chemical variation upon the tumor-inhibiting activity was investigated. Principally, a metallocene dihalide molecule offers three different positions to be modified (Figure 1): (i) At the position of the central metal atom M, one of eight different early transition metals of the titanium, vanadium, and chromium subgroups of the Periodic Table can be introduced. (ii) The positions of the acido ligands X can be occupied by various halide as well as pseudohalide ligands. (iii) Single hydrogen atoms of the two cyclopentadienyl rings may be replaced by other groups in different substitution modes such as monosubstitution, 1,1'-disubstitution, or bridging of the two rings by a bifunctional group.

Studies on the structure-activity relation of the metallocene dihalides were generally performed using as experimental system the Ehrlich ascites tumor (EAT) growing in female CF1 mice. The therapeutic effect was judged by determining the mean survival time (MST) and by calculating the increase in life span (ILS) compared to the untreated controls. The key-date for the survival studies was day 180 after tumor transplantation (Table I, III) or day 60 (Table VIII).

Variation of the Metal Atom. Considering the influence of the central metal M within the metallocene dichloride system $(C_5H_5)_2MCl_2$ upon the tumor-inhibiting activity, there is a strong dependence of the antitumor action upon the metal atom present (3 - 7). Whereas the complexes containing the first and second row transition metals Ti, V, Nb, or Mo effect marked tumor inhibition with distinct dose-activity relations and with cure rates of 100 % at optimum dose (Table I), the metallocene dichlorides of the higher homologues Ta or W only sporadicly induce the survival of treated tumor-bearing mice. The extreme case of this tendency is reached at the metallocene dichlorides of Zr and Hf, for which no tumor-inhibiting properties could be observed against EAT.

Regarding the position of the central metal atoms in the Periodic Table, a diagonal relation Ti - Nb and V - Mo is obvious of those metals which display as central atoms in metallocene dichlorides marked cancerostatic activity (6). This corresponds to

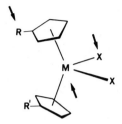

Figure 1.   Molecular structure of the metallocene dihalides, $(\eta^5\text{-}C_5H_5)_2MX_2$. The arrows indicate the three positions that can be chemically modified.

Table I

Pharmacological data of metallocene dichlorides

M< (Cl, Cl)	Optimum dose (mg/kg)	Cure rate at optimum dose (%)	ILS at optimum dose[a] (%)	LD_{50} (mg/kg)	T I [b]	Ref.
M = Ti	30–60	80–90[c]	842–951	100	3.3	(3,4)
M = Zr	–[d]	–[d]	–[d]	75	–[d]	(4)
M = Hf	–[d]	–[d]	–[d]	220	–[d]	(4)
M = V	80–90	100	984	110	1.4	(5)
M = Nb	20–25	100	1076	35	3.5	(6)
M = Ta	80–220[e]	–[e]	570[f]	220	–[e]	–
M = Mo	75–100	100	1039	175	2.9	(7)
M = W	100–525[e]	–[e]	360[f]	500	–[e]	(6)

a) I L S (increase in life span) values are defined as percentual increase of the mean survival time (MST) of a dose group related to the untreated tumor-bearing control group (key-date: day 180). With Ti, V, Nb, Mo in optimum doses, the MST values are significantly different from control values (Wilcoxon-Mann-Whitney U-statistics). b) T I (therapeutic index), defined as the relation LD_{50}/ED_{75}. c) 100 % after application in buffered solution (17). d) No cures or any therapeutic effect observed. e) Only sporadic cures within the indicated dose range. f) Maximum value.

the similarity of atomic radii within a diagonal pair of elements, e.g. Ti (1.32 Å) and Nb (1.34 Å), and points to the significance of effects of size for the mechanism of action.

Thus, the size of M influences the Cl‒M‒Cl bonding angle,
the M‒Cl bonding distance and the non-bonding Cl...Cl distance
(bite) within the dichlorometal moiety of the complexes. These
structural parameters are given in Table II for metallocene dichlorides (8‒11) and for the inorganic cytostatic drug DDP (12).

For DDP the Cl...Cl bite amounts to 3.35 Å and corresponds
to the distance between two appropriate DNA-base donor atoms of
a DNA helix (13) in a manner that cross-links can be built up
after dissociation of the Cl atoms (13‒16). If the simplifica-
tion is admitted that the bite between the Cl atoms as the leaving groups is directly correlated to the distance of adjacent
coordination sites at the metal atom against another given pair
of entrant ligands, the possibility of a similar molecular attack
for complexes exhibiting similar bite values has to be taken in
account. It is remarkable that with all tumor-inhibiting metallocene dichlorides this bite is of a similar size as with DDP, i.e.
the value is at the most by 0.12 Å higher or 0.11 Å lower than
the bite of DDP. In contrast, the zirconocene and hafnocene dichlorides, which do not induce antiproliferative activity, are
characterized by a bite which is markedly (by 0.25 or 0.31 Å)
larger than that of DDP. These two Cl...Cl distances exceed a
critical value lying between 3.50 and 3.60 Å which seems to be an
upper limit for the formation of DNA-metal cross-links, and are
therefore possibly responsible for the therapeutic ineffectivity
of zirconocene and hafnocene dichlorides.

From these considerations it can be deduced that the cis-di-
chlorometal moiety within the metallocene dihalides is apparently
of critical significance for the mechanism of action. The formation of adjacent, perhaps chelating bonds to biological macromolecules after dissociation of the halide ligands seems to be an
important step.

Variation of the Acido Ligands. In contrast to the variation of the central metal atoms, the exchange of the Cl ligands
in the titanocene model system $(C_5H_5)_2TiX_2$ by the halide or pseudohalide ligands X = F, Br, I, NCS, N_3 does not affect the antitumor activity (17). Table III shows that all investigated compounds lead to cure rates of 100 % when applied in optimum doses.
This means that the antitumor activity of the metallocene species
is independent of the halide ligand X; provided that a central
metal is present which causes marked antitumor activity, the acido ligands can apparently be widely varied without loss or diminution of the cancerostatic effectivity. In some cases, especially in the case of X = Br, the therapeutic range is even enlarged
leading to an increase of the therapeutic index (T I) to 4.5,
compared to 3.3 after treatment with titanocene dichloride.

Moreover, the application of the titanocene dihalides in so-

Table II

Structural parameters
of DDP and some metallocene dichlorides

Compound	M	$M-Cl$ [a] (Å)	$Cl-M-Cl$ (°)	$Cl...Cl$ [b] (Å)	Ref.
$(C_5H_5)_2MoCl_2$	Mo	2.471(5)	82.0(2)	3.242	(8)
$(C_5H_4CH_3)_2VCl_2$	V	2.398(2)	87.06(9)	3.303	(9)
$cis-(NH_3)_2PtCl_2$	Pt	2.330(1)	91.9(3)	3.349	(12)
$(C_5H_5)_2NbCl_2$	Nb	2.470(4)	85.6(1)	3.356	(8)
$(C_5H_5)_2TiCl_2$	Ti	2.364(3)	94.43(6)	3.470	(10)
$(CH_2)_3(C_5H_4)_2HfCl_2$	Hf	2.423(3)	95.87(8)	3.598	(11)
$(C_5H_5)_2ZrCl_2$	Zr	2.441(5)	97.1(2)	3.660	(8)

a) Mean $M-Cl$ distance. b) Calculated non-bonding $Cl...Cl$ distance (bite).

Table III

Pharmacological data of titanocene dihalides

Ti<$_X^X$	Optimum dose[a] (mg/kg)	Cure rate at opti- mum dose (%)	I L S at opti- mum dose[b] (%)	LD_{50} (mg/kg)	T I	Ref.
X = F	40	100	1039	60	2.0	(17)
X = Cl	30-60	75[c]	960-971	100	3.3	(17)
X = Br	40-80	100	1162	135	4.5	(17)
X = I	60-100	100	1011	145	2.6	(17)
X = NCS	80	100	1081	135	3.4	(17)
X = N_3	50-70	100	1084	95	2.4	(17)

a) After application in buffered solutions, toxic levels are shifted to higher doses so that the optimum dose ranges are broadened and the T I values are enlarged (for details see ref. 17). b) The basic MST values are in all cases significantly different from the control values. c) 100 % after application in buffered solution.

lutions buffered to pH 5.1 - 5.7 leads to a further increase of the T I values and to a reduction of the substance-induced side effects; especially the appearance of postperitonitic symptoms several weeks after intraperitoneal application of high doses of titanocene dihalides is strikingly reduced by pH elevation in the drug solutions before injection (17).

This phenomenon may be explained by the tendency of all titanocene dihalides to partially cleave off their acido ligands X within a hydrolysis equilibrium in aqueous systems (18). This leads to acid properties of the drug solutions which are responsible for the side effects and which can be reduced by buffering.

On the other hand, the reason for the similar tumor-inhibiting potencies of the titanocene dihalides with X = F, Cl, Br, I, NCS, N_3 can be seen in their similar ability to dissociate the ligands X in aqueous solutions, which apparently means a similar ability to release the metals' coordination sites for interaction with the target molecule in the biological system. In consequence, titanocene derivatives with strongly bonded ligands X such as $(C_5H_5)_2Ti(SR)_2$ (19) or $(C_5H_5)_2TiS_5$ (20) do not show any cancerostatic activities against EAT. Thus, the leaving ability of the X ligands within the dihalometal moiety plays apparently an important role for the tumor-inhibiting properties of the metallocene dihalides, as was similarly postulated for the DDP-type complexes (21).

Modification of the Cyclopentadienyl Ligands. The results described so far suggest that the MX_2 moiety within the metallocene dihalides represents the active center of the molecules. However, modification of the cyclopentadienyl rings in $(C_5H_5)_2TiCl_2$ as the model system also has a significant influence on the tumor-inhibiting potency of titanocene dichloride.

The variation of one of the two rings by ethyl or trimethylsilyl monosubstitution reduces the cure rates to 60 or 80 % (Table IV, top). Whereas these values are only moderately diminished in comparison to the unsubstituted titanocene dichloride, the tumor-inhibiting activity of complexes containing two modified rings is much more reduced. Thus, for 1,1'-disubstituted or 1,1'-bridged compounds (Table IV, middle and bottom) at the best sporadic cures can be observed. For $(C_5H_5)(C_5H_4Me)TiCl_2$, $(C_5H_4Me)_2TiCl_2$, $(CH_2)_3(C_5H_4)_2TiCl_2$ (LD_{50} = 35 mg/kg), and $SiMe_2(C_5H_4)_2TiCl_2$ cancerostatic inactivity is noted; because of the outstanding toxicity of the first three compounds it may be argued that here the toxic effect interferes with a possible cytostatic action (22).

In continuation of the modification of the cyclopentadienyl ligands, one or two of these can be replaced by the related η^5-bound systems indenyl or tetrahydroindenyl. The tested compounds of this type include $(C_9H_7)_2TiCl_2$, $(C_9H_7)(C_9H_{11})TiCl_2$, and $(C_9H_7)(C_5H_5)TiCl_2$ (Table V). Whereas for the mixed cyclopentadienyl complex, which reveals a maximum cure rate of 100 %, no di-

Table IV

Pharmacological data of monosubstituted,
1,1'-disubstituted, and 1,1'-bridged titanocene dichlorides (22)

R–Cp Ti Cl₂	OD [a] (mg/kg)	Maximum cure rate within OD (%)	OC [b]	LD$_{50}$ (mg/kg)
R = Me	_[c]	_[c]	_[c]	45
R = Et	50–70	60	9/15	100
R = SiMe$_3$	40–70	80	16/20	100

(1,1'-disubstituted)	SD [d] (mg/kg)	SC [e]	LD$_{50}$ (mg/kg)
R = Me	_[c]	_[c]	30
R = SiMe$_3$	280–300	2/10	360
R = SiMe$_2$^{n}Bu	320–360	3/15	420
R = GeMe$_3$	240–320	7/25	400

(1,1'-bridged)	SD [d] (mg/kg)	SC [e]	LD$_{50}$ (mg/kg)
Z = CH$_2$	220–260	2/15	360
Z = CHMe	200–260	2/20	320
Z = SiHMe	160–220	6/20	300
Z = SiMe$_2$	_[c]	_[c]	220
Z = SiEt$_2$	140–200	3/20	220
Z = GeMe$_2$	220–260	2/15	280

a) OD = Dose range with optimum tumor-inhibiting activity (cure rates > 50 %).   b) OC = Number of cures in the OD, related to the total number of animals in the OD.   c) No cures or any therapeutic effect observed.   d) SD = Dose range of sporadic cures. e) SC = Number of sporadic cures, related to the total number of animals within SD.

Table V

Pharmacological data of
indenyl and tetrahydroindenyl derivatives LL'TiCl$_2$ (**22**)

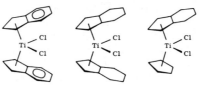

L	L'	S D [a) (mg/kg)	S C [b)	LD$_{50}$ (mg/kg)
C$_9$H$_7$	C$_9$H$_7$	280–320	2/15	360
C$_9$H$_{11}$	C$_9$H$_{11}$	260–300	2/15	320
C$_9$H$_{11}$	C$_5$H$_5$	80–120	11/15[c)	120

a) and b) see Table IV.   c) 100 % cures at optimum dose (100 mg/kg).

Table VI

Pharmacological data of
monocyclopentadienyl complexes C$_5$H$_5$TiX$_2$Y

X	Y	S D [a) (mg/kg)	S C [b)	LD$_{50}$ (mg/kg)
Cl	Cl	50–130	10/45	120
Cl	SPh	60–100	6/25	100
NCS	NCS	70–110	6/25	130

a) and b) see Table IV.

minution of the cancerostatic activity can be observed in comparison to the unaltered titanocene dichloride, again the tumor-inhibiting properties of the complexes containing two modified ring ligands are strongly reduced (22).

On extending the modification of cyclopentadienyl ligands to the total replacement of one C_5H_5 ring by an additional acido ligand Y, an exhaustion of the cancerostatic activity is to be observed in no case (Table VI). Instead, sporadic cures occur with all tested compounds leading to a reduced antitumor effectivity in a range which is comparable to that of the majority of the compounds in Tables IV and V.

From the results of this chapter the hypothesis is deduced that the cyclopentadienyl rings act as carrier ligands which enable the transport of the active centers of the molecules to the intracellular targets. Modification of the rings apparently injures the tumor-inhibiting activity by affecting the transportation properties of the molecules. Possible reasons for this behavior are steric effects, changes in the solubility properties, or alterations of ring ligand-metal bond stabilities of the modified metallocene dihalides (22).

Effect of Hydrolytically Formed Species. As the metallocene dihalides are applied under aqueous conditions, possible effects of the hydrolytically formed species are of interest. Some dissociation, aquation, and hydrolysis reactions of titanocene dihalides have recently been elucidated in more detail (23 - 30). In aqueous solutions, the parent compounds $(C_5H_5)_2TiX_2$ do not only form the neutral oxo-bridged dinuclear complexes $(C_5H_5)_2(X)Ti-O-Ti(X)(C_5H_5)_2$ (18), but additionally seem to coexist in pH-dependent reversible equilibria with the cationic aquo species $[(C_5H_5)_2Ti(OH_2)_2]^{2+}$, $[(C_5H_5)_2Ti(OH_2)OH]^+$, and $[(C_5H_5)_2(H_2O)Ti-O-Ti(OH_2)(C_5H_5)_2]^{2+}$ (23). X-ray structure determinations of the neutral complex $(C_5H_5)_2(Cl)Ti-O-Ti(Cl)(C_5H_5)_2$ (24) as well as of crystalline salts of the mononuclear diaquo (25, 26) and the dinuclear μ-oxo (27, 28) cations show them to have the suggested structures with still valid bis(cyclopentadienyl)titanium skeletons.

On the other hand, on reaction of titanocene dichloride with equimolar amounts of water and diethylamine in tetrahydrofuran the trinuclear monocyclopentadienyl hydrolysis product $[C_5H_5Ti(Cl)O]_3$ together with unchanged $(C_5H_5)_2TiCl_2$ could be isolated (29). Thus, the possibility of hydrolytic cleavage of cyclopentadienyl rings during the biological action has also to be taken in account.

As typical examples of a $(C_5H_5)_2TiCl_2$ and a $C_5H_5TiCl_3$ hydrolysis product, we have tested against EAT the dinuclear $[(C_5H_5)_2Ti(Cl)]_2O$ and the tetranuclear $[C_5H_5Ti(Cl)O]_4$, respectively, which are easily accessible in pure form (24; 29, 30). Compared to their parent compounds, both μ-oxo-complexes show reduced antitumor activity. Thus, hydrolysis seems not to be a step producing the intrinsicly active species.

Tumor Systems Tested in vivo

The cancerostatic activities of titanocene dichloride and vanadocene dichloride as typical representatives of the metallocene dihalides were tested against various experimental tumor systems (Table VII). The two complexes exhibit cancerostatic properties against fluid ascitic tumors such as EAT in early and advanced stages, lymphoid leukemia L1210, and lymphocytic leukemia P388 (31). The growth of solid tumors, e.g. of a subcutaneously implanted solid EAT, is inhibited in a highly significant manner by intraperitoneal application of the metallocene dichlorides (31); this result demonstrates that the substances are capable to achieve antiproliferation by a systemic effect. Test series against other experimental tumor systems are presently under investigation.

Cell Growth Inhibition in vitro

For determination of the growth-inhibiting potencies in vitro, the influence of the metallocene dichlorides $(C_5H_5)_2MCl_2$ (M = Ti, Zr, Hf, V, Mo) upon the proliferation of in vitro cultured tumor and embryonic cells both of animal and of human origin, was investigated. Three main conclusions can be drawn: (i) There are no hints to a cell specifity of the growth-inhibiting action. (ii) Vanadocene dichloride is the most effective growth-inhibiting representative in vitro and accomplishes highly significant diminution of cell proliferation in a concentration as low as 5×10^{-6} mol/l. Titanocene and molybdocene dichlorides inhibit cellular growth only in concentrations of 5×10^{-4} or 10^{-3} mol/l, respectively, whereas zirconocene and hafnocene dichlorides, which are ineffective against EAT in vivo, require even higher concentrations (32). (iii) The growth inhibition is apparently caused by a cytotoxic action of the compounds, as is demonstrated by application of the dye lissamine green (32).

Investigations Concerning the Mechanism of Action

The investigations concerning the mode of action of the metallocene dihalides represented by titanocene dichloride and vanadocene dichloride are based on four experimental pillars: (i) Incorporation studies with ^{3}H-labelled, specific precursors of the DNA, RNA, or protein synthesis were performed to reveal different influences of the substances upon these synthesis pathways. (ii) The cytokinetic behavior of EAT cells after treatment was pursued to recognize alterations in the cell transit through the cell cycle. (iii) The light-microscopic and ultrastructural alteration patterns were observed to gain informations about the cellular events during the inhibition of

Table VII

Tumor-inhibiting properties of $(C_5H_5)_2MCl_2$
in optimum doses against various experimental tumor systems

M	Fluid EAT day 1[a]	Fluid EAT day 5[a]	L1210 day 1[a]	P388 day 1[a]	Solid EAT days 1,3,(5)[a]
Ti	70 mg/kg: 100 % survivors[b]	70 mg/kg: 90 % survivors[b]	70–90 mg/kg: I L S[c] 21–26 %	40–70 mg/kg: I L S[c] 26–30 %	2 x (30–50) mg/kg: T/C[d] 14–25 %
V	80 mg/kg: 100 % survivors[b]	80 mg/kg: 20 % survivors[b]	50–60 mg/kg: I L S[c] 24–29 %	30–50 mg/kg: I L S[c] 18–24 %	3 x 50 mg/kg: T/C[d] 31 %

a) Day after tumor transplantation on which the animals were treated with a single dose. b) On key-date (day 180 after transplantation). c) For definition see Table I. d) T/C = mean tumor weight of a dose group related as percentage to the mean tumor weight of the controls (key-date: day 8 after transplantation).

proliferation. (iv) Using the electron energy loss spectroscopy (EELS), a new microanalytical method which combines the ultra-structural representation of biological objects with the analysis of metals like titanium or vanadium in low concentrations, it was intended to determine the localization of the central metal atoms of $(C_5H_5)_2MCl_2$ (M = Ti, V) within the tumor cells after treatment.

Precursor Incorporation Studies. Studies of the incorporation of tritiated precursors of the DNA, RNA, or protein synthesis, i.e. of thymidine, uridine, or leucine, into the acid-insoluble fraction of EAT cells were accomplished after in vivo as well as in vitro treatment with $(C_5H_5)_2MCl_2$ (M = Ti, V). In all experiments, the nucleic acid metabolism turns out to be much more sensitive to the metallocene dihalide action than the protein metabolism (33, 34). In particular, treatment with vanadocene dichloride induces an extended and persistent suppression of the DNA synthesis without signs of regeneration processes (Figure 2).

In this connection it is worth mentioning that an interaction between metallocene dichlorides and nucleic acids can be demonstrated in vitro by the fact that, dependent on the substance concentration, the UV absorptions of both calf thymus DNA and calf liver RNA are influenced. The maximum at 258 nm is shifted to lower wave lengths, while the absorbance of the band increases which is indicative of an alteration of the secondary structure of the nucleic acids.

Cytokinetic Studies. Marked mitotic depressions and cell accumulations in the late S and in the premitotic G_2 phases are the main results after in vivo treatment of EAT cells with optimum tumor-inhibiting doses of metallocene dichlorides (35). Whereas the G_2 block after $(C_5H_5)_2VCl_2$ application is reversible and gives rise to slow partially synchronized waves and, later-on, to the desintegration of the cells, the $(C_5H_5)_2TiCl_2$-treated EAT cell populations are removed several days after substance application by cells belonging to the defensive system of the host animals.

Considering the cytokinetic behavior of EAT after in vitro treatment with metallocene dihalides, the appearance of cell arrests in the premitotic G_2 phase is again the dominant result. The reversibility of this G_2 block depends on the applied concentrations. Additionally, cell accumulations at the G_1/S boundary can be recognized during the exposure to the substances in low concentrations. Following short exposure periods, these cells escape the arrest at G_1/S and continue their transit through the cell cycle as synchronized populations which can be pursued during one following cycle (36).

The comparison with the cytokinetic behavior after treatment with other cytostatic drugs shows that many substances for which the molecular attack upon DNA molecules is generally assumed pro-

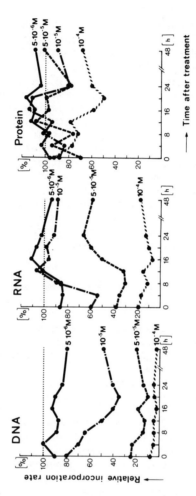

Figure 2. Incorporation rates related as percentage to the controls (· ·) of [methyl-³H]thy-midine (left), [5-³H]uridine (middle), and L-[4,5-³H]leucine (right) as a measure of the DNA, RNA, and protein synthesis activities respectively after a 90-min treatment of EAT cells with vanadocene dichloride in vitro.

voke similar findings: Alkylating agents such as cyclophosphamide (37) and melphalan (38), the anthracyclines (39, 40), and DDP (41) cause cell arrests in the G_2 phase, whereas cell accumulations at the G_1/S boundary are observable under the influence of antimetabolites (40, 42) and DDP (41).

Morphological Studies. In analogy to other cytostatic drugs such as alkylating agents, bleomycin, or DDP, the treatment with the metallocene dichlorides of titanium and vanadium induces the formation of giant cells with one or several nuclei as well as the appearance of abnormal mitotic figures (43).

At the ultrastructural level (Figure 3) the first observable alterations after in vivo and in vitro treatment consist in chromatin condensation and in nuclear segmentation. The further-on developing morphological features show many similarities to the results after treatment with alkylating agents (44, 45) or with DDP (46) and can be described as the development of the morphological signs of an unbalanced cellular growth and, later-on, as the formation of necroses of the tumor cells (43).

A surprising event after in vivo and in vitro treatment with titanocene dichloride, but not with vanadocene dichloride, is the appearance of complete type-A virus particles within the cytoplasm some days after treatment as well as of probable early stages of the viruses (Figure 3). Thus, titanocene dichloride is apparently able to activate the formation of previously unexpressed endogenous viruses. In animals, a massive immigration of cells such as macrophages, leukocytes, or lymphocytes which belong to the defensive system of the host animals, can be observed during the following days. It might be supposed that this process is the consequence of the virus activation and acts as a fortifying factor in the course of tumor inhibition by titanocene dichloride (43).

The final events after metallocene dichloride application are the destruction of the tumor cells and/or their phagocytosis by macrophages in vivo (Figure 3).

Microanalytical Studies. The EELS investigations after in vivo as well as after in vitro treatment of EAT with the antitumor agents titanocene dichloride and vanadocene dichloride reveal reproducibly the main enrichment of the central metals Ti and V within the nuclear heterochromatin. To a minor extent, the metals are associated with the euchromatin, the nucleolus, and the cytoplasmic ribosomes. In most cases, no metal atoms can be detected in other cellular regions by EELS. This means that the treatment with titanocene or vanadocene dichloride results apparently in an accumulation of the central metals Ti and V within those cellular regions which are rich in nucleic acids.

In connection with the structure-activity relation and the other experimental results, the described intracellular distribution pattern of the central metal atoms which apparently repre-

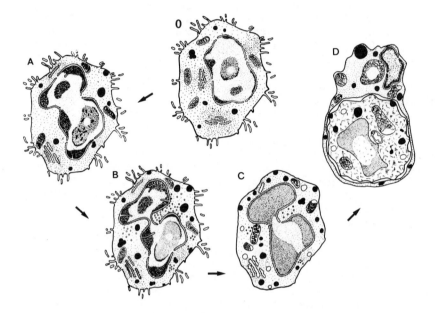

Figure 3.   Schematic representation of ultrastructural alterations of EAT cells after treatment with titanocene dichloride or DDP in vivo. Key to treatment (time after treatment): O, untreated; A, titanocene dichloride (2–6 h); B, titanocene dichloride (8–10 h) or DDP (4–12 h); C, titanocene dichloride (12–24 h) or DDP (24–36 h); and D, titanocene dichloride (36–120 h) or DDP (48–120 h).

Table VIII

I L S values determined on day $60^{a)}$
after transplantation of the fluid EAT

$(C_5H_5)_2MCl_2$	I L S (%)	$(C_5H_5)_2TiX_2$	I L S (%)
M = Ti	217-244	X = F	280
M = V	261	X = Cl	237-241
M = Nb	292	X = Br	323
M = Ta	164	X = I	270
M = Mo	280	X = NCS	294
M = W	97	X = N_3	295

a) This Table was included to facilitate comparison with I L S values of other tumor systems.

sent the active centers of the molecules is indicative of a molecular attack of the metal-containing species upon the nucleic
acids within the treated cells.

Acknowledgments

The authors are indebted to the Deutsche Forschungsgemeinschaft, the Deutsche Krebshilfe, and the Fonds der Chemischen
Industrie for financial grants.

Literature Cited

1. Rosenberg, B.; VanCamp, L.; Trosko, J. E.; Mansour, V. H.
    Nature 1969, 222, 385.
2. Rozencweig, M.; von Hoff, D. D.; Slavik, M.; Muggia, F. M.
    Ann. Intern. Med. 1977, 86, 803.
3. Köpf, H; Köpf-Maier, P. Angew. Chem. Int. Ed. Engl. 1979,
    18, 477.
4. Köpf-Maier, P.; Hesse, B.; Köpf, H. J. Cancer Res. Clin.
    Oncol. 1980, 96, 43.
5. Köpf-Maier, P.; Köpf, H. Z. Naturforsch. 1979, 34b, 805.
6. Köpf-Maier, P.; Leitner, M.; Köpf, H. J. Inorg. Nucl. Chem.
    1980, 42, 1789.
7. Köpf-Maier, P.; Leitner, M.; Voigtländer, R.; Köpf, H.
    Z. Naturforsch. 1979, 34c, 1174.
8. Green, J. C.; Green, M. L. H.; Prout, C. K. J. Chem. Soc.,
    Chem. Commun. 1972, 421.
9. Petersen, J. L.; Dahl, L. F. J. Am. Chem. Soc. 1975, 97,
    6422.
10. Clearfield, A.; Warner, D. K.; Saldarriaga-Molina, C. H.;
    Ropal, R.; Bernal, I. Can. J. Chem. 1975, 53, 1622.
11. Saldarriaga-Molina, C. H.; Clearfield, A.; Bernal, I.
    Inorg. Chem. 1974, 13, 2880.
12. Milburn, G. H. W.; Truter, M. R. J. Chem. Soc. (A) 1966,
    1609.
13. Roos, I. A. G. Chem. Biol. Interact. 1977, 16, 39.
14. Munchausen, L. L.; Rahn, R. O. Cancer Chemother. Rep. 1975,
    59, 643.
15. Macquet, J.-P.; Butour, J.-L. Biochimie 1978, 60, 901.
16. Chiang, C. C.; Sorrell, T.; Kistenmacher, T. J.; Marzilli,
    L. G. J. Am. Chem. Soc. 1978, 100, 5102.
17. Köpf-Maier, P.; Hesse, B.; Voigtländer, R.; Köpf, H.
    J. Cancer Res. Clin. Oncol. 1980, 97, 31.
18. Samuel, E. Bull. Soc. Chim. France 1966, 3548.
19. Köpf, H.; Schmidt, M. Z. Anorg. Allg. Chem. 1965, 340, 139.
20. Köpf, H.; Block, B.; Schmidt, M. Chem. Ber. 1968, 101, 272.
21. Cleare, M. J. Coord. Chem. Rev. 1974, 12, 349.
22. Köpf-Maier, P.; Kahl, W.; Klouras, N.; Hermann, G.; Köpf, H.
    Eur. J. Med. Chem. 1981, 16, 275.
23. Döppert, K. J. Organomet. Chem. 1979, 178, C3.

24. Le Page, Y. J. Organomet. Chem. 1980, 193, 201.
25. Thewalt, U.; Klein, H.-P. J. Organomet. Chem. 1980, 194, 297.
26. Klein, H.-P.; Thewalt, U. Z. Anorg. Allg. Chem. 1981, 476, 62.
27. Thewalt, U.; Schleußner, G. Angew. Chem. 1978, 90, 559.
28. Thewalt, U.; Kebbel, B. J. Organomet. Chem. 1978, 150, 59.
29. Köpf, H.; Grabowski, S.; Voigtländer, R. J. Organomet. Chem. 1981, 216, 185.
30. Skapski, A. C.; Troughton, P. G. H. Acta Cryst. B 1970, 26, 716.
31. Köpf-Maier, P.; Wagner, W.; Hesse, B.; Köpf, H. Eur. J. Cancer 1981, 17, 665.
32. Köpf-Maier, P.; Wagner, W.; Köpf, H. Cancer Chemother. Pharmacol. 1981, 5, 237.
33. Köpf-Maier, P.; Köpf, H. Naturwiss. 1980, 67, 415.
34. Köpf-Maier, P.; Wagner, W.; Köpf, H. Naturwiss. 1981, 68, 272.
35. Köpf-Maier, P.; Wagner, W.; Liss, E. J. Cancer Res. Clin. Oncol. 1981, 102, 21.
36. Köpf-Maier, P.; Wagner, W. Verh. Anat. Ges. 1982, 76, in press.
37. Göhde, W.; Schumann, J.; Büchner, T.; Barlogie, B.; in "Pulse-Cytophotometry", Haanen, C. A. M.; Hillen, H. F. P.; Wessels, J. M. C., Eds.; European Press Medikon: Ghent, 1975, p. 138.
38. Barlogie, B.; Drewinko, B. Proc. 3rd Int. Symp. Pulse-Cytophotometry 1977, p. 26.
39. Göhde, W.; Dittrich, W. Arzneim.-Forsch. (Drug Res.) 1971, 21, 1656.
40. Büchner, T.; Barlogie, B.; Göhde, W.; Schumann, J.; in "Pulse-Cytophotometry", Haanen, C. A. M.; Hillen, H. F. P.; Wessels, J. M. C., Eds.; European Press Medikon: Ghent, 1975, p. 293.
41. Bergerat, J.-P.; Barlogie, B.; Göhde, W.; Johnston, D. A.; Drewinko, B. Cancer Res. 1979, 39, 4356.
42. Ernst, P.; Faille, A.; Killmann, S.-A. Scand. J. Haema. 1973, 10, 209.
43. Köpf-Maier P. J. Cancer Res. Clin. Oncol. 1982, in press.
44. Bienengräber, A.; Putzke, H.-P.; Tessmann, D. Z. Krebsforsch. 1965, 66, 438.
45. Brandes, D.; Anton, E.; Lam, K. W. J. Nat. Cancer Inst. 1967, 39, 385.
46. Aggarwal, S. K. J. Clin. Hematol. Oncol. 1977, 7, 760.

RECEIVED October 4, 1982

Ruthenium Anticancer Agents and Relevant Reactions of Ruthenium—Purine Complexes

MICHAEL J. CLARKE

Boston College, Department of Chemistry, Chestnut Hill, MA 02167

Attempts to incorporate ruthenium into pharmaceutical agents have typically followed two avenues of approach. Early studies were directed toward ruthenium-containing chemotherapeutic agents[1] and more recently workers have begun to explore the possibility of using ^{97}Ru for diagnostic organ imaging.[2,3] While ruthenium complexes have shown promise along both directions, there has been only one clinical trial of a ruthenium compound, which involved $^{103}RuCl_3$ for radio-imaging tumors.[4] At present, the only commonly used ruthenium compound for biomedical purposes is the cytological stain, ruthenium red.[5] The interactions of ruthenium complexes with biologically important molecules have recently been reviewed and the early literature dealing with the metabolic fate of different types of ruthenium compounds has been summarized elsewhere.[1,3,6]

Antitumor Agents

With few exceptions,[7] approaches to ruthenium antineoplastic agents have related to the putative mechanism of action of the clinically employed $cis-Cl_2(NH_3)_2Pt$.[1,8] The binding of ammine complexes of both Ru(II) and Ru(III) to nucleotides and nucleic acids is, in many ways, analogous to that of cisplatin.[8,9] On the other hand, ruthenium(II) complexes usually undergo ligand substitution somewhat more rapidly and the tripositive oxidation state is much more accessible under mild conditions.[10] Advantage can be taken from the ready availability of both the Ru(II) and Ru(III) oxidation states under physiological conditions and the general inertness of these ions toward substitution, when coordinated to nitrogen ligands.[1] Studies reported in an earlier symposium revealed the general anticancer activity of compounds containing the tetraammineruthenium(III) ion or its congeners.[3] Due to the hypoxic conditions often holding in tumor cells, the dipositive oxidation state is more likely to occur. Rapid coordination to nitrogen or sulfur ligands can then fix the metal in its environment. A corollary of this hypothesis is that these complexes should tend to accumulate in tumors relative to more aerobic normal tissue. While the exact mechanism of action is difficult to prove with certainty, the hypothesis accomodates most of the available data and such complexes tend to concentrate in tumors as predicted.[1-3]

In harmony with the cis-platinum drugs, biological studies have also indicated that cellular DNA is the target site for this class of ruthenium complexes.[11,12,14] In contrast to cis-$Cl_2(NH_3)_2$Pt, ruthenium compounds screened in the Ames test were able to cause mutations by frame shift as well as by base pair substitution; however, these compounds were approximately a hundredfold less active in the generation of mutations. The platinum compound also shows greater activity in inducing the bacterial SOS DNA repair mechanism in the B. subtilis Comptest.[12] In general, the ruthenium complexes are an order of magnitude less toxic than cisplatin; however, they must also be administered at higher doses to achieve the same therapeutic effect.[1,12]. Thus the therapeutic indices of these agents are no better than that of cisplatin.

The compound, cis-$Cl_2(DMSO)_4$Ru, exhibits marginal antitumor activity, inhibits nucleic acid synthesis and exerts a pattern of cell damage and mutagenicity similar to that of cis-$Cl_2(NH_3)_2$Pt [13]. Some purine and pyrimidine adducts of the DMSO compound have recently been reported.[15] In contrast to the ammine complexes, the dimethylsulfoxide complexes appear to coordinate at the N-7 of adenine owing to hydrogen bonding between DMSO and the exocyclic amine protons on adenine.[16]

Ruthenium red, $[(NH_3)_5Ru-O-Ru(NH_3)_4-O-Ru(NH_3)_5]^{6+}$, selectively stains cell membrane mucopolysaccharides[5], specifically inhibits cell membrane Ca^{2+}-ATPase[17] and inhibits calcium ion transport across the mitochondrial membrane[18]; however, impurities may be responsible for at least some of these biological effects. It also exhibits fairly good antitumor activity against Lewis lung carcinoma in mice (T/C = 141 at a dose of 2.5 mg/kg·day) and caused a 39% reduction in tumor volume at 5 mg/kg·day.[19,20]

While adenine containing coenzymes are easily complexed by amineruthenium ions, studies with the NAD-requiring enzymes alcohol dehydrogenase, lactate dehydrogenase and glucose-6-phosphate dehydrogenase, the NADH-requiring malate dehydrogenase, and isocitrate dehydrogenase, which utilizes NADP, revealed no inhibition or utilization when these

coenzymes were coordinated to $(NH_3)_5Ru(III)$ at the N-6 site
of the adenine residue.[21]   Therefore, it is unlikely that
complexation of these coenzymes plays a significant metabolic
role, except at very high ruthenium concentrations. Recent
work by Matthews has shown that ribonuclease is mildly
inhibited by a mixture of 2,3'-CMP coordinated to
$(NH_3)_5Ru(III)$ at the exocyclic nitrogen.[22]

Radiodiagnostic Agents

The isotope ^{97}Ru emits an essentially monoenergetic
gamma ray at 216 keV, which is well suited for use in present
radioscintigraphic equipment. Moreover the half-life of the
isotope (2.9 days) is sufficiently long to allow for chemical
synthesis and quality control of these radio-imaging agents.
Ruthenium radiopharmaceuticals would be especially useful
when periodic or delayed scans are necessary in order to
diagnose or monitor the progress of disease. Owing to the
relatively scant availability of this isotope at the present
time, the longer-lived isotope, ^{103}Ru, is often used for
initial tissue-distribution studies. Refinement of earlier
studies has now verified that ^{103}Ru introduced into animals
as cis-$[Cl_2(NH_3)_4Ru]^+$ or related complexes exhibits a
concentration in tumors comparable to that of the widely used
tumor-imaging agent, ^{67}Ga-citrate [2,23]. Unfortunately, these
complexes do not provide high tumor to blood contrast ratios,
so that improvement is necessary for medically useful agents.
Earlier studies with rat-liver microsomes indicated that
NADH-dehydrogenase systems readily reduced
ammineruthenium(III) complexes.[9] Crane has since discovered
plasma membrane NADH-dehydrogenase enzymes on a number of
different types of cells.[24] Experiments with pig
erythrocytes showed that ammineruthenium(III) ions are fairly
readily reduced by the plasma membrane NADH-dehydrogenase.[25]
As expected, the reduction rates are a function of the metal
ion's reduction potential and its intrinsic electron-transfer
rate. Comparison of the hexammineruthenium(III) reductase
activities of subcellular fractions of mouse liver revealed
the plasma membrane and Golgi apparatus to be about
equivalent (when measured per mg of protein) and the
endoplasmic reticulum to be 3-4 times more effective [24]. It
is possible that erythrocyte plasma membrane dehydrogenases
may be partially responsible for the reduction of ruthenium
complexes and their subsequent binding to blood proteins.
Surface NADH-dehydrogenase activity has also been shown to
occur with at least one tumor cell line,[25] so that these
systems may also be indirectly responsible for the binding of
ruthenium complexes to tumor sites. This is in harmony with

Pitha's earlier suggestion that cellular toxicity of
cis-$[Cl_2(NH_3)_4Ru]^{2+}$ occurred through initial binding of the
metal to the cell surface and subsequent uptake into the cell
by pinocytosis.[26]

An important finding by Srivastava et al. is that a
portion of the metal administered as $^{103}RuCl_3 \cdot 3H_2O$ is
complexed by the glycoprotein transferrin, and so mimics iron
metabolism to some extent.[23] Since rapidly growing tumor
cells require substantial quantities of iron, a
Ru-transferrin complex should be readily received by the
tumor. Substantiation of this is the higher uptake of the
purified Ru-transferrin relative to $RuCl_3$ alone. Assuming
the presence of transferrin receptor sites on the tumor cell
surface, initial accumulation by this mechanism should also
occur on the cell membrane followed by subsequent transport
to the cell interior. The recent report that ^{103}Ru
introduced as $RuCl_3$ specifically binds to glycoproteins on
the surface of rat acites hepatoma (AH-130) cells in vitro
may correlate with this [27]. Subcellular distribution of
^{103}Ru in tumor and liver cells isolated from Ehrlich's solid
tumor-bearing mice, which had been injected with $^{103}RuCl_3$,
are similar to those of ^{67}Ga and, by implication, to those of
iron. Fractionation of these and AH-130 cells innoculated in
tissue culture revealed particular accumulation of the metal
ion in the mitochondria followed by the cell debris plus
nuclear portion.[27]

The antitumor antibiotic bleomycin has long been of
interest in radiopharmacy since it selectively localizes in
tumors. In vitro, the drug requires the presence of Fe(II)
and oxygen to exhibit its full biochemical activity, which
involves introducing both single- and double-strand breaks
into cellular DNA through an as yet unidentified radical
intermediate [28]. Stern and coworkers have recently reported
a remarkable Ru-bleomycin complex, which, it is claimed,
retains 100% of native bleomycin's cytotoxic activity,
remains stable through injection and excretion, and exhibits
the same tissue distribution and tumor accumulation as
^3H-labelled bleomycin.[29] A drug of this type may have the
highly desirable advantage of simultaneous chemotherapeutic
and diagnostic activities. Independent work involving direct
combination of $[(H_2O)_6Ru]^{2+}$ with bleomycin also yielded
stable products, which exhibited Sephadex chromatographic
behavior similar to those of native bleomycin and the complex
cited above [30]. However, given the multiple coordination
sites available on this antibiotic and the normal
substitution-inert character of ammineruthenium ions
coordinated to these types of sites, it is unlikely that
either mode of preparation yields a single structural
product. Further characterization of these complexes will be
necessary before mechanistic conclusions can be drawn.

Ruthenium red has shown some tendency to localize in tumors, with the likely receptor sites being mucopolysaccharides on cell surfaces[20,31]. Ruthenocenes have provided a versatile ogranometallic approach to the synthesis of radioruthenium agents, however, no high specificity has been shown for organs which are not already well-imaged by existing agents [32-39]. A number of ruthenium complexes with chelating ligands either similar or identical to the those employed with clinically used ^{99m}Tc radiopharmaceuticals have been tested with similar results. The DTPA complex shows promise for cerebrospinal fluid imaging [40], 8-hydroxyquinoline, 3,4,7,8-tetramethyl-1,10-phenanthroline and iminodiacetate complexes may be useful for delayed hepatobiliary studies [41], complexes of dimercaptopropanesulfonic acid and dimercaptosuccinic acid are potential long-term renal imaging agents [42,43], phosphate and phosphonate derivatives yield bone-imaging agents[44].

Reaction Mechanisms of Purine and Pyrimidine Complexes with (NH$_3$)$_5$Ru(III)

While a substantial amount of structural information has been collected on metal complexes of purine and pyrimidines,[1,45-50] much less is known about their reactivities. Of particular interest are the effects of the metal ion on the organic chemistry of nucleosides and the reactions of the metal ion when coordinated to the heterocyclic base, since these may contribute to either oncogenesis or anticancer activity.

Since the most common coordination position for relatively ''soft'' transition metal ions in nucleic acids is the N-7 of guanine, the reaction chemistry of N-7 bound guanosine and deoxyguanosine complexes is of special importance. It has long been speculated that such complexes may behave analogously to N-7 protonated or alkylated nucleosides, which undergo fairly rapid sugar hydrolysis[51]. However, early studies at low pH showed that the effect of the metal ion was to hinder the proton assisted reaction by blocking protonation at the more catalytically effective N-7 site and making the formation of the conjugate acid of the nucleoside more difficult by virtue of the cationic charge on the metal.[52] HPLC analysis of the decomposition of (dGuo)(NH$_3$)$_5$Ru(III) at neutral pH reveals a complicated product distribution.[53] Assuming the general type of reaction scheme outlined in Figure 1, it is possible to determine: the net rate of disappearance for the dGuo complex ($k_{d1} = k_1 + k_2 + k_3$), the net rate of formation of the Gua

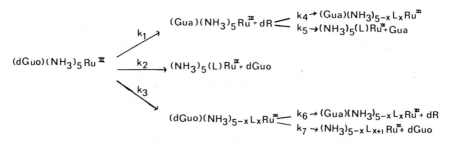

Figure 1.   Proposed reaction scheme for the decomposition of (dGuo)(NH₃)₅-Ru(III) in neutral solution. dGuo is deoxyguanosine; Gua is guanine; and dR is deoxyribose. (Reproduced with permission from Ref. 53.)

complex (k_1), and the net disappearance of this species (k_{d2} = $k_4 + k_5$). At pH 7.0 plots of the yield of
(Gua)(NH$_3$)$_5$Ru(III) as a function of time give rate constants
of: k_{d1} = 8.2 x 10^{-5} sec^{-1}, k_1 = 5.8 x 10^{-6} sec^{-1} and k_{d2} =
4.8 x 10^{-5} sec^{-1}. In harmony with studies on the hydrolysis
of N-7 protonated and alkylated nucleosides,[54-57], the value
of k_1 distinctly decreases in the range of the pK$_a$ (7.6) for
proton loss from the N-1 site[58], so that this pathyway
becomes negligible above pH 8. However, over the same pH
range (6-8.5) a second pathway becomes dominant and yields an
as yet unidentified product (see below).

Under physiological conditions the half-life for the
decomposition of (dGuo)(NH$_3$)$_5$Ru(III) is approximately 4.5
days.[53] Since both free guanine and deoxyguanosine are
observed to form, ligand dissociation is a competetive
reaction. Ammine ligand loss is known to be catalyzed by
base, so that it is likely that at least one of the as yet
unidentified products involves substitution of ammonia.
Another possibility is imidazole ring opening of the purine,
which is known to occur with N-7 alkylated nucleosides in
basic media[54]. Since comparable rates for the hydrolysis of
free deoxyguanosine are not available under the same
conditions, it is difficult to assess the effect of metal ion
coordination in depurinating nucleic acids; however, the
sugar hydrolysis rates probably represent an acceleration of
10^2 to 10^3 over those for the free ligand below pH 7.0.
Since the half-life of these reactions are relatively long
under physiological conditions, immediate metal ion induced
genetic effects are probably the result of the presence of
the metal ion on the nucleic acid rather than metal-catalyzed
depurination. This should be particularly true of ions of
lower charge such as Pt(II). However, in a slightly basic
environment at somewhat elevated temperatures a major side
reaction takes place, which may be a significant process for
metal ions of tripositive or higher charge.

Free Energy Correlations

A substantial amount of structural and acidity data on
pentaammineruthenium(III) complexes with purines and similar
ligands has been correlated through the modification of the
Kirkwood-Westheimer equation[59] given in Eq.(1). Such a
correlation can only be expected to hold when dealing with
the same metal ion similarly coordinated to the identical
tautomeric form of a rigid ligand for which the pK$_a$ value is
known. In addition, this relationship is valid only over a
fairly narrow range of r (between 3.3 and 5.6 A).

Nevertheless, these restrictions obtain for most purine and pyrimidine complexes with $(NH_3)_5Ru(III)$, so that this and related equations have considerable predictive power (as will be seen below.)

$$\Delta pK_a = 1.4/r^2 - 2.6 \qquad (1)$$

In this approach ion-dipole interactions are assumed to predominate and all other terms are simply collected into the intercept value. An analogous correlation can be extracted from reduction potential data and relates ΔE, the change in reduction potential between the complex and its conjugate base, and r. This relation has the distinct advantage of lifting the requirement that identical tautomeric forms be compared, which allows a significantly larger number of complexes to be accomodated.[45]

$$\Delta E = 0.056/r^2 - 0.1$$

Using these two equations it is easily possible to derive additional relationships to predict the difference in pK_a values between isostructural complexes of Ru(II) and Ru(III).

Metal-Ion Movement on Purines and Pyrimidines

Even though metal ions such as Ru(II), Ru(III) and Pt(II) are usually fairly inert to substitution with the type of nitrogen ligands found on nucleic acids, the close juxtaposition of intrabase, intrastrand and interstrand sites may facilitate metal ion movement so as to modulate mutagenic or anticancer effects. Two clear examples of this have now been studied with ruthenium ammine complexes which point out the effects of both pH and electrochemical environments on these linkage isomerization reactions.

Pentaammineruthenium(III)-hypoxanthine complexes undergo a facile linkage isomerization from N-3 to N-9. Figure 2 shows that the rate of this reaction is substantially decreased in the pH range above the pK_a for the N-3 coordinated complex, owing to the residual anionic charge on the pyrimidine. The negative activation entropy is in the range predicted for a mechanism in which the metal ion is simultaneously coordinated to both the N-3 and N-9 sites in the activated complex leading to the loss of five degrees of rotational freedom (four for the cis ammonias and one for the metal center). The decrease in the linkage isomerization rate between pH 1 and 2 (see Figure 2) may be due to the partial protonation of the N-9 site ($pK_a = -0.4$). The

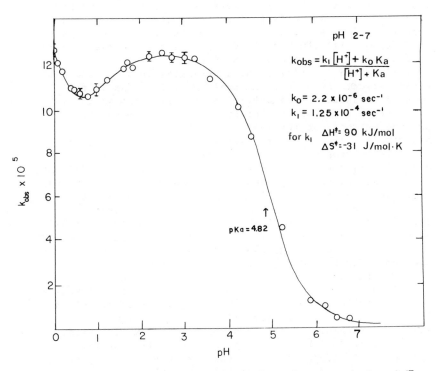

Figure 2. Plot of k_{obs} vs. pH for the N3 to N9 linkage isomerization of (7-MeHyp)(NH$_3$)$_5$Ru(III).

subsequent increase in the rate in the pH range 0 – 1 is surprising and may be due to a change in the ionic media from predominately Li$^+$ to H$^{+45,62}$.

Despite the generally high stability of pentaammineruthenium(II) complexes with aromatic nitrogen heterocycles, complexes of this ion with adenosine and cytidine ligands have proven to be somewhat unstable due to the presence of the adjacent exocyclic amine. However, owing to its greater pi–acceptor ability, the ligand 2–aminopyrimidine (2–AmPm) affords a complex suitable for model studies. The effect of the exocyclic amine on the stability of these complexes is apparent from a comparison of (Pm)(NH$_3$)$_5$Ru(II) (Pm = pyrimidine), which remains stable in acid solution for extended periods, and 1–[(2–AmPm)(NH$_3$)$_5$Ru(II)], which undergoes an acid catalyzed dissociation. Even under neutral conditions the latter complex persists with a half–life of only about an hour.[62]

Figure 3 indicates that it is possible to add two protons to this complex and that both catalyze the hydrolysis. The first protonation undoubtedly occurs at the free ring nitrogen, whereas the second may be at the exocyclic nitrogen or directly on the metal. Space–filling models suggest that a proton of the exocyclic amine impinges on an octahedral face of the metal ion coordinated at the adjacent ring nitrogen. Such a juxtaposition should facilitate protonation of the metal center to form a labile seven–coordinate intermediate[64]. Interestingly, 1–[(4–aminopyridine)(NH$_3$)$_5$Ru]$^{2+}$ has also been shown to undergo a rapid acid catalyzed dissociation.[63]

The formation of exocyclically coordinated ruthenium(III) complexes of adenine and cytidine derivatives has been proposed to proceed through initial coordination of Ru(II) to the adjacent ring nitrogen[65] (see Figure 4). An analogous mechanism, but not necessarily requiring oxidation of the metal ion, has recently been suggested for the synthesis of exocyclically coordinated platinum complexes with these ligands[66], so that this type of linkage isomerization may well be pertinent to the activity of platinum group anticancer agents[8].

Use of Eq.(1), with an estimate of the pK$_a$ for the exocyclic nitrogen on adenosine to be in the range of 18, allows prediction of the pK$_a$ of the N–1 coordinated Ru(III) complex to be approximately 8. This can be verified through a determination of the pH dependence of the reduction potential of this complex which is predicted to be:

$$E_h = E - .059 \log \left[\frac{[H^+]K^{II} + K^{II}K^{III}}{[H^+]^2 + [H^+]K^{II}} \right]$$

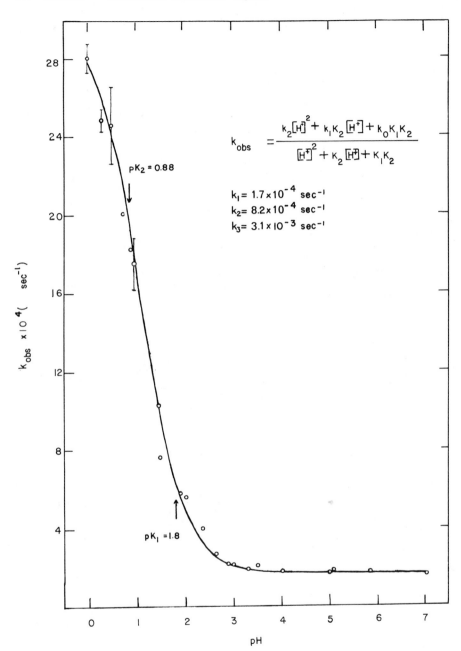

$$k_{obs} = \frac{k_2[H^+]^2 + k_1 K_2 [H^+] + k_0 K_1 K_2}{[H^+]^2 + K_2 [H^+] + K_1 K_2}$$

$k_1 = 1.7 \times 10^{-4} \ sec^{-1}$
$k_2 = 8.2 \times 10^{-4} \ sec^{-1}$
$k_3 = 3.1 \times 10^{-3} \ sec^{-1}$

$pK_2 = 0.88$

$pK_1 = 1.8$

$k_{obs} \times 10^4 (\ sec^{-1})$

pH

Figure 3. Plot of k_{obs} vs. pH for the dissociation of 2-(AmPm)(NH₃)₅Ru(III). pK₁ has been determined to be 1.79 by independent spectrophotometric titration. pK₂ is derived from the kinetic data.

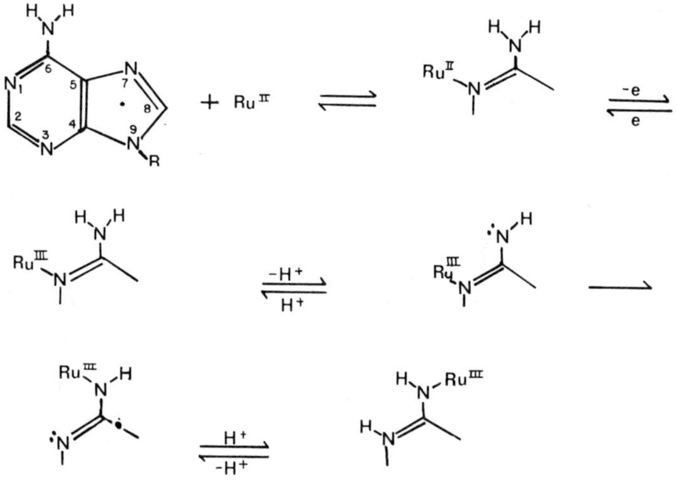

Figure 4.   Reaction mechanism for the formation of exocyclically coordinated complexes of adenosine and cytidine. Step 4 is taken to be rate-limiting.

where K^{II} is the acid dissociation constant for the conjugate acid of the Ru(II) form (with the proton presumably at N-3 or N-7) and K^{III} is the equilibrium constant for the loss of a proton from the exocyclic amine of the Ru(III) complex. Electrochemical data fitted to this equation (see Figure 5) determines the actual pK_a for $1-[Ado(NH_2)_5Ru(III)]$ to be 8.2. The corresponding potential-pH curve for the model complex, $1-[(2-AmPm)(NH_3)_5Ru(III)]$, is similar with $pK^{II}=1.8$ and $pK^{III}=8.9$. The higher E^o value of the 2-AmPm complex (363 mV) is consistent with stronger retrodative bonding between Ru(II) and 2-AmPm than with Ado (342 mV).

Confirmation of the reaction mechanism is provided by kinetic data dependent upon the same pK_a for the N-1 coordinated ruthenium(III) complex (see Figure 6). Owing to the instability of $1-[(Ado)(NH_3)_5Ru(II)]$ and severe restrictions required of the oxidizing partner, isomerization kinetic rates were derived from cyclic voltammetric data using the method of Nicholson and Shain[68-70], after forming the N-1 coordinated Ru(II) complex at the electrode surface by electrolytic reduction of the N-6 bound Ru(III) species. Since the specific rates estimated by this method were independent of concentration, the rate law is taken to be first order in the complex.

The reverse (N-6 to N-1) linkage isomerization has also been studied and requires the metal to be in the dipositive oxidation state on the protonated (neutral) ligand. Previous electrochemical work determined the pK_a of $6-[(Ado)(NH_3)_5Ru(II)]$ to be 11.3, with deprotonation probably occuring at N-1. A plot of specific rate constants for the exo- to endocyclic movement of Ru(II) (as determined by the cyclic voltammetric method) versus pH shows that the kinetic pK_a value of 10.6 falls within the range of the thermodynamic value. The limiting rate of the N-6 linkage isomerization of $6-[(5'-AMP)(NH_3)_5Ru(II)]$ has been spectrophotometrically determined to be 1.6 sec^{-1} following reduction of the corresponding Ru(III) complex by either Cr(II) or Eu(II) over the pH range 1 to 5.[71] The electrochemical results indicate that this rate becomes insignificant in the pH range substantially above the pK_a. The activation parameters for this reaction when measured at pH 3 are $\Delta H^* = 86$ kJ/mol and $\Delta S^* = 43.5$ J/mol·K. Since both forward and reverse isomerizations can occur at neutral pH, the adenine coordination site on cellular nucleic acids should be determined by the environmental electrochemical potential and the relative efficiencies of the electron-transfer agents present.

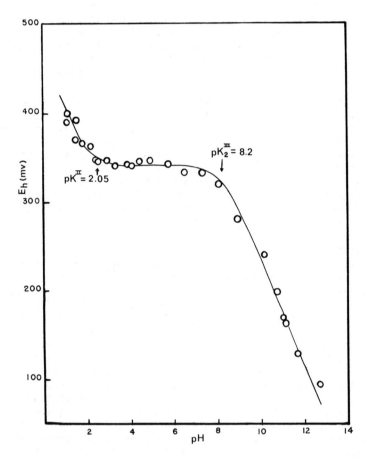

Figure 5.   Plot of reduction potential vs. pH for 1-(Ado)(NH₃)₅Ru(III).

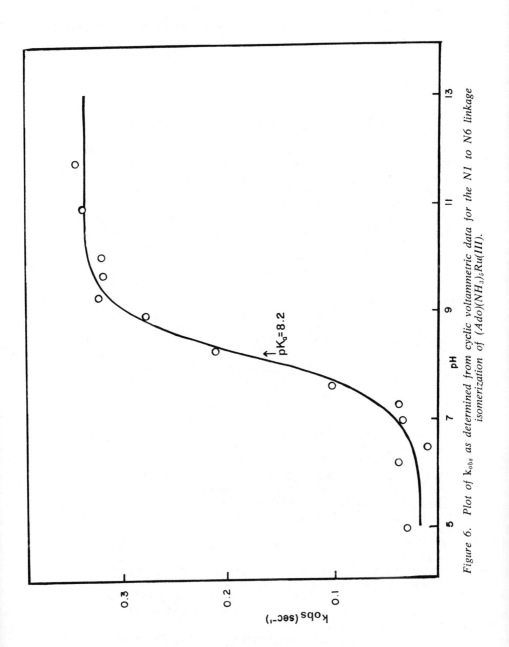

Figure 6.   Plot of k_{obs} as determined from cyclic voltammetric data for the N1 to N6 linkage isomerization of $(Ado)(NH_3)_5Ru(III)$.

Acknowledgments   This work was supported by PHS grant
GM26390. Particular acknowledgement is made of the
substantial assistance provided by P.H. Fackler, A. Abelleira
and J. Lacava in the preparation of the manuscript.

Literature Cited

1. Clarke, M. J., Met. Ions Biol. Syst., 1980, 11, 231-83
and references therein.
2. Srivastava, S. C., Richards, P., Meinken, G. E., Som, P.,
Atkins, H. L., Larson, M. S., Grunbaum, Z., Rasey, J. S.,
Dowling, M., Clarke, M. J., ''Radiopharm. 2, Proc. Int.
Symp., 2nd'', Sorenson, J. A., Ed., Soc. Nucl. Med., Inc.,
New York, 1979, pp. 265-74.
3. Clarke, M. J., in ''Inorganic Chemistry in Biology and
Medicine'', Martell, A. E., Ed., Am. Chem. Soc., Washington,
D.C. 1980, pp. 157-80.
4. Tanabe, M., Radioisotopes, 1976, 25, 44.
5. De C.T. Carrondo, M.A.A.F., Griffith, W.P., Hall, J P.,
Skapski, A.C., Biochem. Biophys. Acta., 1980, 627, 332-334,
and references therein.
6. Clarke, M. J., Rev. Inorg. Chem., 1980, 2, 27-52.
7. Dwyer, F. P., Mayhew, E., Roe, E. M. F., Shulman, A.,
Brit. J. Cancer, 1965, 19, 195.
8. Clarke, M. J., Inorg. Chem., 1980, 19, 1103.
9. Clarke, M. J., Bitler, S., Rennert, D., Buchbinder, M.,
Kelman, A. D., J. Inorg. Biochem., 1980, 12, 79-87.
10. Taube, H., Comments in Inorg. Chem., 1981, 1, 17-31.
11. Kelman, A. D., Clarke, M. J., Edmonds, S. D., Peresie, H.
J., J. Clin. Hematol. Oncol., 1977, 7, 274.
12. Yasbin, R. E., Matthews, C. R., Clarke, M. J., Chem.
Biol. Interact., 1980, 31, 355-65.
13. Giraldi, T., Sava, G., Bertoli, G., Mestroni, G.,
Zassinovich, G., Cancer Res., 1977, 37, 2662-66.
14. Durig, J. R., Danneman, J., Behnke, W. D., Mercer, E. E.,
Chem. Biol. Interact., 1976, 13, 287.
15. Khan, B. T., Mehmood, A., J. Inorg. Nucl. Chem., 1978,
40, 1938-9.
16. Farrell, N., de Oliveira, N.G., Inorg. Chim. Acta., 1982,
in press.
17. Scott, R. I., Gibson, J. F., Poole, R. K., J. Gen.
Microbiol., 1980, 120, 183-98.
18. Fiskum, G., Cockrell, R. S., FEBS Lett., 1978, 92, 125-8.
19. Tsuruo, T., Iida, H., Tsukagoshi, S., Sakurai, Y., Jap.
J. Can. Res., 1980, 71, 151-4.
20. Matsunaga, K., Okayama Igakkai Zasshi, 1979, 91, 141-52.
21. Coffey, K. F., Clarke, M. J., unpublished results, 1980.
22. Matthews, C. R., unpublished results, 1981.

23. Srivastava, S. C., Richards, P., Meinken, G. E., Larson, S. M., Grunbaum, Z., ''Radiopharm.: Stuct.-Act. Relat.'', Spencer, R. P., Ed., Grune and Stratton, New York, **1981**, pp. 207-23.

24. Cherry, M. J., Mackellar, W., Morre, D. J., Crane, F. L., Jacobsen, L. B., Schirrmacher, V., <u>Biochim. Biophys. Acta</u>, **1981**, <u>634</u>, 11-18.

25. Laliberte, J.-F., Crane, F. L., Clarke, M. J., submitted for publication, **1982**.

26. See citations in reference 1.

27. Mizukawa, K., <u>Okayama Igakkai Zasshi</u>, **1979**, <u>91</u>, 127-34 and 135-40.

28. Umezawa, H., Takita, T., <u>Struct. Bonding</u>, **1980**, <u>40</u>, 73-100.

29. Stern, P. H., Halpern, S. E., Hagan, P. L., Howell, S. B., Dabbs, J. E., Gordon, R. M., <u>J. Nat. Can. Inst.</u>, **1981**, <u>66</u>, 807-11.

30. Clarke, M. J., unpublished results, **1980**

31. Anghileri, L. J., <u>J. Nucl. Med.</u>, **1975**, <u>16</u>, 795.

32. Wenzel, M., Schenider, M., <u>Int. J. Appl. Radiat. Isot.</u>, **1981**, <u>32</u>, 5-11

33. Taylor, A. J., Macha, J., Wenzel, M., <u>J. Nucl. Med.</u>, **1980**, <u>21</u>, 63-6.

34. Schneider, M., Wenzel, M., <u>J. Labelled Compd. Radiopharm.</u>, **1981**, <u>18</u>, 293-301.

35. Hoffman, K., Riebelmann, B., Wenzel, M., <u>J. Labelled Compd. Radiopharm.</u>, **1980**, <u>17</u>, 421-30.

36. Schneider, M., Wenzel, M., <u>J. Labelled Compd. Radiopharm.</u>, **1980**, <u>17</u>, 1-20.

37. Wenzel, M., Schneider, M., Macha, H., <u>Int. J. Appl. Radiat. Isot.</u>, **1981**, <u>32</u>, 797-802.

38. Wenzel, M., Hoffmann, K., <u>Naturwissenschaften</u>, **1979**, <u>66</u>, 313-14.

39. Wenzel, M., <u>Strahlentherapie</u>, **1978**, <u>154</u>, 506-7.

40. Oster, Z. H., Som, P., Gil, M. C., Fairchild, R. G., Goldman, A. G., Schachner, E. R., Sacker, D. F., Atkins, H. L., Meinken, G. E., Srivastava, S. C., Richards, P., Brill, A. B., <u>J. Nucl. Med.</u>, **1981**, <u>22</u>, 269-73.

41. Schachner, E. R., Gil, M. C., Atkins, H. L., Som, P., Srivastava, S. C., Badia, J., Sacker, D. F., Fairchild, R. G., Richards, P., <u>J. Nucl. Med.</u>, **1981**, <u>22</u>, 352-7.

42. Anghileri, L. J., Ottaviani, M., Ricard, S., Raynaud, C., <u>Eur. J. Nucl. Med.</u>, **1981**, <u>6</u>, 403-5.

43. Oster, Z. H., Som, P., Gil, M. C., Goldman, A. G., Fairchild, R. G., Meinken, G. E., Srivastava, S. C., Atkins, H. L., Richards, P., Brill, A. B., <u>Radiology</u>, **1981**, <u>141</u>, 185-90.

44. Srivastava, S. C., Som, P., Meinken, G. E., Sewatkar, A., Ku, T. H., **1981**,

45. Kastner, M. E., Coffey, K. F., Clarke, M. J., Edmonds, S.

E., Eriks, K., J. Am. Chem. Soc., 1981, 103, 5747-52.
46. Graves, B. J., Hodgson, D. J., J. Am. Chem. Soc., 1979,
101, 5608.
47. Marzilli, L. G., Kistenmacher, T. J., Eichhorn, G. L.,
Met. Ions in Biol., 1980, 1, 179-250.
48. Marzilli, L. G., Prog. Inorg. Chem., 1977, 23, 255-378.
49. Hodgson, D. J., Prog. Inorg. Chem., 1977, 23, 211-254.
50. Gellert, R. W., Bau, R., Met. Ions Biol. Syst., 1979, 8,
1-49.
51. Thomson, A. J., Williams, R. J. P., Resolva, S., Struct.
Bonding, 1972, 11, 1.
52. Clarke, M. J., Taube, H., J. Am. Chem. Soc., 1974, 96,
5413-18.
53. Clarke, M. J., Perpall, H., Coffey, K. E., Anal.
Biochem., 1982, in press.
54. Zoltewicz, J. A., Clark, D. F., Sharpless, T. W., Grahe,
G., J. Am. Chem. Soc., 1970, 92, 1741-50.
55. Zoltewicz, J. A., Clark, D. F., J. Org. Chem., 1972, 37,
1193-97.
56. Romero, R., Stein, R., Bull, H. G., Cordes, E. H., J. Am.
Chem. Soc., 1978, 100, 7620-24.
57. Hevesi, L., Wolfson-Davidson, E., Nagy, J. B., Nagy, O.
B., Bruylants, A., J. Am. Chem. Soc., 1972, 94, 4715-20.
58. Morrissey, P. E., Clarke, M. J., unpublished results,
1982
59. Perrin, D. D., Dempsey, B., Sergeant, E. P., ''pKa
Prediction for Organic Acids and Bases'', Chapman and Hall,
New York, 1981.
60. Clarke, M. J., Inorg. Chem., 1977, 16, 738.
61. Coffey, K. F., M. S. Thesis, Boston College, 1981.
62. Maldonado, I., Clarke, M. J., 1981, unpublished results.
63. Sutton, J. E., Taube, H., Inorg. Chem., 1981, 20,
4021-23.
64. Taube, H., Surv. Prog. Chem., 1973, 6, 1.
65. Clarke, M. J., J. Am. Chem. Soc., 1978, 100, 5068-5075.
66. Faggiani, R., Lippert, B., Lock, C. J. L., Speranzini, R.
A., J. Am. Chem. Soc., 1981, 103, 1111.
67. McConnell, B., Biochem, 1974, 13, 4516-4523.
68. Nicholson, R., S., Shain, I., Anal. Chem., 1966, 38,
1406.
69. Nicholson, R., S., Anal. Chem., 1965, 37, 667.
70. Kuempel, J., R., Schaap, W., B., Inorg. Chem., 1968, 7,
2435.
71. Clarke, M. J., Kirvan, G.E. and Jian W., unpublished
results, 1979.

RECEIVED October 4, 1982

GOLD ANTIARTHRITIC DRUGS: BIOCHEMISTRY AND CHEMISTRY

Overview and Current Status of Gold-Containing Antiarthritic Drugs

BLAINE M. SUTTON

Smith Kline and French Laboratories, Philadelphia, PA 19101

Auranofin, (2,3,4,6-tetra-O-acetyl-1-thio-β-
D-glucopyranosato-S)(triethylphosphine)gold is a new
compound for treating rheumatoid arthritis (RA).
Gold has a long medical history. Gold compounds
were first investigated for RA treatment because of
the reported relief of joint pain in tubercular
patients being treated unsuccessfully with sodium
aurothiosulfate. Use of gold therapy and its
mechanism of therapeutic benefit have long been
controversial. However, clinical studies reported
in 1960 confirmed its antiarthritic value.
Auranofin has several potential advantages over gold
compounds in use today, most important is its route
of administration. It is clinically effective when
administered orally. Other gold compounds must be
given by injection. Auranofin's unique therapeutic
properties may be due in part to physical and
chemical characteristics which differ markedly from
those of currently used agents.

Excellent studies of the interaction of platinum
compounds with biologically important small and
macromolecular species have been reported both in this
volume and elsewhere (1). Consequences of these
observations have been associated with proposed modes of
antineoplastic action of cis-platinum (II) compounds. The
relatively recent discovery of this new class of antineoplastic agents (2) has led to an intensification of research
into the therapeutic potential of transition metal
compounds. It is surprising that the intensity of
scientific zeal directed towards this class of
antineoplastic agents has not focused on gold compounds,
probably one of the first metals to be used in treatment of

0097-6156/83/0209-0355$06.00/0
© 1983 American Chemical Society

disease and one that still holds a prominent position as a
specific therapeutic form for treatment of active rheumatoid
arthritis (RA).

History

    Gold unlike platinum is an ancient metal and has a long
medical history. It was probably one of the first to
attract the attention of man, because it is one of the few
that existed in the elemental state in nature. Being
relatively inert it retains its luster and does not tarnish
on exposure to air. Since pure gold was too soft to form
useful implements, primitive man valued gold for ornamental
purposes. The ancient Egyptians obtained their gold in
alluvial diggings from the sand and gravel in several
districts between the Nile and the Red Sea, the Nubian
area. The 'Rameside papyrus', the oldest map in the world,
locates these districts (3). Ornamental gold became a sign
of chieftainship and remains today as evidence of personal
wealth. Its acquisition has enslaved unknown numbers of
people from ancient to modern times and has motivated
unbelievable acts of violence and crime: these lines from
the Greek writer Phyoclides (4).
    "Gold and silver are injurious to mortals: gold is the
    source of crime, the plague of life and ruin of all
    things. Would be that thou were not such an attractive
    scourge: because of these arise robberies, homicide,
    brothers are maddened against brothers and children
    against parents".
The biological mystique attributed to gold in history
equaled and possibly surpassed its monetary attraction (5).
The Egyptian Sun God Ra in the Pyramid Age was believed to
be the procreator of kings. The liquid of Ra, the gold of
the gods and goddesses, flowed in their veins and gave them
strength and endurance. Search for the golden liver of life
was prevalent in ancient India and Persia. Thus there is
little wonder that gold easily occupied a magically honored
place when it was considered for therapeutic purposes.
Older races respected its curative power when laid upon
parts of the body with suitable incantations or worn as
rings or amulets. Its golden color identified it as a
remedy for jaundice "the Golden Disease" among the Hindus
and later the Greeks, southern Persians and Germans (6).
    As early as 2500 BC the Chinese employed gold for
biological benefit (7). Ancient Arabic physicians also
record its benefit. Gold was revered in medieval medicine
and held an honored place in pharmacopoeias of those days.
Pliney describes manifold efficacious uses of gold in
wounded persons, to ward off sorcerous curses; in ashen form

to cure fistulas and discharges, putrid ulcers and sores; boiled in honey as a purgative liniment (5). Gold in some form has been recommended as a panacea for all diseases from the 8th Century by Abn Moussa the Wise to as recently as 1500 AD by Paracelsus (7). Homeopathic medicine in the 18th and 19th century valued the benefit of gold therapy (8). Hahnemann praised the virtue of gold in homeopathy, published a pharmacodynamic study of powdered gold and in association with ten other physicians experienced and described bizarre biological responses after the ingestion of triturated gold leaf (aurum foliatium). He also reported in 1879 treatment of a 55 year old women with bacterial endocarditis, noting improvement in the heart as well as the joints, freed of rheumatism.

Robert Koch reported the first experimental antibacterial activity of gold salts in 1890 (9). He described in vitro antitubercular activity of gold cyanide at a dilution of 1 to 2 million, a concentration much too dilute to invoke cyanide ion as the active agent. When he later failed to demonstrate antitubercular activity with gold salts in experimental animals, Koch terminated his work with gold compounds. However his observations did not go unnoticed. Different physicians administered inorganic gold salts often intravenously in large doses and reported beneficial results in skin tuberculosis, syphilis (10), lupus vulgaris (11) and pulmonary tuberculosis (12). As one might suspect in many of these cases the treatment was probably more terminal than the disease. The introduction of gold sodium thiosulfate (Sanochrysin) by Mollgaard in 1924 rekindled use of gold compounds for tuberculosis therapy (13) and sparked what P. D'Arcy Hart termed the "Gold Decade" (1925-1935) (14). The mystique of gold therapy again caught the public imagination. Different chemical forms (15) and smaller dosages reduced fatalities due to the therapy. However toxicity and inconclusive therapeutic benefit contributed to a decline in the use of gold compounds for treatment of tuberculosis. Although the real value of gold therapy for tuberculosis may never be answered, the clinical benefit, historically, did not outweigh the persistent risk associated with its toxicity.

Development of Chrysotherapy for Rheumatoid Arthritis

Lande first used aurothioglucose (Solganal, Schering) to treat non-tuberculosis infections (16). He treated a group of 39 patients with bacterial endocarditis and various poorly defined diseases including rheumatic fever. His observation of the significant loss of joint pain in these patients and recommendations for trial studies in chronic arthritis led J. Forestier to investigate the use of gold

compounds for treatment of rheumatoid arthritis (17). Six
years later (1935) Forestier reported evidence of the
beneficial action of gold salts on the evolution of chronic
rheumatoid arthritis (18). In his initial studies he used
sodium aurothiopropanolsulfonate (Allochrysine). Later he
used other preparations sodium aurothiomalate (Myochrysine),
aurothioglucose (Solganal) and others. He recommended that
the preparations be administered intramuscularly and noted
that colloidal gold, gold chloride and gold cyanide were not
useful.

Chrysotherapy was not readily accepted in the United
States. As late as 1934, Cecil reported that drugs played a
relatively minor role in treatment of rheumatoid arthritis
and that his experience with gold compounds had never shown
striking results (19).

The first report of the successful use of gold compounds
in treating arthritis induced in experimental animals was
that of Sabin and Warren in 1940 (20). Intravenous
injection of a pleuropneumonia-like microorganism (Type B
strain) with a particular affinity for the joints of the
animals (mice) produced a migratory and progressive
polyarthritis leading to ankylosis in two to four months. A
variety of gold(I) thiolates exhibited prophylactic
prevention as well as therapeutic reversal of the arthritic
syndrome in the infected mice. It was noted that the
infectious agent was cleared quickly from the vascular
system and localized in the joint areas. Gold(I) thiolates
did not inhibit growth of the pleuropneumonia-like
microorganism in vitro leading the authors to hypothesize an
in vivo activation of the reticuloendothelial system as a
mechanism whereby the gold salts produced their effects.
Gold(III) in the form of sodium tetrachloroaurate was
somewhat beneficial at a near toxic dose level. Colloidal
gold was ineffective. Freyberg and co-workers later
reproduced this arthritic mouse model and demonstrated that
the beneficial effects of gold coordination compounds
resided in the gold containing complexes and not in the
thiol ligand (21). Sodium aurothiomalate was 100% protective
when administered intravenously at a dose of 2 or 4 mg/mouse
on alternate days until 9 or 10 injections had been given.
Sodium thiomalate was ineffective at doses as high as 15.4
mg administered in the same regimen. Sodium succinimide
aurate, a compound not containing a thiol ligand was equally
effective as sodium aurothiomalate, raising further question
as to the role of the thiol ligand in the therapeutic
response.

Conflicting reports of the benefit of chrysotherapy in
rheumatoid arthritis motivated Sir Stanley Davidson of the
Empire Rheumatism Council (Great Britain) to plan for a

multicenter, double blind study of the treatment in 1938.
The Second World War took priority so that the study was not
initiated until 1957. The first report of this study in
1960 stated that "by all criteria except radiological,
patients with acute rheumatoid arthritis treated, over a
period of five months, with a total treatment dose of 1g of
sodium aurothiomalate fared better than those treated with a
total dose of 0.01g of the same substance given in a double
blind trial over the same period" (22). The final report as
recent as 1961 compared the results of 77 patients treated
with a five months course of twenty weekly gold injections
with 81 controls followed for a total of 30 months. In
general "gold treated patients fared better than controls
from the third to sixth month and on the whole up to month
18, one full year after completion of the 5 month course of
treatment. Thereafter gold treated patients deteriorated to
an appreciable extent although they retained some small
advantage over controls at 30 months". No significant
radiological difference was found between the gold treated
and control groups (23). Data from this study supported the
efficacy of chrysotherapy in patients with rheumatoid
arthritis but did not describe a dosage regimen that was
consistent with a reliable clinical response.

Current Applications

Although the report of the Empire Rheumatism Council
established the benefit of gold therapy, it was only
subsequent to the rise and fall of the corticosteroid
arthritic panacea period (24) that rheumatology reevaluated
gold preparations as major therapeutic modalities for RA
(25). Recent studies have presented radiological evidence
that gold therapy slows and often terminates the progress of
degenerative joint changes associated with the disease
process (26). However there is yet no universal agreement
upon the patient population that should receive
chrysotherapy, the most appropriate time to initiate therapy
nor the most appropriate dosage regimen. There also does
not appear to be a correlation between blood gold levels and
a therapeutic response. The degree of allowable side effect
severity for continued therapy is unresolved and the
mechanisms of the antiarthritic activity of gold compounds
are receiving continued but not necessarily conclusive
attention. However, it is now accepted that benefit of gold
therapy outweighs the risk associated with its use and that
low maintenance therapy is appropriate in those patients who
have responded to treatment (27).

Since the Report of the British Rheumatism Council,
there has been little change in the chemical forms of gold

used to treat RA (sodium aurothiomalate and aurothioglucose) in the United States. However, there have been notable modifications of the dosage regimens employed with the intent of decreasing toxic reactions and increasing therapeutic responses. The present conventional treatment procedure involves an initial intramuscular injection of a gold compound containing 10 mg of gold. This initial small dose identifies those patients that might be hypersensitive to gold therapy and should not continue treatment. Thereafter the dose is increased stepwise in the next two to three weeks to 25 mg and 50 mg (based on Au content of the compound). After a dose level of compound containing 50 mg of gold has been reached, it is continued for twenty weeks until a total of 1g of gold has been administered. If a clinical response occurs, weekly dosing is gradually changed to a maintenance regimen consisting of a single monthly injection of compound containing 50 mg of gold (28) .

Serum gold levels in patients on this therapeutic regimen are quite variable reaching 4 to 8 ug/ml after the injection and falling off to 0.75 to 1.25 ug/ml when the gold compounds are administered on a monthly bases. Lorber (29) has claimed that a more enhanced and prolonged clinical response can be obtained if the gold compounds are administered at weekly doses sufficient to maintain a steady state serum gold level of 3 ug/ml, however, correlation of serum gold levels with clinical response has been challenged repeatedly (28). Gold thiolates comprise the major class of gold compounds used today to treat RA, sodium aurothiomalate, Myochrisine (1), and aurothioglucose, Solganal (2), being the drugs of choice in the United States. The former is administered as an injectable aqueous solution and the latter as an injectable suspension in oil.

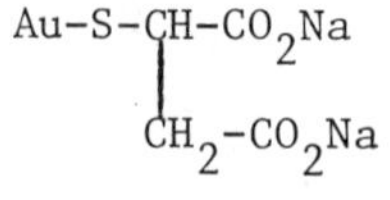

Au–S–CH–CO$_2$Na
|
CH$_2$–CO$_2$Na

1

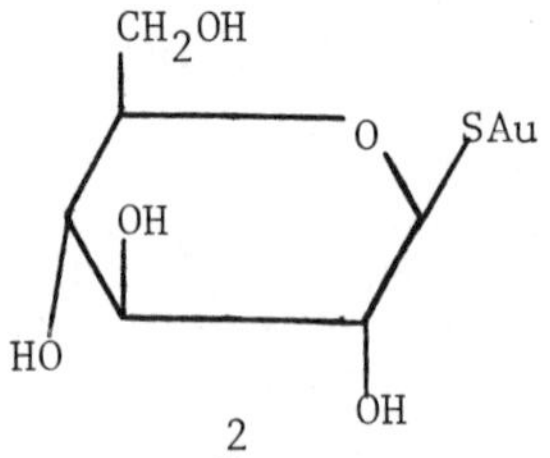

2

New Developments

The mechanisms whereby gold(I) compounds arrest
progression of the disease syndrome in RA are not well
understood. Leibfarth and Persellin in a recent review
highlight this fact (30). They evaluated the antimicrobial,
antiinflammatory, antienzyme and immunosuppressive
activities reportedly observed with different injectable
gold products. Their conclusions favored antiinflammatory
and antienzyme activities of gold(I) compounds as being the
best documented mechanisms involved in arresting the
progressive crippling processes associated with RA (Table
I). Interference with other proposed mediators of
inflammation (macrophage activation, release of mast cell
reactors, chemotactic factors, prostaglandin participation)
were considered in need of further study.

We reported previously on a series of phosphine gold
coordination compounds that produced antiarthritic activity
in adjuvant induced arthritis in rats when administered by
the oral route (32). All other gold compounds are effective
only when administered parenterally. One member from this
group, (2,3,4,6-tetra-O-acetyl-1-thio-β-D-glucopyranosato-S)
(triethylphosphine)gold, auranofin (3), exhibited potent
activity of this type and is now undergoing clinical trial.

$$AcO \quad CH_2OAc \quad O$$
$$AcO \quad OAc \quad S-Au-P-Et_3$$

3

This compound differs from currently used gold thiolates
in that the gold(I) in the molecule is two coordinated
through thiol and phosphine ligands. This novel molecular
environment appears to endow auranofin with physical and
biological properties unique to gold compounds in current
therapeutic use. Auranofin exists as a monomolecular
species in the solid state and in solution as determined by
x-ray crystallographic studies and osmometric molecular
weight determinations (33, 34). Mossbauer spectroscopic
studies confirm both the monovalent state of gold in the
molecule as well as the monomolecular nature of the compound
(35). Earlier Mossbauer Spectroscopic studies have shown
that there is a linear relationship between isomer shift
(IS) and quadrupole splitting (QS) for two coordinate,
monovalent gold compounds which differs significantly from
that of trivalent gold (36). The plot in Figure 1 locates
aurothiolates, aurothioglucose and sodium aurothiomalate in
the lower region of that linear plot in an area where gold
is coordinated to two sulfur atoms, i.e. bis-(ethylenethio-

Table I

Inhibition of Enzyme Activity

by Gold Compounds, in vitro (30)

Enzyme	Enzyme Source	Compound	Molar Inh. Conc.
Acid Phosphatase	guinea pig peritoneal macrophage	Sodium Aurothiomalate	5×10^{-3}
	human synovial fluid		2×10^{-4}
β-Glucuronidase*	guinea pig peritoneal macrophage	Sodium Aurothiomalate	5×10^{-3}
	human synovial fluid		5×10^{-5}
β-Glucosaminidase	human synovial fluid	Sodium Aurothiomalate	1×10^{-4}
	plasma leukocytes		
Elastase	human leukocytes	Sodium Aurothiomalate	5×10^{-3}-10^{-4}
Cathepsin	human synovial fluid		4×10^{-4}
Collagenase	human leukocyte	Sodium Aurothiosulfate	1×10^{-2}

*Lewis et al. recently reported that sodium aurothiomalate (1×10^{-2}M) failed to inhibit β-glucuroni-
dase and β-glucosaminidase derived from mouse macrophages (31).

Reproduced with permission from Ref. 30.

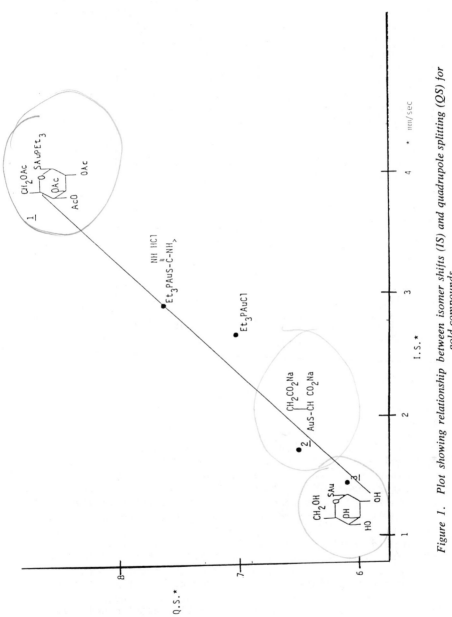

Figure 1. Plot showing relationship between isomer shifts (IS) and quadrupole splitting (QS) for gold compounds.

uronium)gold(I) chloride, etc. The close fit to the
two-coordinate line indicates that in the solid state these
compounds are two-coordinate through two sulfur ligands. In
contrast auranofin is located in upper region of the plot, a
location occupied by monomeric molecular species.

These data as well as nmr, EXAFS and gel filtration
studies indicate that gold thiolates, sodium aurothiomalate
and aurothioglucose, exist in polymeric states (37, 38,
39). Suitable crystalline forms have not been prepared to
investigate these molecules by x-ray crystallography. In
fact the structure of gold thiolates is better represented
by 4 rather than those structures described earlier.
Auranofin is a lipophilic, nonionic compound whereas gold
thiolates in general are hydrophilic (40, 41). The
characteristic physical

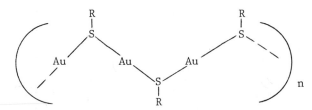

R= ($SCHCO_2CH_2CO_2$) $^{2-}$ Na $^{2+}$, sodium aurothiomalate
R= $SC_6H_{12}O_5$, aurothioglucose

4

properties of auranofin (lipophilicity, monomolecular,
non-ionic) are different from those of gold thiolates in
clinical use and may contribute to its novel biological
properties.

No exact experimental model of rheumatoid arthritis has
been developed. However in numerous biological assays
designed to interpret drug effect on models of or events
associated with RA, auranofin produced distinctly different
responses than gold thiolates. Auranofin inhibited the
development of experimentally induced adjuvant arthritis in
rats when administered orally. Sodium aurothiomalate
inhibited only when administered intramuscularly (31, 42).
Serum gold levels in animals treated effectively with
auranofin were approximately one third of those treated with
sodium aurothiomalate. Kidney retention of gold in the
sodium aurothiomalate animals was ten or more times that of
auranofin treated animals. Thus auranofin produced
antiarthritic activity in this arthritic animal model after
oral administration at lower serum concentrations than those
required by sodium aurothiomalate with much less kidney gold
retention.

Gold in the blood following the administration of sodium aurothiomalate is associated primarily with proteins in the serum. In contrast gold from oral administration of auranofin is equally distributed between the cellular components and serum proteins of the blood during the 24-48 hr. period after administration./After seventy hours auranofin gold is also localized in the serum proteins (43). The biological significance of the property has not been interpreted.

Tissue damage present in RA is attributed in part to action of lytic lysosomal enzymes released by phagocytic cells in inflammed tissue. Auranofin inhibits the release of lysosomal enzymes from phagocytizing leukocytes at micromolar concentrations (1-10 uM) (44, 45). It did not produce leukocyte cytotoxicity nor inhibition of cell free lysosomal enzyme activity at these effective concentrations. Sodium aurothiomalate, aurothioglucose and sodium aurothiosulfate did not exhibit this potent activity.

The etiology and pathogenesis of RA are unknown, however both humoral and cell mediated immune responsiveness are thought to play a role in the pathogenesis of chronic inflammation (46, 47). Auranofin has been shown to suppress humoral immunity (antibody production) in assay systems in which sodium aurothiomalate was either ineffective or stimulated antibody production (48). In other studies both auranofin and sodium aurothiomalate were shown to be capable of stimulating low-level delayed hypersensitivity in mice but only auranofin was capable of restoring immunosuppressed (methotrexate) cell mediated immunity (49). These contrasting immunopharmacological properties of auranofin, suppression of humoral immunity and enhancement of cell mediated immunity, appear ideally suited to correct immunological abnormalites observed in RA (hyperactive humoral immunity, suppressed cell mediated immunity).

Unlike the transition elements, copper and iron, which are normal body constiuents, gold does not have a well defined transport, storage or enzyme function within the body. Gold thiolate compounds used clinically to treat RA have limiting side effect liability, i.e. mild dermatitis, proteinurea, nephrosis, exfoliative dermatitis, leukopenia, thrombocytopenia. Auranofin, first studied clinically by Finkelstein (50) and Berglof (51), is now undergoing extensive clinical evaluation. The results of its use in treatment of 1200 RA patients for periods up to 3 years have been reported to the Food and Drug Administration. Both symptomatic and serological improvement was seen in patients after six months treatment. A dose of 6mg/day of drug was observed to be safe and effective. Side effects requiring

discontinuance of therapy have been minimal, about 10%. The
most prevalent of these were mild diarrhea and skin rash.
The majority of patients showing these symptoms continued
treatment without further complications. Data collected to
date indicate that auranofin is a safe and effective form of
chrysotherapy for treatment of RA. It has several potential
advantages: oral dose form, no pain from injection, no
nitritoid reaction, potential low tissue accumulation of
gold (52).

Future Applications

     As a result of auranofin, chrysotherapy promises to find
a new position in the treatment of RA. Continued research
into its mechanism of action is necessary. Development of
more effective gold agents should be the object of continued
attention which will require extensive comparative
laboratory and clinical study with heavy research investment.
     Metal containing compounds are attracting increasing
attention as antineoplastic agents. Cisplatin is
established as useful therapy for treatment of testicular
and ovarian tumors, although associated severe side effects
limit the doses that may be given to patients. Work is
underway to develop less toxic, equally efficacious agents
(53). Palladium (II) complexes recently have been reported
to exhibit antineoplastic potential in in vitro studies, in
vivo activity has not been reported (54, 55). Simon et al
observed in vitro inhibition of DNA synthesis and
antiproliferative activity with auranofin (56, 57). In
light of the low level of serious side effects observed in
clinical studies, these authors speculated on its
antineoplastic potential. Other workers have observed
inhibition of lymphocyte DNA synthesis with auranofin,
however their data indicate that the inhibition was a result
of interference with membrane transport activity rather than
direct action on DNA synthesis (58).
     Simon et al also reported antitumor activity with
auranofin using mouse lymphocytic leukemia P388 (59).
Studies carried out at the Southern Research Institute
indicated that auranofin at maximum non-toxic doses
exhibited minimal activity in the P388 system and that
continued treatment failed to reduce the tumor burden or
prolong animal survival time. In contrast cisplatin both
reduced tumor burden and prolonged animal survival (60).
     Although auranofin, itself, does not appear to have
potent antineoplastic activity, results obtained are
encouraging. Investigation of the antineoplastic activity
of other gold(I) as well as gold(III) compounds appears
justified. Gold(III) compounds may be more attractive in
light of the similar structural characteristics of

gold(III), platinum(II) and palladium(II) coordination
compounds.

Literature Cited

1. Prestayko, A.W.; Crooke, S.T.; Carter, S.K. "Cisplatin",
    Academic: New York, 1980.
2. Rosenberg, B.; VanCamp, L.; Trosko, J.E.; Mansour, V.H.
    Nature 1969, 222, 285.
3. Rickard, T.A. "Man and Metals"; McGraw Hill: New York,
    1932; Vol. 1, p. 219.
4. Hoover, H.C.; Hoover, L.H. Translation, "De Re
    Metallica"; (by Georgius Agricola, 1st Latin Ed. 1556)
    Salsbury House: London, 1912; p. 7.
5. Smit, P. P. Mine Med. Officers, 1968, 47, 90.
6. Ellery, R.S. Med. J. Aust. 1954, 41, 762.
7. Block, W.; VanGoor, K. "Metabolism, Pharmacology and
    Therapeutic Use of Gold Compounds"; Charles C. Thomas:
    Springfield, Ill., 1956; p.1.
8. Burnett, J.C. "Gold As A Remedy in Disease"; The
    Homeopathic Pub. Co.: London, 1879; p. 28, 127.
9. Koch, R. Dtsch. Med. Wochenschr. 1890, 16, 756.
10. Bruck, C. and Gluck, A. Moench. Med. Wochenschr. 1913,
    60, 57.
11. vonPoor, F. Dtsch. Med. Wochenschr. 1913, 39, 2303.
12. Junker, . Moench. Med. Wochenschr. 1913, 60, 1376.
13. Mollgaard, H. "Chemotherapy of Tuberculosis"; Nyt.
    Nordisk Forlag-Copenhagen, 1924.
14. Hart, P.D. Brit. Med. J. 1946, 2, 805, 849.
15. Nineham, A.W. Arch. Interam. Rheumatol. 1963, 6, 113.
16. Lande, K. Moench. Med. Wochenschr. 1927, 74, 1132.
17. Forestier, J. B. Soc. Med. Hop. Paris. 1929, 53, 323.
18. Forestier, J. J. Lab. Clin. Med. 1935, 20, 827.
19. Cecil, R.L. J. Am. Med. Assoc. 1934, 103, 1583.
20. Sabin, A.B.; Warren, J. J. Bact. 1940, 40, 823.
21. Preston, W.S.; Block, W.D.; Freyberg, R.H. Proc. Soc.
    Exp. Biol. Med. 1942, 50, 253.
22. Empire Rheumatism Council, Ann. Rheum. Dis. 1960, 19, 95.
23. Empire Rheumatism Council Subcommittee, Ann. Rheum. Dis.
    1961, 20, 315.
24. Kendall, E.C. "Cortisone"; Charles Scribner's Sons: New
    York, 1971; p 121.
25. Castles, J.J. "Arthritis and Allied Conditions";
    McCarty, D.J. Ed.; Lea and Febiger: Philadelphia, 1979;
    p 391.
26. Sigler, J.W.; Bluhm, G.B.; Ducan, H.; Sharp, J.T.;
    Ensign, D.C.; McCrum, W.R. Ann. Intern. Med. 1974, 80,
    21.
27. Bluhm, G.B. Seminars in Arthritis and Rheumatism, 1975,
    5, 147.

28. Zvaifler, N.J. "Arthritis and Allied Conditions";
    McCarty, D.J., Ed.; Lea and Febiger: Philadelphia,
    1979; p 358.
29. Lorber, A.; Simon, T.M.; Leeb, J.; Carroll Jr., P.E.; J.
    Rheumatol. 1975, 2, 401.
30. Liebfarth, J.H.; Persellin, R.H. Agents Actions, 1981,
    11, 458.
31. Lewis, A.J.; Cottney, J.; White, D.D.; Fox, P.K.;
    McNeillie, A.; Dunlop, J.; Smith, W.E.; Brown, D.H.
    Agents Actions, 1980, 10, 63.
32. Sutton, B.M.; McGusty, E.; Walz, D.T.; DiMartino, M.J.
    J. Med. Chem., 1972, 15, 1095.
33. Hill, D.T., Sutton, B.M. Cryst. Struct. Comm. 1980, 9,
    279.
34. Warren, R., personal communication, Mol. Wt. calcd.
    678.49; found 679 (acetone) 650 (CHCl$_3$).
35. Hill, D.T.; Sutton, B.M.; Isab, A.A.; Razi, M.T.;
    Sadler, P.J.; Trooster, J.M.; Calis, G.H.M. Manuscript
    in preparation.
36. Viegers, M.P.A., Ph.D. Thesis, Catholic University,
    Nijmegen, Netherlands, 1976.
37. Sadler, P.J. Struct. Bonding, 1976, 29 191.
38. Mazid, M.A.; Razi, M.T.; Sadler, P.J.; Greaves, G.N.;
    Gurman, S.J.; Koch, M.H.J.; Phillips, J.C. J. Chem. Soc.
    D. Chem. Commun. 1980, 1261.
39. Shaw, III, C.F.; Schmitz, G.; Thompson, H.O.;
    Witkiewicz, P. J. Inorg. Biochem. 1979, 10, 317.
40. Webb, R.L.; Wawro, J.E., Middleton, A. personal
    communication.
41. Baldinus, J.; Mentzer, M. personal communication.
42. Walz, D.T.; DiMartino, M.J.; Chakrin, L.W.; Sutton,
    B.M.; Misher, A. J. Pharmacol. Exp. Ther. 1976, 197, 142.
43. Walz, D.T.; Griswold, D.E.; DiMartino, M.J.; Bumbier,
    E.E. J. Rheumatol. 1980, 7, 820.
44. DiMartino, M.J.; Walz, D.T. Inflammation, 1977, 2, 131.
45. Finkelstein, A.E.; Roisman, F.R.; Walz, D.T.
    Inflammation 1977, 2, 143.
46. Zvaifler, N.J. "Arthritis and Allied Conditions";
    McCarty, D.J. Ed.; Lea and Febiger: Philadelphia, 1979;
    p. 417.
47. Miller, M.L.; Glass, D.N. Bull. Rheum. Dis. 1981, 31, 21.
48. Walz, D.T.; DiMartino, M.J.; Griswold, D.E. J.
    Rheumatol. 1979, 6, (S5), 74.
49. Walz, D.T.; Griswold, D.E. Inflammation, 1978, 3, 117.
50. Finkelstein, A.E.; Walz, D.T.; Batista, V.; Misradi, M.;
    Roisman, F.; Misher, A. Ann. Rheum. Dis. 1976, 35, 351.
51. Berglof, F.E.; Berglof, K.; Walz, D.T. J. Rheumatol.
    1978, 5, 68.
52. Heuer, M. personal communication.

53. Cleare, M.J. Platinum Metals Rev. 1982, 26, 33.
54. Newkome, G.R.; Kawato, T.; Kohli, D.K.; Puckett, W.E.; Oliver, B.D.; Chiari, G.; Fronczek, F.R.; Deutsch, W.A. J. Am. Chem. Soc. 1981, 103, 3423.
55. Graff, G.M. Chem. Week 1982, 130, 35.
56. Simon, T.M.; Kunishima, D.H.; Vibert, G.J.; Lorber A., J. Rheumatol. 1979, 6 (S5), 91.
57. Simon, T.M.; Kunishima, D.H.; Vibert, G.J.; Lorber, A. Cancer 1979, 44, 1975.
58. Finkelstein, A.E.; Burrone, O.R.; Walz, D.T.; Misher, A. J. Rheumatol. 1977, 4, 245.
59. Simon, T.M.; Kunishima, D.H.; Vibert, G.J.; Lorber, A. Cancer Res. 1981, 41, 94.
60. Shabel, F.; Laster, R.; Corbett, T. personal communication.

RECEIVED October 4, 1982

Ligand Exchange Reactions of Gold Drugs in Model Systems and in Red Cells

M. TAHIR RAZI, GABRIEL OTIKO, and PETER J. SADLER

Birkbeck College, Department of Chemistry, Malet Street, London, WC1E 7HX England

80 MHz ^{31}P NMR and 400 MHz ^{1}H spin-echo NMR are
used to compare and contrast reactions of aurothiomalate (Myocrisin) Et$_3$PAuCl, and Et$_3$PAu(TATG),
where TATG is 2,3,4,6-tetra-0-acetyl-1-thio-B-D-
glucopyranosato-S, (auranofin) with intact red
blood cells, glutathione in model reactions, and
dimercaptopropanol (dmp), an agent thought to be
useful for reversal of gold toxicity. The hydrophobic phosphine complexes readily penetrate cells,
and their exchange reactions are more rapid on the
NMR timescale than those of aurothiomalate. In red
cells, Et$_3$PAuCl is partitioned between GSH and a
second site, and (Et$_3$P)$_2$Au$^+$ is also formed at high
Au levels. Significant Et$_3$P release and oxidation
to OPEt$_3$ is observed inside cells only when dmp is
added. (Et$_3$P)$_2$Au$^+$ is not auranofin-treated red
cells. We also show that auranofin, when added to
whole blood, is partitioned between plasma and
cells. It is suggested that a key feature in the
molecular pharmacology of gold(I) is its ability
to transport, store, and release reducing equivalents (thiols and phosphines).

Gold compounds were originally brought into clinical use
accidentally for the treatment of rheumatoid arthritis (1,2,3).
However, controlled clinical trials (4) confirmed their effectiveness, and gold therapy ("chrysotherapy") is now considered to be
as good as that using any other drug for the difficult cases, and
one of the few that can lead to repair of joint tissue.
Currently, the most widely used gold drugs are gold(I) thiolate
complexes such as aurothiomalate ("Myocrisin") and aurothioglucose
("Solganal"), administered by intramuscular injection. These have
now been supplemented (5) by the orally-active complex (2,3,4,6-
tetra-0-acetyl-1-thio-β-D-glucopyranosato-S)(triethylphosphine)
gold(I) (auranofin), see Figure 1. The initial clinical pictures

0097-6156/83/0209-0371$06.00/0

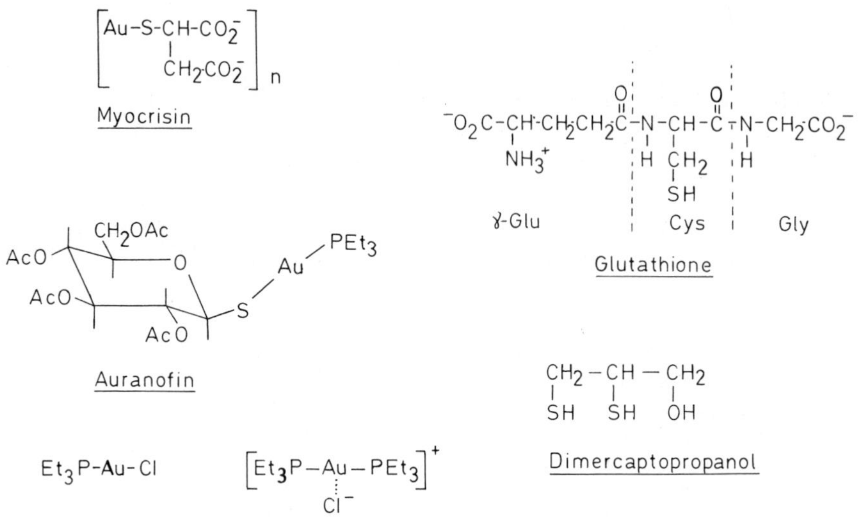

$$\left[\begin{array}{c} Au-S-CH-CO_2^- \\ | \\ CH_2CO_2^- \end{array}\right]_n$$

Myocrisin

$$^-O_2C\text{-}CH\text{-}CH_2CH_2\overset{O}{\underset{||}{C}}\text{-}N\text{-}CH\text{-}\overset{O}{\underset{||}{C}}\text{-}N\text{-}CH_2CO_2^-$$
$$NH_3^+ \qquad H \;\; CH_2 \;\; H$$
$$SH$$

γ-Glu $\qquad$ Cys $\qquad$ Gly

Glutathione

Auranofin

$$CH_2-CH-CH_2$$
$$|\qquad|\qquad|$$
$$SH \quad SH \quad OH$$

Dimercaptopropanol

$$Et_3P\text{-}Au\text{-}Cl \qquad \left[Et_3P-Au-PEt_3\right]^+$$
$$Cl^-$$

Figure 1.   Molecular structures.

emerging from use of thiolate and phosphine complexes appear to be similar, although responses seem to be earlier with auranofin and side-effects fewer.   The aim of chrysotherapy is usually to establish a constant serum gold level (ca. 15 µM with aurothiomalate administration) and to maintain it with further doses, although clinical responsiveness is not necessarily correlated with serum gold levels.

The results described here suggest that the effectiveness of gold in therapy may be related to its very strong preference for thiolate sulphur as a ligand compared to others that are available in the biological system.   Depletion of protein thiol groups in serum through oxidation is thought to be a contributing factor to connective tissue diseases such as rheumatoid arthritis (6,7). Polymeric Au(I) thiolates can bind further thiolates reversibly to form $[Au(SR)_n]^{1-n}$ species ($1 \leq n \leq 2$) with favourable exchange energies (8,9).   Au(I) avoids chelation sites, that might trap other metal ions with similar ligand preferences, through its strong tendency toward linear two-coordination.   However, there seems to be a certain "floppiness" in its coordination sphere.

The intriguing possibility arises that gold phosphine biochemistry may differ markedly from that of gold thiolates.   Many gold phosphines are hydrophobic and too little attention has been paid in the past to differences in metal ion affinity for ligands in aqueous compared to non-aqueous media. Since cells are "mixed solvents" the question arises as to the correct conditions under which to carry out model reactions. Little is known, too, about phosphine biochemistry. In this paper we describe the development of NMR methods for the observation of ligand exchange reactions on gold(I) and phosphine biochemistry directly in cells, and in comparison with analogous reactions in model systems.

Experimental

Solid Myocrisin, as an off-white powder, Au(I) thiomalate 0.3 glycerol .2H$_2$O, was the gift of May and Baker Ltd.(Dagenham). Auranofin, trademark 'Ridaura', was the gift of S,K and F Laboratories (Philadelphia).

Blood was drawn from male volunteers and placed in Sterilin plastic vials containing K$_2$EDTA as anti-coagulant. NMR experiments were usually carried out within the next few hours.

^{1}H NMR spectra at 400 MHz were obtained on the Bruker WH400 instrument of the ULIRS service, with the help of Mr. M. Buckingham, using 5 mm tubes. For SEFT spectra, 300 repetitions of a (90°-τ-180°-τ)-collect sequence with τ = 60 msec was used (10). The reference was DSS or TSS.

^{31}P NMR spectra at 80 MHz were recorded on the Bruker WM200 spectrometer at the MRC Biomedical NMR Centre, Mill Hill, using 15 mm tubes and ca. 4 ml of sample. Typically, 3 ml of packed red cells, previously washed twice with saline solution, were resuspended in 1 ml of D$_2$O-saline. Compounds which were insoluble in water were added in ca. 5-20 μl of MeOH. Spectra are usually the result of ca. 1 hour accumulations : 2000 pulses, 1.8 sec pulse repetition time, 16 K computer points, 45° pulse, and peaks are referenced to external H$_3$PO$_4$ (85% in H$_2$O)/15% D$_2$O.

Thiol Uptake and Exchange Reactions of Aurothiomalate ("Myocrisin")

Model systems. Aurothiomalate is a 1:1 complex of Au(I) and disodium thiomalate. Many commercial samples are hydrated and also contain glycerol (8). EXAFS, Mössbauer spectroscopy and gel permeation chromatography all indicate that the complex is polymeric both in the solid state and in solution (11,12,13). Linear AuS$_2$ coordination is attained through bridging thiomalate S atoms. It is possible that Au(I)-Au(I) bonds stabilise ring or chain structures, and there is evidence that such polymeric structures are flexible, changing in response, for example, to ionic strength changes (14,15). We have recently obtained evidence that up to 23% of gold in solid samples is structurally different to the remainder (14).

Further thiomalate, added to aqueous solutions of the 1:1 complex at pH 7, binds to Au(I) and all thiomalate is in fast exchange (ca. 10^3 sec^{-1}) until a ratio of Au(I):thiomalate of 4:7 is reached, then resonances for free thiomalate appear. It is still not clear whether $[Au(tm)_2]^-$ monomers are actually formed, or whether cluster species of the type $[Au_4(tm)_7]^{3-}$ exist. There are no reports of crystal structures of bis(thiolato)Au(I) complexes from aqueous solution, although a few well-characterised complexes have been isolated from non-aqueous media (16). Clusters may contain 3-coordinate Au(I), although a recent attempt to prepare such species lead to $[Au(I)_2M_2(II)_2SR_4]^{2-}$ heteronuclear clusters (M=Ni or Pd, SR=D-penicillamine) containing two coordinate AuS_2 and stabilised by short Au-Au contacts of 2.9Å (17). It is now known that three- and four-coordinate Au(I) phosphines exist and that there is a degree of "floppiness" in their coordination bonds (18). However P cannot bridge gold ions and so stabilize Au(I)-Au(I) bonds as S can.

Thiols with pK_a's > 8 exhibit slow exchange with $[Au(SR)_n]^{1-n}$ on the ^{13}C NMR time scale and we have determined exchange parameters for thiomalate, N-acetylcysteine and mercaptoacetate (8). The activation free energies are ca. 16 Kcal $mole^{-1}$ and activation entropies are negative, consistent with associative intermediates. Thiol displacement orders tend to follow the pK_a(SH) order: those with the lowest pK_a's bind most strongly at pH 7.

Using high field ^1H NMR we have now observed free and bound glutathione (GSH) when added to aurothiomalate solutions. This we were unable to do in previous ^{13}C experiments. Most of the thiomalate is displaced by two equivalents of GSH at pH 7, Figure 2, and integration of the Cys αCH resonance of GSH suggests that a species of stoichiometry $[Au(SG)_{1.5}]$ is formed as indicated by our previous measurements on other thiolates by ^{13}C NMR. Again, this emphasizes the instability of monomers relative to polymers and clusters. It is interesting to note that at a GSH:Au(tm) ratio of 1:2, peaks for bound tm are broadened but not those of free. This suggests that exchange reactions are occurring within cluster species.

Using SEFT NMR we can observe resonances from GSH in intact red cells and we therefore studied the entry of Au(tm) into cells. These studies will be reported in more detail elsewhere (19).

Entry of aurothiomalate into red cells. Figure 3 shows 400 MHz ^1H SEFT NMR spectra of GSH (ca. 2 mM) and other small molecules in red cells. Resonances for larger molecules such as haemoglobin which have short T_2 values disappear during the refocussing period (10). Upon addition of Au(tm), the GSH resonances for Cys αCH, βCH_2 and Gly CH_2 all decrease in intensity. We interpret this to mean that some gold enters cells forming $Au(SG)_{1.5}$ complexes, as above, in slow exchange with free GSH. Increasing the Au(tm) concentration from 0.5 mM to 1 mM causes little further change in the spectrum. It is possible that polymeric Au(tm) coats the surface of the cells preventing entry of more gold. This could be an important function of polymeric gold thiolates in vivo and could alter the antigenic determinants on lymphocyte cell surfaces. Red cells from patients treated with Myocrisin usually have a low gold

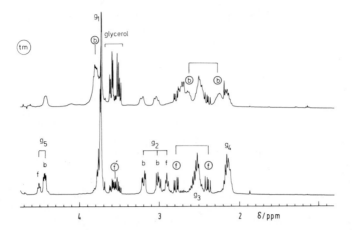

Figure 2. ¹H-NMR spectra (400 MHz) of glutathione (20 mM) in the presence of 2 equivalents (top) and 0.5 equivalents (bottom) of aurothiomalate in D_2O at pH* 7 and 298 K showing the displacement of coordinated thiomalate by GSH and the slow exchange of the latter between free (f) and bound (b) forms. Thiomalate CH and CH_2 resonances are circled. Key to the glutathione assignments: g_1, Gly CH_2; g_2, Cys CH_2; g_3, Glu γ-CH_2; g_4, Glu β-CH_2; g_5, Cys CH.

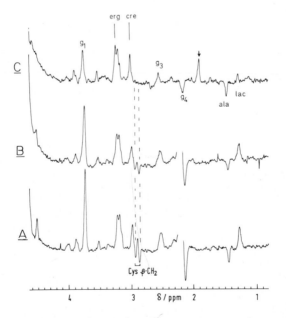

Figure 3. SEFT ¹H-NMR spectra (400 MHz). Key: top, 500 μM auranofin B; middle, 500 μM aurothiomalate (note the decrease in intensity of the inverted multiplet for Cys β-CH_2 relative to ergothioneine or lactate); and bottom, packed red cells 0.45 mL plus 0.05 mL D_2O–saline. The singlet near 2 ppm is from auranofin acetyls; other assignments are g_1, Gly CH_2; g_3, Glu γ-CH_2; g_4, Glu β-CH_2 (all GSH); erg, ergothioneine; cre, creatine; ala, alanine; and lac, lactate.

content, except for smokers (20)! Most gold in blood is carried
on albumin. We have yet to study Au(tm) in whole blood, but have
done so with auranofin, vide infra.

Reactions of Gold Phosphines with Thiols

These are relevant to both the oral absorption of gold and
entry into cells. We compare auranofin with Et_3PAuCl since reactions with thiols could lead to the same products if the Et_3P-Au
bond stays intact. Et_3PAuCl could also be a product of auranofin
reactions with HCl media in the stomach, although NMR investigations (21,22) suggest that slow deacetylation of the sugar is the
major reaction under such conditions. We have also studied the
bis(phosphine) species $(Et_3P)_2AuCl$. Not only is this orally-
active (23), but curiously also appears as an intermediate via
Et_3P transfer reactions both in some model systems and in red
cells.

Model reactions of gold phosphines. Figure 4 shows ^1H NMR
spectra of Et_3PAuCl in the presence of varying amounts of GSH at
pH 7. It is clear from the shift and separation of resonances for
the two Cys βCH_2 protons that GS^- displaces Cl^-, as deduced from
our previous ^{31}P NMR studies (24):

$$Et_3PAuCl + GSH \rightarrow Et_3PAuSG + Cl^- + H^+$$

A small amount of $(Et_3P)Au^+$
is also produced presumably via disproportionation of Et_3PAuSG.
It is interesting to note that the Gly CH_2 protons also become
non-equivalent suggesting that secondary interactions occur within
the Et_3PAuSG complex. The presence of Et_3P bound to Au also
appears to enhance thiol exchange rates. The Cys αCH ^1H resonance
is a single peak even with two equivalents of GSH present (βCH_2 is
more complex). We also observe (25) fast exchange of Et_3PAu^+ with
N-acetyl cysteine on the ^{13}C NMR time-scale, in contrast to Au(tm).
The high trans influence of phosphines (weakening of the trans
bond) has a parallel in Pt(II) chemistry.

The bis complex $(Et_3P)_2AuCl$, which is ionized in H_2O (24),
does not react rapidly with thiols, but is a good reducing agent
toward disulphides (24,25), due to the lability of one of the
phosphines which acts as the reducing agent. This lability is
neatly illustrated by the NMR spectra of $(Et_3P)_2Au^+$. In H_2O, Et_3P
exchange is slow and effects due to virtual coupling are observed
in ^1H and ^{13}C spectra, whereas in $CDCl_3$ or MeOD exchange is slow
only at low temperatures (25).

The choice of solvent presents a problem in the study of
thiol exchange reactions of auranofin. The clinically-used
crystalline polymorph, auranofin A, is soluble to only 20 μM in
H_2O and does not dissolve to the mM level on shaking with GSH
solutions, as does Et_3PAuCl. This suggests that GSH does not

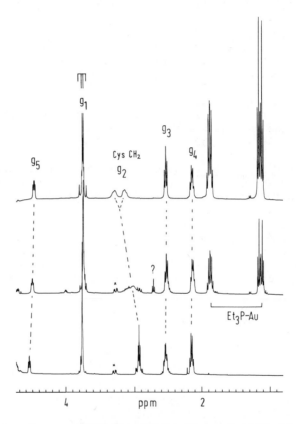

Figure 4. *¹H-NMR spectra (400 MHz) of Et₃PAuCl reacted with 20 mM solutions of GSH. Key to GSH: Et₃PAuCl molar ratios: top, 1:1; middle, 1:0.5; and bottom, 1:0. Final pH values were adjusted to pH* 7. Note the large shift of the GSH Cys β-CH₂ protons and AB coupling pattern for Gly CH₂(g₁) at 1:1 ratio. GSH is in fast exchange between free and bound forms at 1:0.5 molar ratio, but the Cys β-CH₂ resonances are complex and have yet to be analyzed.*

readily displace TATG. However, TATG is hydrophobic and therefore
not a good leaving group in H_2O! Using the polymorph auranofin B
(H_2O solubility 0.7 mM), we have observed some broadening but
little shift of the Cys βCH_2 resonance of GSH at auranofin: GSH
ratios of 1:1 to 1:4 in D_2O. This suggests that GSH exchange
occurs at intermediate rates, but that there is little displacement of TATG. Similar results were obtained for GSH-auranofin A
in $MeOD-D_2O$ solutions.

The exchange behaviour of TATG with auranofin is curious. At
0.2M concentrations the ^{13}C NMR spectrum in MeOH is a superposit-
ion of resonances for auranofin and added TATG, whereas the peak
for the anomeric C_1H proton is broadened beyond detection in 400
MHz ^1H spectra of similar solutions at 1:1 (10 mM) to 1:4 ratios
and a single set of averaged resonances is observed for the
remaining protons. It would appear therefore that the TATG
exchange rate increases with decrease in the concentrations of
auranofin and TATG. This is being further investigated.

Reactions of gold phosphines with red cells. $(Et_3P)_2AuCl$
does not appear to penetrate red cells, but when added to whole
blood, reacts readily with albumin, reducing disulphide crosslinks, so denaturing it (24).

Et_3PAuCl, on the other hand, rapidly enters cells and occu-
pies two sites (24). We have now been able to investigate the
titration curve in more detail. It can be seen (Figure 5) that
two resonances A and B for Au-bound phosphine are seen at low
Et_3PAuCl concentrations. Above 2 mM, a third resonance assignable
to $(Et_3P)_2Au^+$ appears. We had previously assigned resonance A at
40.1 ppm to $Et_3PAu-SG$ since its chemical shift is similar to that
in model reactions. However, since the population of Site B (42.1
ppm) saturates, this is more likely to arise from the GSH complex.
It is notable that site A is populated at Et_3PAuCl levels well
below the GSH concentration (ca. 1.5 mM in the cell suspension
used). We considered that site A might be due to Et_3PAuCl in the
membrane but when cells are lysed and the ghosts removed, both
resonances A and B are retained. Thus we observe a marked difference between cell and model reactions.

Confirmation of intracellular GSH binding was obtained by ^1H
SEFT studies, Figure 3: at 0.5 mM Au the Cys βCH_2 resonance disappears from the spectrum and the marked decrease in intensity of
the Gly CH_2 resonance indicates non-equivalence, as seen for model
reactions. It remains to be seen whether GSH protects oxyhaemo-
globin from Et_3PAuCl-induced spin-state changes (26) similar to
those we have observed with cytochrome c (27).

Auranofin also leads to the disappearance of the GSH Cys βCH_2
resonance on reaction with red cells, Figure 3. All the GSH in
the cell is evidently in intermediate exchange on the NMR time-
scale, thus the peak is broadened (shorter T_2) and it disappears
from the SEFT spectrum.

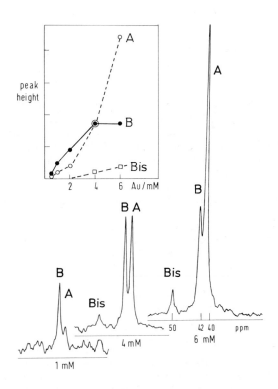

Figure 5. {¹H}–³¹P-NMR spectra (80 MHz) of Et₃PAuCl (left, 1 mM; middle, 4 mM; and right, 6 mM) on reaction with red cells (3 mL of packed cells) in D₂O–saline solution (1 mL) at 297 K. The inset shows the variation in peak heights with Au concentration.

Reaction of Auranofin with Whole Blood

^{31}P NMR spectra of whole blood containing 1 mM auranofin (20 μl of an MeOH solution added to 5 ml of blood) at average reaction times of 2, 3.25 and 4.25 hours, showed a single peak at 42.8 ppm. After 7 hr, the red cells were separated, washed three times with saline, resuspended in saline and NMR spectra recorded at 39.5, 40.5 and 41.5 hr. Spectra taken from both separated plasma and resuspended red cells showed single peaks at 42.8 ppm. From the peak intensities it could be concluded that auranofin was partitioned between plasma (45%) and red cells (55%). The ^{31}P NMR shift suggests that the species could be intact auranofin although other Et$_3$PAuSR species in cells may have similar shifts.

Previous studies, using radio-labelled auranofin (μM) incubated with rat and dog blood for 20 min, have also indicated partitioning between plasma (60%) and cells (40%) (28). The reported data appears to show that when Au is transferred to cells it leaves behind the TATG ligand (mostly bound to protein) and half of the Et$_3$P (as OPEt$_3$). We did not observe formation of OPEt$_3$ and, as yet, have no NMR information about TATG transfer, but further studies are in progress.

Dimercaptopropanol as an Intracellular Au-binding Ligand

2,3-Dimercaptopropanol (dmp, Figure 1, also called British Anti-Lewisite) is thought to be useful for the treatment of toxic side effects arising from gold therapy (29). We report here studies on reactions of dmp with red cells treated with Et$_3$PAuCl or auranofin.

^{31}P NMR spectra of these reactions are shown in Figures 6 and 7. It seems likely that dmp promotes migration of gold in Et$_3$PAuCl-treated cells into hydrophobic regions of the cell, probably as the complex CH$_2$(SAuPEt$_3$)CH(SAuPEt$_3$)CH$_2$OH. In a hydrophobic environment, Et$_3$P transfer would probably be facile, giving (Et$_3$P)$_2$Au$^+$. This may dissociate or act as a reducing agent (although there is no obvious intracellular candidate for reduction) leading to OPEt$_3$ and Et$_3$PAu$^+$, which in turn binds to thiol forming Et$_3$PAuSR. Hence we see an increase in intensity of resonance B after an initial fall and the intermediate formation of (Et$_3$P)$_2$Au$^+$. In the presence of one equivalent of dmp, equilibrium was reached after ca. 9 hr, by which time just under half of the phosphine had been converted to the oxide. Addition of a second equivalent of dmp causes further conversion, Figure 6.

No intermediate formation of (Et$_3$P)$_2$Au$^+$ is seen in the reaction of dmp with auranofin-treated red cells, perhaps another indication that little TATG is displaced inside the cells under these conditions although it is possible that the bis species is shorter-lived. After ca. 2.5 hr in the presence of one equivalent of dmp about half of the coordinated Et$_3$P has been converted to Et$_3$PO, Figure 7.

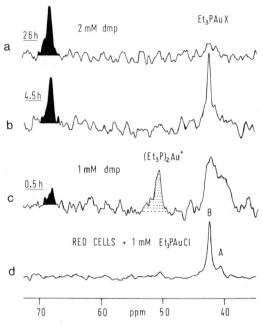

Figure 6a. {^1H}–^{31}P-NMR spectrum (80 MHz) of red blood cells that had reacted with 1 mM Et_3PAuCl for 3 h (a). One molar equivalent dimercaptopropanol (dmp) was then added and spectra were taken after 0.5 h (b) and 4.5 h (c). The reaction appeared to reach equilibrium after ca. 9 h at 297 K. After 24 h a second equivalent of dmp was added and 2 h later another spectrum (d) was obtained.

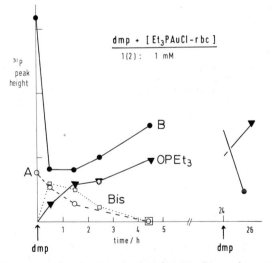

Figure 6b. Plot of peak heights from spectra shown in Figure 6a vs. time after dmp addition showing the formation of intermediates. Because the peak heights do not appear to account for all the phosphine present during the reaction, they may be subject to relaxation effects.

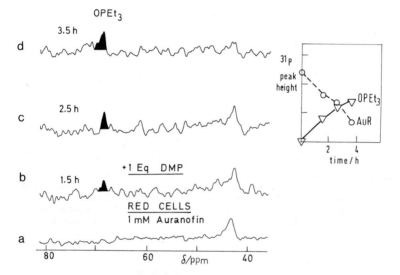

Figure 7. {¹H}–³¹P-NMR spectrum (80 MHz) of red cells (4 mL packed cells + 1 mL D₂O/saline) that had reacted with 1 mM auranofin (added in 20 μL of MeOH) for 9 h (a). One molar equivalent of dimercaptopropanol (dmp) was then added and spectra were recorded after 1.5 h (b), 2.5 h (c), and 3.5 h (d) at 297 K. The insert shows the variation of peak heights with time after dmp addition.

Dimercaptopropanol is insoluble in H_2O, and attempts to model the above reactions by addition of a MeOH solution of dmp to an aqueous solution of Et_3PAuSG (Et_3PAuCl + GSH, 1:1, pH 7) gives a yellow precipitate, probably the dmp-$(AuPEt_3)_2$ complex. We have previously studied a mixed Au(I), Au(III)-dmp complex by Mössbauer spectroscopy (30).

The ability of dimercaptopropanol to induce the formation of $OPEt_3$ is of biological interest since rapid degradation of auranofin to produce the oxide has been observed in rats and dogs (28). Once the phosphine is released, Au molecular pharmacology could resemble that of gold thiolate drugs, although there are two important differences. Firstly, gold may have been delivered to hydrophobic intracellular sites which gold thiolates could not reach, and secondly the phosphine, on release, may carry out biochemically significant reductions.

Finally, we note that it may be possible for strong oxidants to remove thiolate ligands even from 1:1 Au(I) thiolates. This may generate a highly reactive Au(I) ion. Experiments to explore this area are in progress.

Acknowledgments   We thank the MRC, SERC and ULIRS for the provision of NMR facilities. We also thank the Arthritis and Rheumatism Council and Smith Kline and French Laboratories (Philadelphia) for support. We are grateful to Drs. D. Hill and B. Sutton (S, K and F Labs.) for fruitful discussions.

Literature Cited

1. Sadler, P.J. Structure and Bonding (Berlin) 1976, 29, 171.
2. Shaw, C.F. Inorg. Perspec. Biol. Med. 1979, 2, 287.
3. Brown, D.M., Smith W.E. Chem. Soc. Revs. 1980, 9, 217.
4. Empire Rheumatism Council, Ann. Rheum. Dis. 1960, 19, 95.
5. Walz, D.T., DeMartin, M.J., Chakrin, L.W., Sutton, B.M., Misher, A. J. Pharm. Exp. Therap. 1976, 197, 1.
6. Haafaja, M. Scan. J. Rheum. 1975, 4 (Suppl. 7) 1.
7. Lorber, A., Simon, T.M. Gold Bull., 1979, 12, 149.
8. Isab, A.A., Sadler, P.J. J.C.S. Dalton, 1982, 135.
9. Isab, A.A., Sadler, P.J. J.C.S. Chem. Comm. 1976, 1051.
10. Brown, F.F., Campbell, I.D., Kuchel, P.W., Rabenstein, D.L. FEBS Lett. 1977, 82, 12.
11. Mazid, M.A., Razi, M.T., Sadler, P.J., Greaves, G.N., Gurman, S.J., Koch, M.H.J., Phillips, J.C. J.C.S. Chem. Comm. 1980, 1261.
12. Hill, D.T., Sutton, B.M., Isab, A.A., Razi, M.T., Sadler, P.J., Trooster, J.M., Calis, G.H.M. Submitted for publication.
13. Shaw, C.F., Schmitz, G., Thompson, H.O. Witkiewics, P. J. Inorg. Biochem. 1979, 10, 317.
14. Grootveld, M.C., Sadler, P.J. Submitted for publication.
15. Isab, A.A., Sadler, P.J. J.C.S. Dalton, 1981, 1657.

16. Bowmaker, G.A., Dobson, B.C. J.C.S. Dalton Trans, 1981, 267.
17. Birker, P.J.M.W.L., Verschoor, G.C. Inorg. Chem. 1982, in press.
18. Jones, P.G. J.C.S. Chem. Comm., 1980, 1031.
19. Otiko, G., Razi, M.T., Sadler, P.J., Isab, A.A., Rabenstein, D.L. Manuscript in preparation.
20. Graham, G. Personal communication.
21. Malik, N.A., Otiko, G., Razi, M.T., Sadler, P.J. Symposium on "Bioinorganic Chemistry of Gold Coordination Compounds" Philadelphia Nov. 16-17, 1981.
22. Smith, I.C.P. Symposium on "Bioinorganic Chemistry of Gold Coordination Compounds" Philadephia Nov. 16-17, 1981.
23. Hill, D.T. US Patent 4,057,630, Nov. 8, 1977.
24. Malik, N.A., Otiko, G., Sadler, P.J. J. Inorg. Biochem. 1980, 12, 317.
25. Malik, N.A. Ph.D Thesis, University of London, 1980.
26. Otiko, G. Ph.D Thesis, University of London, 1981.
27. Otiko, G., Sadler, P.J. FEBS Lett. 1980, 116, 227.
28. Intoccia, A.P., Flanagan, T.L., Walz, D.T., Gutzait, L., Swagzdis, J.E., Flagieollo, J., Hwang, B.Y-H., Dewey, R.H. "Symposium on Bioinorganic Chemistry of Gold Coordination Compounds", Pennsylvania Nov. 16-17, 1981.
29. Margolis, H.M., Kaplan, P.S. Ann. Intern. Med. 1947, 27, 353.
30. Calis, G.H.M., Trooster, J.M., Razi, M.T., Sadler, P.J. J. Inorg. Biochem. 1982, in press.

RECEIVED October 4, 1982

Gold-Based Antiarthritic Drugs and Metabolites
Extended X-Ray Absorption Fine Structure (EXAFS) Spectroscopy and X-Ray Absorption Near Edge Spectroscopy (XANES)

R. C. ELDER, M. K. EIDSNESS, and M. J. HEEG—University of Cincinnati, Department of Chemistry, Cincinnati, OH 45221

K. G. TEPPERMAN—University of Cincinnati, Department of Biological Sciences, Cincinnati, OH 45221

C. F. SHAW III and NANCY SCHAEFFER—University of Wisconsin–Milwaukee, Department of Chemistry, Milwaukee, WI 53201

Gold oxidation state and local structure in biologically relevant samples have been probed by X-ray absorption spectroscopy. XANES, X-ray absorption near edge spectroscopy, distinguishes gold(III) from gold(I) and gold(0), due to a 2p 5d transition which occurs only for gold(III). Also XANES apparently indicates the presence of any Au-P bonds in a sample. EXAFS, extended X-ray absorption fine structure, spectroscopy has been used with curve fitting techniques to show that the gold atoms in solutions of sodium gold(I)thiomalate (GTM) are coordinated to two sulfur atoms at 2.29 Å. Aurosomes, gold-containing lysosomal bodies formed in the kidneys of rats given chronic doses of GTM, have two sulfur atoms bound to gold(I) at 2.30 Å. Administration of gold(III) to rats results in rapid reduction and renal deposition of gold(I) containing aurosomes.

Considering that tens of millions of people suffer from rheumatoid arthritis (1) and that gold-based anti-arthritis pharmaceuticals have been proven to induce remission of this frequently crippling disease (2), it is surprising how little is known about gold biochemistry (3,4,5). Significant medical progress has been made in fine-tuning protocols for drug administration (chrysotherapy) (6) and a new orally-administered, gold-based drug, auranofin, has undergone clinical trials (7), yet the metabolism, mode of action, site of action, cause of toxicity, etc. of these drugs are not understood. A partial explanation may lie in the fact that gold is spectroscopically "quiet," that is gold has no useful NMR or ESR spectra (excepting rare gold(II) complexes (8)) and its visible-UV spectrum is either nonexistent or difficult to interpret in terms of structural implications. Another explanation might be that gold chemistry has been considered uninteresting. Two oxidation states, III and I, dominate the aqueous chemistry. Gold(I) complexes are frequently unstable with respect to disproportionation to gold(0) metal and gold(III). "Soft" ligands binding through sulfur and phosphorus stabilize gold(I). The structural chemistry of gold(III) is largely that of four coordinate square planar species, whereas gold(I) chemistry is dominated by two coordinate linear complexes. Recently,

however, an increasing number of three (trigonal) and four coordinate
(tetrahedral) gold(I) complexes have been characterized (9,10). Finally,
gold has no known biological function in the body (11). This simple
observation has had two results: first, it has reduced interest in gold
biochemistry and, second, it makes gold biochemistry difficult. There
are no evolved storage systems or transport mechanisms for gold. As a
result, once introduced, gold is found throughout the body, involved in
seemingly non-specific interactions.

For whatever reasons, gold biochemistry is not well understood.
Any attempt to improve the situation seemed to require the introduction of a new, more sensitive technique for the characterization of
gold complexes in a biological milieu. X-ray absorption spectroscopy,
XAS, (12,13,14) offered such a tool. This type of spectroscopy has
enjoyed a recent revitalization due to the advent of intense new sources
(13) and to the suggestion of a new theoretical basis for interpretation
(15). XAS may be divided into two categories: XANES (X-Ray
Absorption Near Edge Spectroscopy) and EXAFS (Extended X-Ray
Absorption Fine Structure). From XANES it may be possible to
discover oxidation state and specific ligands bound to the absorbing
atom (16) and from EXAFS one determines the types of atom bound,
numbers of neighbors and coordination distances. XAS has several
extremely attractive features. First, it is element specific, that is
absorption edges for each element are well separated and few direct
interferences occur. Second, the sample may be in any state. We have
obtained spectra from amorphous solids, solutions, gums, oil suspensions
and animal tissues. Third, the sample size is relatively small, typically
less than 50 mg of material is required. Fourth, the technique is
relatively sensitive, permitting examination of samples containing as
little as 1 ppm of the atom of interest. Fifth, the technique is
relatively non-destructive, causing much less radiation damage to
samples than might be anticipated (vide infra). Disadvantages are that
XAS does have limited sensitivity, that the information discovered is
limited in scope (vide infra) and that an extremely intense source of x-
rays is required.

Experimental Considerations for X-Ray Absorption Spectroscopy

A typical spectrum, that of a 0.015 M solution of sodium
gold(I)thiomalate, is shown in Figure 1 and a diagram of the experimental setup is given as Figure 2. The spectrum which is a plot of
$\log(I_o/I)$ versus x-ray energy may be discussed most easily in terms of
three regions. At the lowest energy is the pre-edge region. Here there
is general background absorption by all the atoms in the sample with
absorption decreasing as the energy of the incident x-rays increases.
This region is of no interest other than it provides a measure of the
background to subtract. At higher energy there is a sudden rise in
absorption known as the absorption edge. For gold compounds this
feature occurs at ca. 11.9 Kev. The absorption increase results once
the incident x-ray photons have sufficient energy to promote the gold
2p electrons into some available excited state or to ionize them. If a
2p electron is excited into a bound state having significant ligand

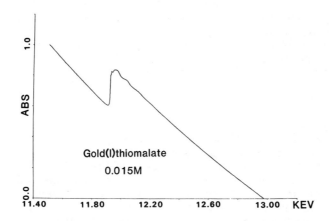

Figure 1. X-Ray absorption spectrum at the L_{III} edge of a 0.015 M solution of the drug Myocrisin (sodium gold(I)thiomalate).

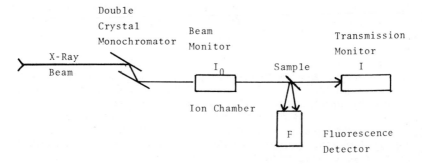

Figure 2. Schematic diagram of experimental setup to measure x-ray absorption spectra showing both transmission and fluorescence modes.

character, it may give a signal characteristic for the particular ligating atom. For example, vanadyl complexes give a signal typical of the "yl" oxygen (16). If, on the other hand the excited state is largely centered on the metal atom there may be an indication of the metal oxidation state. Both types of features occur in the near edge region for gold compounds. Beyond the L_{III} edge the 2p electron is ionized and excess energy is carried off by the ejected photo-electron. In this, the EXAFS region, which extends for roughly 1000 ev beyond the edge, there is again a gradual decrease in absorption with increase in x-ray energy. The decrease is not smooth, however. There is a series of wiggles, some of which can be seen in Figure 1. It is this wiggling modulation of the x-ray absorption which is known as EXAFS and which can be interpreted in terms of local structure around the absorbing atom. Most simply, it is due to interference phenomena arising from back-scattering of the ejected photo-electron by the neighbor atoms.

Apparatus Used to Measure X-Ray Absorption Spectroscopy. To obtain a sufficiently intense source of x-rays, we and most others use synchrotron radiation from an electron storage ring (13). All of the experiments described here have been performed at the Stanford Synchrotron Radiation Laboratories. Electrons are injected into the storage ring and held at high energy (typically 3.0 Gev). Since the electron path must be bent around the ring there is necessarily an acceleration applied and this results in the emission of synchrotron radiation. The spectrum of this radiation is continuous with the intensity peaking in the x-ray region. The x-ray beam is extracted from the storage ring through a series of beryllium windows and brought down a beam pipe where it is available for experimenters. The x-ray beam is extremely intense (several orders of magnitude more intense than the continuous spectrum from a high intensity x-ray tube) and intensity decreases slowly with time as electrons are lost from the storage ring.

The x-ray beam first is diffracted by a double crystal mono-chromator which passes a narrow energy band (typically a few ev wide) as indicated on the left of Figure 2. Next the beam intensity, I_o, is monitored by an ion chamber which absorbs a few percent of the beam to ionize a gas such as nitrogen or argon. The ion current which flows between charged plates is then a measure of beam intensity. Subsequently the beam passes through the sample where it is partially absorbed and, in transmission mode, on to a second ion chamber to measure I, the remaining intensity. In a fluorescence mode, a detector placed at $90°$ to the beam is used to measure the fluorescent L α x-ray which may be emitted in the relaxation of the 2p hole. Fluorescence yields are acceptably high (ca. 30% for gold); however, the emission is nearly isotropic, so a large area fluorescence detector is desirable. The fluorescence technique is more sensitive and so preferred for dilute samples.

Sample preparation is relatively simple. Solids are packed into a slot cut into aluminum or plastic sheet of 1 mm or less thickness. The area of the sample is larger than the beam which is normally 3 x 25 mm. The samples are covered front and back with a thin adhesive tape, typically Kapton. Liquid holders follow an equally simple design with injection ports on the top. For fluorescence detection the sample is placed at $45°$ to the beam.

Problems of Gold-Arthritis to be Considered

The questions which arise concerning the gold-based, anti-arthritis drugs may be categorized as arising from chemical or medical points of view. Chemical questions concerning the interactions of gold at the molecular level include: what are the structures of the drugs themselves (sodium gold(I)thiomalate - Myochrisin and gold(I)thioglucose - Solganol are both amorphous solids), what happens at the molecular level to these and other drugs in the body, do they proceed to a common metabolite and, most generally, what is involved in gold biochemistry? More medical questions include: what is the mode of action of the gold drugs, what is the site of action, what causes the toxic side effects such as renal failure and how can side effects be prevented or reduced?

We have attempted to answer several of these questions and will dwell here on our results concerning drug structure in solid and solution and on a somewhat detailed knowledge of the form of gold deposits accumulated in the kidneys.

Kidney Deposits - The Separation of Aurosomes. That gold concentrates in pre-existing lysosomal bodies called aurosomes has been known for some time (17). These electron-rich areas are seen on electron micrographs and considerable morphological characterization of them has taken place. However, the oxidation state of the gold was not known, nor were the chemical identities of the ligands (if any) bound to gold known. We have developed a method of separating aurosomes from bulk kidney tissue (18) in order to subsequently examine the aurosomes by XAS. The samples used here were generated by two different procedures. In one case 12 male Sprague-Dawley strain rats (200-225 g initially) were given weekly interperitoneal injections of 0.4 mg Au/Kg body weight as sodium gold(I)thiomalate in 0.9% saline solution for a period of 20 weeks. In another, similar rats were given an acute dose, 35 mg/Kg of body weight, of sodium gold(III)tetrachloride and killed by suffocation with CO_2 18 hours later. In both cases, the kidneys were immediately excised and chilled in ice cold homogenizing medium (0.25 M sucrose, 1 mM EDTA, 5 mM $MgCl_2$, 25 mM KCl and 50 mM Tris/HCl, pH 8.6). During all subsequent steps the tissues and resulting samples were maintained at $0-4°C$. The renal capsules were removed and connective tissue was cut away from the collected kidneys. The renal cortex was diced, washed, and patted dry to yield tissue, which was then homogenized in 4 ml homogenizing medium per gram of tissue using a Thomas glass/Teflon tissue grinder.

The homogenates were centrifuged at 600 g for 10 minutes to pellet the nuclear/aurosomal fraction (18). Because of their anomalously high density, aurosomes pellet with nuclei as shown by electron microscopy. To remove cell debris, the pellet was resuspended in 2.3 M sucrose/3.3 mM calcium acetate to two-thirds of the original volume and centrifuged at 40,000 g for 60 minutes. The pellet was resuspended in 1.0 M sucrose/1 mM calcium acetate to one-half the original volume, then centrifuged at 3000 g for 5 minutes. The pellet was twice resuspended in 0.25 M sucrose/50 mM Tris/HCl, pH 8.6 and pelleted by centrifugation at 3000 g for 5 minutes. The final washed pellet was resuspended in water, frozen at $-78°$ and lyophilized. The lyophilized sample contained ca. 200 μ g gold/g of sample. This technique provided two aurosomal samples from the kidneys of normal rats, one from rats given normal pharmacological doses of a currently used drug over an extended time and the other from rats given a single acute dose of a gold(III) compound and relatively quickly thereafter sacrificed.

XANES - Results and Interpretation

Figure 3 shows x-ray absorption near edge spectra, XANES, taken at the L_{III} edge for Au(III) and Au(I) complexes as well as for gold(0) foil. The plots are typical in that all the gold(III) complexes we have examined are characterized by a sharp spike at 11.920 (1) Kev, whereas the spike is missing from the edge spectra of gold foil and also of all the gold(I) complexes we have examined. These results may be interpreted most simply as follows: the L_{III} edge results from the excitation of a 2p electron. Above the edge energy, this electron is excited to the continuum. However, the 2p electron can also be promoted to a bound state subject to the selection rule, $\Delta \ell = \pm 1$. For a 2p electron this means transitions to s and d states are allowed (19). The electron configuration for Au(0) is Xe $4f^{14}5d^{10}6s^1$, that for Au(I) is Xe $4f^{14}5d^{10}$ and that for Au(III) is Xe $4f^{14}5d^8$. Thus, the gold(III) complexes have a vacancy in the 5d orbitals and the spike in the absorption edge may be ascribed to the $2p \rightarrow 5d$ transition. Since both gold(0) and gold(I) have a filled 5d subshell, this transition is not possible and the spike is not seen. Gold(0) metal has an extremely characteristic absorption spectrum above the edge as may be seen in Figure 3. These two sharp peaks at 11.945 and 11.967 Kev serve to differentiate gold(0) from gold(I). We have also obtained spectra from colloidal gold(0), generated in such a way to give particles of gold metal with a mean diameter of 64 nm (20), much smaller than the size of aurosomes seen in electron micrographs. The sol spectra are identical to that shown from gold foil in Figure 3. XANES for gold foil and the chronic dose sodium gold(I)thiomalate aurosomes are compared in Figure 4. Clearly the spike which characterizes gold(III) complexes is missing in the aurosome spectrum and thus the gold in these aurosomes has not been oxidized to gold(III). Similarly, comparison with the gold(0) foil spectrum indicates that aurosomal gold has not been reduced to colloidal gold(0). Thus, these aurosomes contain gold(I). (Gold(II) may be ruled out on several bases. First, it is extremely rare. Second, the gold(II) cytidine complex (8) which we have examined and which might be of biological relevance shows a spike similar to that for gold(III), a finding not too surprising in view of the Xe $4f^{14}5d^9$ electron configuration expected for gold(II).)

XANES for the gold(III) tetrachloride induced aurosomes and for gold foil are compared in Figure 5. Once again, it is clearly evident that the gold in these aurosomes is gold(I). Thus, the administration of gold(III) tetrachloride has been followed by rapid reduction to gold(I). It

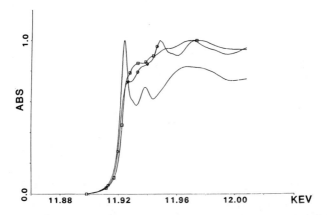

Figure 3.   XANES spectra for —, gold(III); □, gold(I); and ○, gold(0). The inflection point on the gold(0) edge is defined as 11.9212 keV.

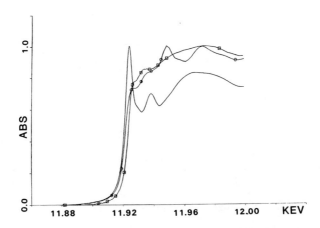

Figure 4.   XANES spectra for chronic dose gold(I) thiomalate aurosomes (□) showing that the gold is still in the + 1 oxidation state as compared with spectra of gold(0) (○); and gold(III) (—).

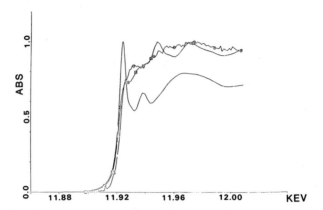

Figure 5.   XANES spectrum for aurosomes (○) produced by injecting gold(III) tetrachloride showing that reduction of gold(III) to gold(I) has taken place. Spectra for gold(0) (□) and gold(III) (—) are given for comparison.

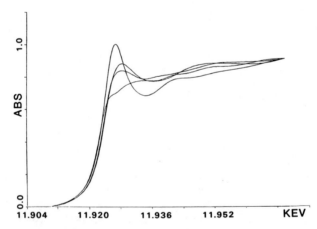

Figure 6.   XANES spectra for a series of gold(I) complexes with zero, one, two, and four phosphorus atoms coordinated to gold. The absorption peak at 11.927 keV increases as the number of bound phosphorus atoms increases. Compound identification given in text.

appears that gold(I) is the predominent oxidation state in a biological milieu.

Interestingly, these samples show little if any evidence of radiation damage. A spectrum taken during the first 10 minutes exposure to the beam is identical with one taken after several hours of x-ray irradiation. Also aurosomal samples reexamined one year after their original irradiation show no changes.

XANES as an Indicator of Ligating Atoms

If the spectral transition which causes a XANES peak is to an unoccupied molecular orbital which contains substantial ligand character, then that peak may be used to identify ligation by a particular atom. This situation is illustrated in Figure 6. XANES for four compounds are shown. In order of increasing absorbance at 11.927 Kev the compounds are sodium bis(thiosulfato)gold(I), triethylphosphine-gold(I)tetraacetylthioglucose (auranofin-Ridaura), bis(diphenylmethyl-phosphine)gold(I)hexafluorophosphate and tetrakis(diphenylmethylphos-phine)gold(I)hexafluorophosphate. Thus, the series progresses through zero, one, two and four bound phosphorus atoms and the peak absorbance increases accordingly. It appears that this peak which occurs at significantly higher energy than the gold(III) spike may be diagnostic of an Au-P interaction. All of the complexes containing phosphorus which we have examined show this peak. Auranofin can be recognized from its XANES Au-P peak, and since this orally administered drug is known to lose triethylphosphine during metabolism (21), the XANES peak may prove quite useful in determining at which stage the Au-P bond is broken.

EXAFS Results and Structural Interpretation

In order to extract useful information from the EXAFS region of an x-ray absorption spectrum considerable data manipulation is necessary. We have chosen to follow the methodology of Keith Hodgson and coworkers (22). First, the general background absorption due to non-gold atoms in the sample may be subtracted by extrapolation of the pre-edge absorption. Second, a smooth curve through the EXAFS portion of the spectrum is subtracted and the EXAFS normalized. This curve, shown for sodium gold(I)thiomalate solution data in Figure 7, is usually a cubic spline of two or three segments. The smooth curve represents the absorption which would occur if the absorbing atom was isolated from all neighbors. The resultant wiggles are then multiplied by $K^{\frac{1}{2}}$ and plotted versus K as shown in Figure 8. K is proportional to $(\Delta E)^{\frac{1}{2}}$ where ΔE is the difference between the energy of a particular point and the energy chosen as the start of the EXAFS region (usually 20-40 ev above the edge inflection point of some standard material such as gold foil). The advantage to working in K space is that the EXAFS now appears as a damped sine wave with a period related to the distance between absorber and back scattering neighbor plus a phase shift characteristic of the absorber-scatterer pair. The amplitude is related to the number of neighbors and the damping factor arises from

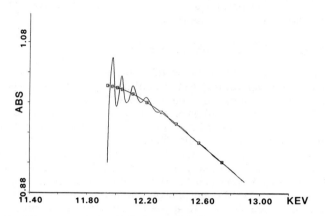

Figure 7. The pre-edge subtracted absorption data for a solution of 0.14 M sodium gold(I)thiomalate (——). The smooth curve (☐) is the three-part cubic spline which is subtracted to give the EXAFS.

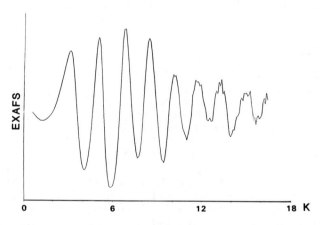

Figure 8. EXAFS times K² vs. K for a solution of 0.14 M sodium gold(I)thio-malate.

thermal and positional disorder, that is, all neighbors in all sites are not at exactly the same distances. If there are several types of neighbor atoms (or the same kinds of atoms but at different distances) then interferences or a beat pattern results in the EXAFS which most simply arises, from the sum of the individual sine waves. Thus, the EXAFS data in this form can show whether the absorber has only one type of neighbor. As shown in Figure 9, the maximum in the amplitude envelope occurs at different K values for different absorber–scatterer pairs. Three scatterers, widely different in atomic number, are used. In general, the peak in the amplitude envelope moves to higher K for higher atomic number scatterers, occurring ca. K=2 for nitrogen, ca. K=5 for chlorine and ca. K=9 for bromine. For a simple EXAFS pattern it is relatively easy to guess the approximate atomic number of the scattering partner. A comparison of Figures 9 and 8 will show there is relatively little difference between the EXAFS when the neighbors are changed from sulfur to chlorine. (The position of the maximum in the amplitude envelope will depend on the power of K used to weight the EXAFS. K^2 is used here.)

Fourier Transforms, Filtering and Curve Fitting. The EXAFS data can be Fourier transformed into R space. The resulting function which is plotted versus distance is not a true radial distribution function since the phase shift now results in a distance shift from true gold–ligand distance. A Fourier transform for sodium gold(I)thiomalate is shown in Figure 10. In practice, the phase shifts are evaluated from model compounds with known crystal structures. From the peak shape(s), position(s) and height(s) reasonable estimates may be made of the number and kinds of scatters and their distance(s) from the absorber. Finally, the data may be filtered by back transforming a selected range of data from R into K space. It is this Fourier filtered data to which curve fitting techniques are applied. The curve is determined by six parameters (22) of which four describe the phase shift, amplitude and disorder for a particular absorber–scatterer pair. All six parameters are varied for a model compound of known structure. These parameters are transferred to an unknown compound and only the two parameters which may be interpreted in terms of coordination number and bond distance are varied to give the best fit.

Aurosome Results

The results of fitting the chronic dose sodium gold(I)thiomalate aurosomes based on a sodium bis(thiosulfato)gold(I) model (23) are presented in Figure 11 and the values derived from the fit are listed in Table I. A first attempt to fit to a gold–nitrogen environment is disasterous, the gold coordination number becomes negative and the bond distance unrealistically short. A fit with sulfur neighbors is much better giving a reasonable coordination numbr of 1.8 and bond distance of 2.30 Å. An attempt to fit two sets of neighbor atoms, nitrogen and sulfur results in an apparently better fit value, however, there are now four variable parameters and the nitrogen coordination number is unreasonably low at 0.4 with an extremely short distance of 1.90 Å.

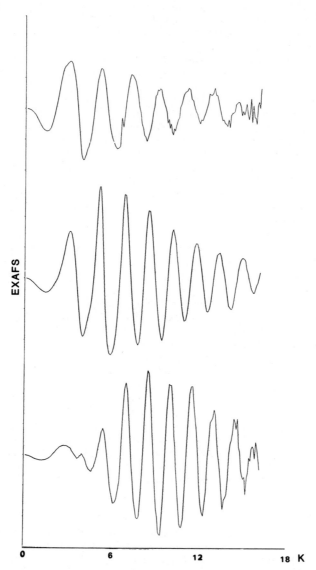

Figure 9.   EXAFS times K^2 *vs.* K. *Key: top, tetraamminegold(III) nitrate (maximum amplitude at ca.* K $= 2$); *middle, potassium gold(III)chloride (maximum amplitude at ca.* K $= 6$); *and bottom, potassium gold(III)bromide (maximum amplitude at ca.* K $= 9$).

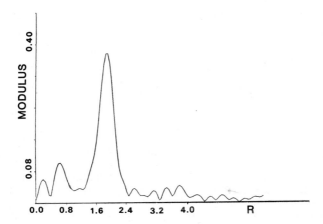

Figure 10. Fourier transform for a solution of 0.14 M sodium gold(I)thiomalate showing the gold–sulfur peak.

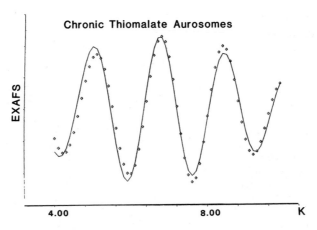

Figure 11. The Fourier-filtered data (boxes) fit to a gold–sulfur scattered pair with coordination number of 1.84 and bond distance of 2.30 Å, (line).

Table I

Chronic Dose Gold Thiomalate Aurosomes

EXAFS Curve Fitting: Single Shell

Atom type	Coord #	R($\overset{\circ}{A}$)	Fit
Nitrogen	<u>negative 1.7</u>	1.95	1.61
Sulfur	1.84	2.30	0.33
Phosphorus	2.07	2.34	0.29

EXAFS Curve Fitting: Double Shell

Nitrogen and	0.41	1.90	
Sulfur	1.89	2.27	0.26

This result merely indicates that nitrogen is not in the gold coordination sphere. A phosphorus fit is included to show that we are unable to distinguish between sulfur and phosphorus neighbors on the basis of curve fitting. However, both on the basis of the XANES data which shows no evidence of phosphorus coordination and chemical sense we are able to rule out phosphorus coordination here. Based on our experience in fitting known compounds and the results of Hodgson's group (22) for an extensive series of molybdenum complexes, the errors which we expect in these calculations are ca. 0.02 $\overset{\circ}{A}$ in distance and ca. 20% in coordination number. Thus, we feel confident that the gold in these aurosomes is bound to two sulfur atoms at a distance of 2.30 $\overset{\circ}{A}$.

Gold-Based Drug Results

These are shown in Table II.

Table II

EXAFS Results Sulfur Ligands

Compound	Coord #	Au–S ($\overset{\circ}{A}$)	Fit
Chronic aurosomes	1.84	2.304	.33
Au thiomalate solid	1.81	2.298	.17
Au thiomalate soln .14 M	1.86	2.292	.17
Au thiomalate soln .015 M	1.81	2.292	.36
Au thioglucose solid	1.72	2.304	.23
Au (cysteine) solid	1.87	2.309	.17
Au (glutathione) solid	1.72	2.304	.23

Sodium gold(I)thiomalate has been fit successfully with sulfur neighbors giving coordination numbers ca. two and bond distances of 2.29 $\overset{\circ}{A}$ in solutions of 0.14 and 0.015 M concentration. This requires the compounds to be polymeric with bridging sulfur atoms since thiomalic acid has a single thiolate function. From the minor differences between the aurosome fit and the fit to the drug Myochrisin it is not possible to exclude that aurosomes might be mere storehouses of the drug. On the basis of rather low circulating concentrations of gold in the blood (24), it seems unlikely that the polymer would remain intact. Also, the similarity of the fit aurosome data to that from the gold(III)tetrachloride aurosomes (which we have yet to fit) would suggest that aurosomes contain a drug metabolite.

Possible metabolites previously suggested include gold complexes of cysteine and glutathione (25). We have examined solid samples of each of these and find them to fit satisfactorily to a model in which gold is coordinated to two bridging sulfur atoms with bond lengths identical to those found in the chronic sodium gold(I)thiomalate aurosomes.

Conclusions

X-ray absorption spectroscopy shows considerable promise as a powerful tool to aid in the elucidation of the role of gold-based pharmaceuticals in the management of rheumatoid arthritis.   This technique has already given considerable new insight into gold oxidation state and binding in aurosomal samples prepared from rat kidneys.

Acknowledgments

We thank the Research Corporation, the National Science Foundation and Smith Kline and French Laboratories for support of this work. XAS experiments were performed at SSRL which is supported by the NSF through the Division of Materials Research and the NIH through the Biotechnology Resource Program in the Division of Research Resources.   We thank Professors K.O. Hodgson and R.A. Scott for immense help in introducing us to these techniques.

Literature Cited

1.   "Primer on the Rheumatic Diseases" 7th Edtion, Rodman, G.P., Ed., The Arthritis Foundation, New York, NY, 1973.
2.   Empire Rheumatism Council, Ann. Rheum. Dis. 1961, 20, 315-354.
3.   Shaw, III, C.F., Inorganic Perspectives in Biology and Medicine 1979, 2, 287-355.
4.   Sadler, P.J., Struct. Bonding 1976, 29, 171-214.
5.   Brown, D.H.; Smith, W.E., Chem. Soc. Rev. 1980, 9, 217-240.
6.   Jessop, J.D., J. Rheumatol. Suppl. 5, 1979, 6, 12-17.
7.   Sutton, B.L., this volume.
8.   Hadjiliadis, N.; Pneumatikakis, G.; Basosi, R., J. Inorg. Biochem., 1981, 14, 115-126.
9.   Jones, P., Gold Bull. 1981, 14, 102-118.
10.   Elder, R.C.; Zeiher, E.H.K.; Onady, M.; Whittle, R.R., J. Chem. Soc. Chem. Commun. 1981, 900-901.
11.   Shroeder, H.A., in "Metal Binding in Medicine," Seven, H.A., ed., J.P. Lippincott, Philadelphia, PA, 1960, 59-67.
12.   Cramer, S.P.; Hodgson, K.O., Prog. Inorg. Chem., 1979, 25, 1-39.
13.   Winick, H., in "Synchrotron Radiation Research," Winick, H. and Doniach, S., eds., Plenum, New York, NY, 1980, 27-58.
14.   Teo, B., in "EXAFS Spectroscopy," Teo, B. and Joy, D., eds., Plenum, New York, NY, 1981, 13-58.

15. Sayers, D.E.; Stern, E.A.; Lytle, F.W., Phys. Rev. Lett., 1971, 27 1204-1207.
16. Tullius, T.D.; Gillum, W.O.; Carlson, R.M.K.; Hodgson, K.O., J. Am. Chem. Soc., 1980, 102, 5670-5676.
17. Ghadially, F.N., J. Rheumatol. Suppl. 5, 1979, 45-50.
18. Shaw, III, C.F.; Thompson, H.O; Witkiewicz, P.; Satre, R.W.; Siegesmund, K., Toxicol. Appl. Pharmacol., 1981, 61, 349-357.
19. Lytle, F.W.; Via, G.H.; Sinfelt, J.H., in "Synchrotron Radiation Research," Winick, H. and Doniach, S., eds. Plenum, New York, NY, 1980, 401-423.
20. Horisberger, Marc, Biol. Cell., 1979, 36, 253-258.
21. Walz, D.T., private communication.
22. Cramer, S.P.; Hodgson, K.O.; Stiefel, E.I. and Newton, W.E., J. Am. Chem. Soc., 1978, 100, 2748-2761.
23. Ruben, H.; Zalkin, A.; Felkens, M.O. and Templeton, D.H., Inorg. Chem., 1974, 13, 1836-1839.
24. Lorber, A.; Wilcox, J.A.; Vibert, G.J.; Simon, T.M., J. Rheumatol., Suppl. 5, 1979, 6, 31-39.
25. Shaw, III, C.F., in "Inorganic Chemistry in Biolgy and Medicine," Martell, A., ed., ACS Symposium Series, No. 140. Washington, D.C., 1980, 349-372.

RECEIVED October 4, 1982

Gold Thiolate Complexes In Vitro and In Vivo

D. H. BROWN and W. E. SMITH

University of Strathclyde, Department of Pure and Applied Chemistry,
Glasgow G1 1XL, Scotland

Naturally occurring thiols and other thiol
ligands used in the complexes administered
during gold therapy react with gold(0), gold
(I) and gold(III). The products formed in
each case are dependent on the ligand, the
solvent and the presence or absence of oxygen. Polymers, clusters, co-precipitates or
mixed crystals and monomeric complexes have
all been identified, as have gold(I), gold
(III) and mixed valence complexes. In vivo
gold distributes widely and reacts readily.
Despite this, the reactivity of serum gold
is dependent on the compound originally administered. It is suggested that the therapeutic effect of gold compounds is dependent
on the ability of gold to bind to the thiol
system on cell membrane.

Gold compounds have been used for many years in
the treatment of rheumatoid arthritis. They have
proved to be effective therapeutic agents in some patients but they are also potentially toxic(1-5). As a
result, enthusiasm for these compounds has waxed and
waned over the years but no drug has yet been developed
to replace them completely, although compounds such as
d-penicillamine have become viable alternatives (6).
They differ from standard anti-inflammatory agents in
that they affect chronic rather than acute inflammation
and they may cause a remission of the disease activity.
Gold compounds and most other compounds claimed to produce remission in rheumatoid arthritis affect the immune system in some way and it seems likely that this
action is responsible for the antirheumatic effect
(4,6,7). All these agents can produce serious toxic
side reactions in some patients and it is hoped that

0097-6156/83/0209-0401$06.00/0

their mode of action might make it possible to differentiate between the therapeutic and toxic action of gold
complexes in conventional therapeutic regimes.
    Most authors agree that gold compounds react with
the thiol/disulphide system in vivo. This system provides the largest source of soft ligands and gold has
been identified bound to proteins in almost every
tissue fraction so far investigated, including brain
tissue (8). Gold compounds affect the results of assays
for the thiol content of proteins (8) and they alter the
thiol balance across the cell walls of circulating
blood cells (9). This paper describes the reaction of
gold compounds with thiol ligands in vitro and uses
this information in interpreting the less direct evidence for thiol/gold reactions in vivo. A possible
mechanism for action of gold compounds in the therapy
of rheumatoid arthritis is suggested.

In Vitro Gold Chemistry

    The ligands considered in the in vitro studies are
shown in Figure 1. Cysteine and the tripeptide glutathione are naturally occurring thiol containing compounds. Penicillamine is an effective drug in the
treatment of rheumatoid arthritis and contains an -SH
group on a tertiary carbon. Thiomalic acid is the
ligand used in the drug Myocrisin. It does not contain
an amine group and, since carboxylate groups do not
complex readily with gold, it is a better model for
comparison with protein sulphydryl groups. The dithiol
2,3-dimercaptopropanol (British Anti-Lewisite or BAL)
has been used to treat cases where an overdose of gold
has been administered (10).

    Spectroscopic Studies. Many of the solids isolated
from the reactions of thiols with gold compounds are
noncrystalline and polymeric. They can, therefore, not
be recrystallized and are often not suitable for X-ray
structural analysis, although auranofin can be crystal-
lized and its structure has been determined (11). As
a consequence, spectroscopic probes of structure and
electronic configuration are widely used in the solid
state as well as in solution.
    The oxidation state of the gold present in these
compounds is usually determined by Mössbauer spectroscopy (12) but X-ray photoelectron spectroscopy has
also been used successfully (13). The major advantages
of the latter technique are simpler sample handling
procedures and the elimination of a need for liquid
helium coolant, but it requires very careful interpre-

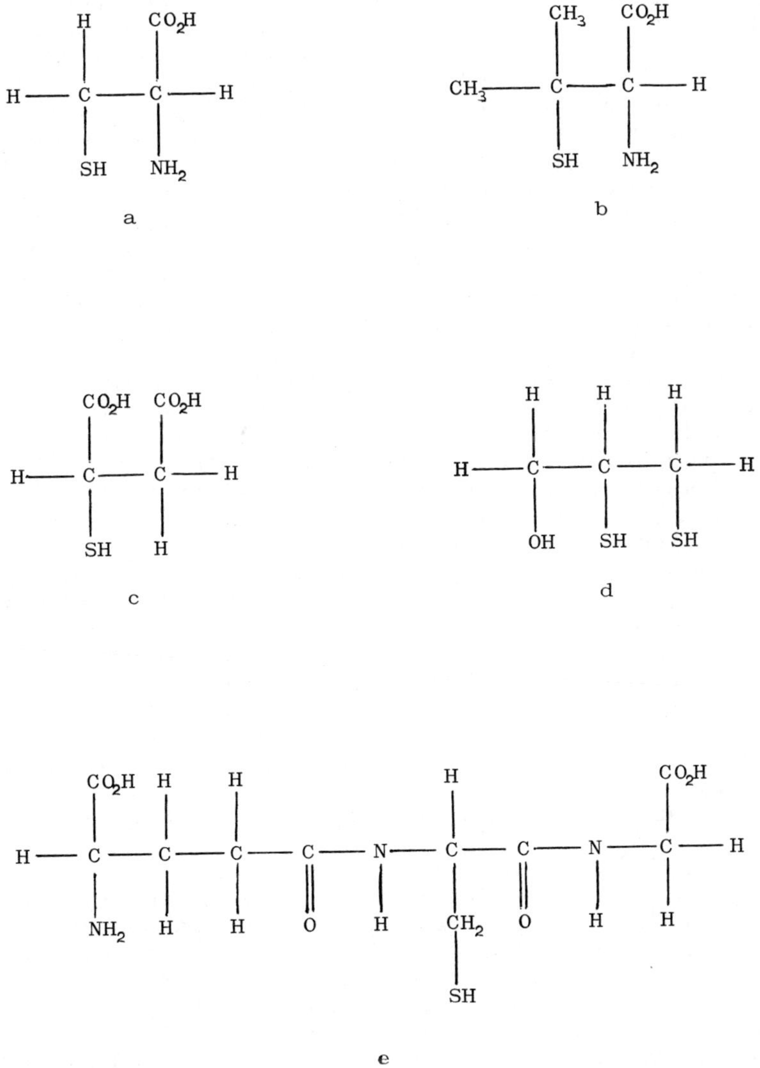

*Figure 1.   The thiol-containing ligands used in most of the reactions considered.
Key: a, cysteine; b, penicillamine; c, thiomalic acid; d, 2,3-dimercaptopropanol
(BAL); and e, glutathione.*

tation of the results. Surface charging of the samples
is overcome by using the C_{1s} signal from the ligand.
Both techniques are insufficiently sensitive for routine
use in biological systems and can cause chemical reactions to occur in the sample. An example of this with
XPS also illustrates the detection of gold(I) and
gold(III) by this technique (Figure 2) and a similar
result has been reported for gold(III) dithiocarbamate
(14). Considerable exposure to the X-ray beam was required to achieve the complete removal of the gold(III)
signal and the compounds used are particularly suitable
for this experiment. EXAFS and related techniques are
also proving to be valuable in understanding these
structures. Sodium gold(I) thiomalate contains an approximately linear S-Au-S grouping (15), and this and
related studies are reviewed in another article in this
volume (16).

If an Au-S bond is present in the sample, a combination of uv-visible spectrometry and circular dichroism (C.D.) produces a spectrum in the visible and near
uv region which is characteristic of this bond (Figure
3) and which is present in both gold(I) and gold(III)
compounds. In gold(III) compounds, however, the bands
are shifted by about 60 nm towards the infrared and,
consequently, an estimation of the gold oxidation state
is possible by this method in both solid and solution
samples and at concentrations down to about 10^{-4} molar
(17). C.D. spectra are very sensitive to environment
and so provide a simple method of following geometry
changes in solution. C.D. is complementary to NMR in
that it is simpler to carry out and is readily applicable in a wider range of solvents and is more suitable
for kinetic studies. NMR methods provide a more detailed analysis of the structure of solution species
(18).

A C.N.D.O. calculation on P-Au(I)-S entities was used
to aid in assigning the spectra. Since an error of
less than 1% is sufficient to prevent an assignment of
individual bands, the calculation was used only to provide a description of the orbitals expected to contribute to transitions in this energy region and for this
purpose, it should be acceptable. Individual band
assignments were made empirically. The bond formed
between gold and sulfur has both a σ and π contribution.
The stronger σ orbital contains a larger proportion of
Au(s) than Au(p), probably because the energy separation of the s and p is quite large compared to bonding
in an equivalent bond with a 3d metal. Thus, gold(I)
with sulfur halide ligands prefers linear coordination.
With phosphorus, the P (p) orbitals mix more readily

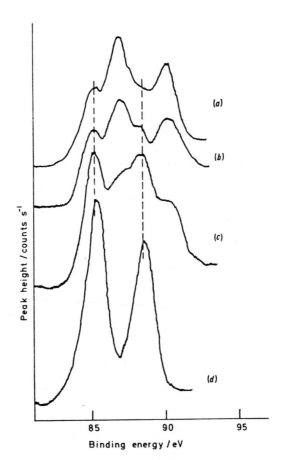

Figure 2. Decomposition of Et_4NAuBr_4 in the x-ray beam of an x-ray photo-electron spectrometer. Peaks 1 and 2 refer to gold(III) and peaks 3 and 4 refer to gold(I). Key to exposure time before spectra were recorded: a, 15 min; b, 3 h; c, 24 h; and d, control spectrum of Et_4NAuBr_2. (Reproduced with permission from Ref. 13.)

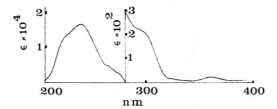

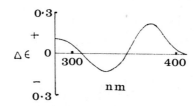

Figure 3.   Near-UV electronic (top) and circular dichroism (CD) (bottom) spectra of gold(I) cysteine attributable to transitions centered on the gold–sulfur bond. The changes in sign in the CD spectrum can be helpful in separating more complex spectra.

with the gold, producing a decreased energy separation
of the gold s and p orbitals and predisposing the phosphine gold entity to further substitution. Thus,
higher coordination numbers are to be expected with
phosphorus-containing ligands.

   Chemical Reactions. The reactions of all of the
ligands with gold compounds are very dependent on the
solvent used. For example, sodium tetrachloroaurate
reacts with thiomalic acid in water to give a gold(I)
thiomalate complex in solution. In thoroughly dried
ethanol, sodium chloride is precipitated and gold(III)
complexes of thiomalic acid and chloride are obtained
in solution, and with acetonitrile a gold(I) complex,
gold(I) thiomalate.NaCl, is precipitated and a gold(III)
solution remains (19). Further, although the usual
form of gold(I) complexes is AuL, in glacial acetic
acid, gold(I) compounds of formula AuL$_3$ have been isolated (20). It is presumed that they contain a disulfide. However, the infrared spectrum of these compounds is not consistent with a mixture of the
component parts, irrespective of the form of disulfide
which is postulated to exist and, therefore, some form
of complexing is believed to exist.
   The solution species appear to be quite labile.
The results of conductiometric titration were dependent
on the speed with which they were carried out (19).
Thus, the solids obtained are often simply the least
soluble component arising from a series of competitive
reactions between clusters. Depending on conditions,
a series of stoichiometric products, Au(tmH$_2$),
Na$_2$[Au(tm)], Ca[Au(tm)]2H$_2$O, Ba[Au(tm)]2H$_2$O, and mixed ligand complexes containing thiomalic acid (tm) and
glutathione or cysteine have been prepared (21).
   The stability of the oxidation state is also dependent on the ligand used. For example, the compound
gold(III)(penicillamine)$_2$ can be prepared by dissolving
penicillamine and sodium tetrachloroaurate in ethanol
but under the same conditions, cysteine produced gold(I)
cysteine (11). Reaction of BAL with sodium tetrachloroaurate in aqueous ethanol produced a range of polymers
of definite stoichiometry Au$_3$(BAL)$_x$Cl$_y$ which include
examples of gold(I) and gold(III) compounds and mixed
valence compounds(22). Further, starting with a solution of Na$_3$Au en$_2$(SO$_3$)$_2$, substitution with different
ligands produced gold(I) complexes and with d-
penicillamine, a gold(III) complex (20) (Figure 4).
The gold oxidation states in this latter study were
determined by XPS.
   Many of the compounds formed are polymeric.

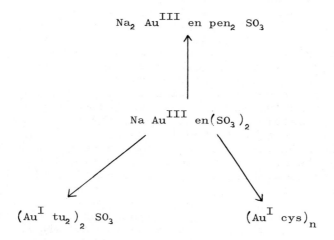

Figure 4. Products identified in the reaction of Na₃Au en₂ (SO₃)₂ with sulfur-containing ligands. Reactions were carried out at 1:1 stoichiometry in aqueous ethanol. Key to abbreviations: cys, 1-cysteine; en, diaminoethane; pen, d-penicilla-mine; and tu, thiourea.

Sodium gold(I) thiomalate has been shown to be a polymer in solution by NMR and there is more than one
polymer present in the solution of this compound used
as the drug Myocrisin (23). In aqueous solution,
cysteine produces an insoluble polymeric gold(I) cysteine in many reactions studied. When this reaction is
started from triethylphosphine gold(I) chloride, at
least four intermediate species can be observed in the
circular dichroism (2). However, starting with triphenylphosphine gold(I) chloride, the reaction stops at
the first stage, producing monomeric triphenylphosphine
gold(I) cysteine (11). The kinetics of substitution
can be quite rapid but some of the more complex reactions, such as the formation of polymeric gold(I)
cysteinate, can be slow, taking from 24 hours to one
week to complete. In in vivo reactions, solubility is
also important. Triethylphosphine gold(I) chloride
reacts readily in ethanol, in which it is soluble and
with difficulty in water, in which it is not appreciably soluble, whereas the reverse is true of sodium gold
(I) thiomalate (24). Insoluble gold(I) polymers,
although they can be made to redissolve with suitable
ligands, are relatively unreactive and in the correct
medium in vivo, they are the most likely storage forms
of gold.
     Gold(0), gold(I) and gold(III) oxidation states
can readily be interchanged, the final product depending on the ligand and on the conditions used. In
addition to the production of gold(I) from gold(III) as
already discussed, reaction of $KAu(CN)_2$ with a five-
fold excess of penicillamine in air in aqueous ethanol
produced gold(III)(penicillamine)$_2$ (11). However,
reaction of sodium tetrachloroaurate with insufficient
penicillamine produces gold(0). Gold(0) colloid can be
oxidized to gold(I) or gold(III) with penicillamine in
the presence of oxygen and gold(III) can be reduced to
gold(I) with disulfides (26). This latter reaction is
unusual in that a disulfide is being used as a reducing
agent. The explanation of this effect is that oxygen
causes further oxidation of the disulfide to form, in
stepwise fashion, sulfenic, sulfinic and sulfonic acids
(26). Further, in the reduction of gold(III) with cysteine the conventional reaction,

$$NaAuCl_4 + RSH \longrightarrow RSAu + RSSR + 3HCl + NaCl$$

requires 3 moles of cysteine per mole of gold compound
and this appears to be the reaction which occurs under
nitrogen. In the presence of oxygen, however, much
less ligand is required, oxygen is consumed in the

reaction (11) and cysteic acid has been identified in
the products (27). In a study of the reduction of gold
(III) to gold(I) with thioethers, a key step in the
reduction process is postulated as a reaction at the coordinated ligand rather than at the metal ion (28) and
it is possible that oxygen complexes to the coordinated
sulfur atom in the reduction of gold(III) by thiols or
disulfides.

In Vivo Chemistry

The approach required for in vivo chemistry is
quite different from that employed in vitro in that not
all the techniques employed in vitro are applicable and
the basic chemistry is more complex. The administration of a gold compound eventually leads to its metabolism and the final storage or excretion of the gold in
a time scale comparable to those observed for in vitro
kinetics and, hence, there is an essentially non-
equilibrium situation chemically as well as metabolic-
ally. Further, there is no guarantee that the largest
fractions of the gold found in vivo are, in fact, the
therapeutic or toxic fractions; it is possible that
very small amounts of gold present in the correct environments are responsible for the drug action. During
the process of metabolism, the gold will pass through
biological compartments in which the dielectric constant will be such as to produce a chemistry more akin
to that in non-aqueous solvents than to that in water.
In spite of these difficulties, sufficient is known
about the reactivity of in vivo gold to enable some
conclusions to be drawn on the basis of a comparison of
the available in vivo data and the in vitro chemistry.
In this respect, the development of auranofin (triethyl-
phosphine(2,3,4,6-tetra-o-acetyl-1-thio-β-D-glucopyra-
nosato) gold(I) (1), which contains the triethylphosphine gold(I) moiety, is helpful in that a comparison
can be made between it and the more conventional gold-
sulfur drugs such as Myocrisin (sodium gold(I) thiomalate).

Myocrisin and auranofin are widely distributed
among the proteins in blood serum (29). For Myocrisin,
the gold content of each protein fraction isolated by
electrophoresis has been shown to vary from patient to
patient but to remain constant for any one patient as
the gold level of the serum increases during therapy
(30). Thus, there seems to be a number of gold binding
sites in serum which are of comparable strength and
which are not saturated at the gold levels achieved
during therapy. These sites are probably thiol groups

or disulfides. The largest single fraction is on albumin, with reports of between 50 and 90% of the gold
being present on this protein. This wide scatter is
due to differences in analysis methods and separation
techniques used, in the time of sampling after injection and in the variation in biochemistry of patients
with rheumatoid arthritis. In addition to the tightly
bound gold, some gold is absorbed on albumin, probably
as the unchanged or partly metabolised drug. There are
fewer results available for auranofin, but there is a
fraction of the gold on albumin as well as a fraction
bound to it and there is a different distribution of
tightly bound gold with higher concentrations on the β
and γ globulin fractions (29,20). Further, the distribution of gold between the circulating blood cells and
plasma is different with the different compounds (Figure 5). Up to 50% of the blood gold in auranofin is
present in the cells. With Myocrisin, up to about 30%
of the gold may be present in some cases but no gold at
all has been detected in others. The difference appears to be that cigarette smoking increases the amount
of intracellular gold, possibly because the additional
cyanide present in blood acts as a transporting agent
but auranofin produces at least one form of serum gold
which can cross the cell membrane in any case (9,31).
    The difference in reactivity of the serum gold
produced by the two drugs can be demonstrated clearly
by incubating the serum from Myocrisin and auranofin
treated patients with blood cells from a placebo
treated patient. Most of the auranofin serum gold is
transferred (9). This conclusion is reinforced by animal experiments with triethylphosphine gold chloride
and Myocrisin. Triethylphosphine gold chloride is very
efficiently absorbed orally (32,33). A very high concentration appears to adhere to the stomach wall initially, suggesting that the absorption may occur by
chemical attack with naturally occurring thiol ligands
in the lipid layers of the stomach wall (8). Myocrisin
reacts readily with zinc metallothionen in vitro with
the gold replacing zinc (34). The way in which different compounds or metabolites react with this protein
in the gut could be an important step in oral absorption. Both Myocrisin and auranofin distribute widely
but the residence time of gold in tissues such as kidney and liver is appreciably shorter for orally administered auranofin than for injected Myocrisin, again
suggesting a different reactivity for the in vivo gold
and demonstrating that the change in reactivity applies
to more biochemical compartments than blood. Thus, it
seems likely that both Myocrisin and auranofin are

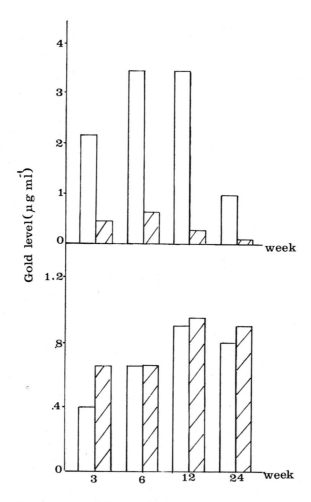

Figure 5. Distribution of gold between the cells and the plasma in patients treated with Myocrisin (top) and auranofin (bottom).

metabolised quite quickly in vivo but the metabolites
formed retain a memory of the parent compound in some
way and produce biochemical fractions of quite different reactivity.

There have been many more studies in which gold
distribution and the reactions of gold with proteins
have been investigated. The general conclusion of
these ex vivo studies is that the gold is coordinated
to the thiol group. A gold-sulfur bond in albumin has
been demonstrated by Mössbauer measurements (35). A
major problem with such studies is that the separation
and subsequent reaction of these biochemical fractions
may well cause changes in reactivity as the matrix is
removed during separation. Using N.M.R. methods, it
has been possible to demonstrate the existence of a
gold glutathione complex in the intact red cell and it
may be that this method of approach may yet provide a
more detailed understanding of the in vivo processes
(36).

Mechanism of Action of Gold Drugs. In only a few
cases is the action of a drug understood in sufficient
detail to be of use to the chemist in postulating a mechanism at the molecular level. In the case of platinum compounds, the effect on cell replication is regarded as a key step which leads to the postulate that the
mechanism of action is due to formation of complexes
of platinum with DNA, as discussed elsewhere in this
volume. The equivalent observation in the case of gold
compounds and of other agents believed to be capable of
producing a remission of the symptoms of rheumatoid arthritis may be that they all modulate the immune response in some way. To date, all the major compounds
claimed to have remission inducing properties and which
are not either cytotoxic agents or steroids, are thiols
or hydrolyse to thiols in vivo, or are compounds such
as the gold compounds or chloroquine which would be expected to react readily with thiols in vivo. However,
the way in which the immune system is affected varies
from compound to compound and is different for each gold
compound, as might have been inferred from their different in vivo reactivity. Further, there is no evidence
of a common factor such as the suppression of activity
of one particular enzyme (1,3,4) and there is no general
consensus that the amount of any gold fraction such as
serum gold, small molecule gold or intracellular gold,
is related to therapeutic response.

One way compounds with such disparate profiles of
activity might affect the immune system is by reaction
with sulfhydril and disulfide groups on cell membrane.

These membranes require metal ions for their stability
(37) and the -SH groups on and in them affect the chemical transport of vital nutrients such as alanine (38),
the synthesis of components such as glutathione (39)
and cell adherence.

The thiol groups on the membranes are in many different environments with different degrees of protection by steric or dielectric constant factors (40).
Thus, they will react differently with different compounds. A related example which has been widely studied
is the determination of the thiol content of hemoglobin
(41). Due to the protection of the thiol groups by the
protein structure, from 1 to 8 thiol groups per molecule have been reported, depending on the estimation
used and one standard reagent, Ellman's reagent, does
not appear to react at all. Thus, each potential therapeutic agent would be expected to react with a different combination of thiol groups and, hence, to affect
cellular functions in a unique way.

The thiol system itself is in a complex and little
understood equilibrium in vivo. The main thiol containing species in serum is albumin and it has between 0.3
and 0.7 thiol groups per molecule, depending on disease
state, with the remaining thiol either blocked by cysteine or other thiol ligands or missing altogether.
The kinetics of reaction of albumin thiol are complex
and there may be more than one microenvironment round
the thiol group. This group is likely to be in equilibrium with other thiols and the way in which gold
adds proportionately to each serum fraction as the level
increases is an indication that gold certainly equili-
brates between different serum proteins. A soluble
small molecule disulfide could equally well accomplish
this in vivo. It would be expected that some form of
equilibrium with each protein and with the membrane
surface would exist. On the inside of the membrane, an
analogous "equilibrium" would also exist. To affect
this equilibrium, the drugs must survive in vivo and
be tolerated well by the patient. Thus, although cysteine would be oxidized to cystine and precipitate at
cell membrane and tissue surfaces at blood pH, penicillamine will form a mixed disulfide and remain in
circulation and potentiate the thiol-disulfide equilibrium (43). Thus, gold would be expected to modulate
the thiol system in an analogous but not identical way
to penicillamine or chloroquine (Figure 6).

In chronic inflammation, the inflammatory response
which begins as a beneficial effect of the immune system remains in action sufficiently long to create
tissue destruction and so produce more antibodies

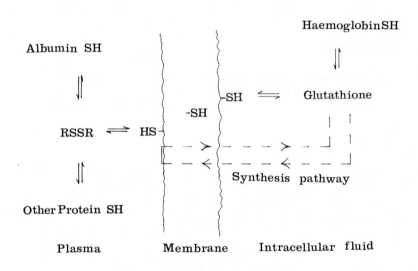

Figure 6.   Schematic diagram of the thiol/disulfide equilibrium inside and outside cells. Gold interacts with different compounds of this system and is expected to modify the equilibrium.

requiring a further inflammatory response. This sustained inflammation is achieved in a slightly different way than the initial inflammation. One effect is that circulating monocytes adhere to the polymorphonuclear cells in the joint and enhance their phagocytic action. Myocrisin is known to reduce this adherence and may affect the immune response in that way (44). This change could well be caused by the interaction of gold with the thiol group on cell membranes. Thus, the mechanism of action of gold drugs may not be known with certainty but a reasonable postulate as to their chemical activity can be given. Much remains to be done to test this hypothesis and to define the precise nature of the effect on the membrane of circulating blood cells and the synovium.

Acknowledgments

We thank Dr. H.A. Capell and the staff at the Centre for Rheumatic Diseases in Glasgow for their encouragement of our work on gold over a number of years.

Literature Cited

1. Walz, D.T; DiMartino, M.J.; Sutton, B.M.; "Anti-inflammatory Agents", Ed.: Scherrer, R.A.; White-house, M.W.: Academic Press: New York, N.Y., 1974; Vol. 1, 217.
2. Brown, D.H.; Smith, W.E.; Chemical Society Reviews 1980, 9, 217.
3. Shaw III, C.F., Inorg.Persp.Med.Biol. 1979, 2, 287.
4. Lewis, A.J. and Walz, D.T., in press.
5. Sadler, P.J. Structure and Bonding 1976, 29, 171.
6. Lyle, W.H.; Kleinman, R.L., Eds., "Penicillamine at 21: Its Place in Therapeutics Now"; Proc.Roy. Soc.Med.Supp. 1977, 3, 70.
7. Leibfarth, J.H.; Persellin, R.A.; Agents and Actions 1981, 11, 458.
8. Kamel, H.; Brown, D.H.; Ottaway, J.M.; Smith, W.E.; Talanta 1977, 24, 309.
9. Lewis, D; Capell, H.A.; Brown, D.H.; Iqbal, M.S.; McNeil, C.J.; Smith, W.E.; Ann.Rheum.Dis. 1982, in press.
10. Margolis, H.M.; Kaplan, P.S.; Ann.Intern.Med. 1947, 27, 353.
11. Sutton, B., this volume.
12. Brown, D.H.; McKinley, G.C.; Smith, W.E.; J.C.S. Dalton 1978, 562.

13. McNeillie, A.; Brown, D.H.; Smith, W.E.; Gibson, M.; Watson, L.; J.C.S. Dalton 1980, 767.

14. van Attekum, P.M.Th.M.; Trooster, J.M.; J.C.S. Dalton 1980, 201.

15. Mazid, M.A.; Razi, M.T.; Sadler, P.J.; Greaves, G.N.; Gurman, S.J.; Koch, M.J.H.; Philips, J.C.; J.C.S. Chem.Comm. 1980, 1261.

16. Elder, D., this volume.

17. Brown, D.H; McKinley, G.C.; Smith, W.E.; J.C.S. Dalton 1977, 1874.

18. Isab, A.A.; Sadler, P.J.; J.C.S.Chem.Comm. 1976, 1051.

19. Brown, D.H.; Paton, M; Smith, W.E.; Inorg.Chim. Acta 1982; 66 L 51.

20. Brown, D.H.; Smith, W.E., unpublished results.

21. Larkworthy, L.F.; Sattari, D; J.Inorg.Nucl.Chem. 1980; 42, 551.

22. Brown, D.H.; McKinley, G.C.; Smith, W.E.; Inorg. Biochem. 1979; 10, 275.

23. Harvey, D.A.; Lock, C.J.L.; Kean, W.F.; Singh, D.; Conf. Abstracts A.C.S. Meeting, Las Vegas, March, 1982.

24. Lewis, A.J.; Cottney, J.; White, D.D.; Fox, P.K.; McNeillie, A.; Dunlop, J.; Smith, W.E.; Brown, D.H.; Agents and Actions 1980; 10, 63.

25. Brown, D.H.; Smith, W.E.; Fox, P.; Sturrock, R.D.; Inorg. Chim.Acta 1982; 67, 27.

26. Shaw III, C.F.; Canero, M.P.; Witkiewicz, P.L.; Eldridge, J.F.; Inorg.Chim. 19. 1980.

27. Annibale, G., Canovese, L., Cattalini, L., Natile, G., J.C.S. Dalton,1980, 1017.

28. Van der Stadt, R.J.; Abbo-Tibstra, B; Ann.Rheum. Dis. 1980; 39, 31.

29. Lorber, A.; Wilcox, S.A.; Vibert, G.J.; Simon,T.M.; J.Rheumatol. Supp. 5 1980, 30.

30. Brown, A.A.; Brown, D.H.; Ottaway, J.M.; Smith, W.E.; in press.

31. Graham, G.G.; Champion, G.D.; Haavisto, T.M.; McNaught, P.J.; Ann.Rheum.Dis. 1981; 40, 210.

32. Kamel, H., Brown, D.H., Ottaway, J.M., Smith, W.E.; Cottney, J.; Lewis, A.J.; Arth. and Rheum. 1978, 21, 441.

33. Kamel, H.; Brown, D.H.; Ottaway, J.M.; Smith, W.E.; Cottney, J.; Lewis, A.J.; Agents and Actions 1978; 8, 546.

34. Schmitz, G.; Minkel, D.T.; Gingrich, D.; Shaw III, C.F.; J.Inorg.Biochem. 1980; 12, 298.

35. Private Communication.

36. Razi, M.T., Otiko, G., Sadler, P.J., Conf. Abstract A.C.S. Meeting, Las Vegas, March 1982.

37. Ludwig, J.S.; Chapvil, M.; in "Trace Elements in
     the Pathogenesis and Treatment of Inflammation",
     Eds.: Rainsford, K.D.; Brune, K.; Whitehouse, M.W.;
     Pg. 65, Birkhauser, 1981, Basel.
38. Young, J.D.; Biochem.Soc. Trans. 1979, 7, 683.
39. Meister, A.; Griffith, O.W.; Novogrodsky, A.; Tate,
     S.S.; in "Sulphur in Biology", Pg. 135, CIBA Sym-
     posium 72, Exerpta Medica, 1980, Amsterdam.
40. Haest, C.W.M.; Kamp, D.; Deuticke, B.; Biochim.
     and Biophys. Acta 1979; 557, 363.
41. The Chemistry and Biochemistry of the Sulphydryl
     Group in Aminoacids, Peptides and Proteins,
     Friedman, M., Pergamon Press, Oxford Press, 1973.
42. Banford, J.C.; Brown, D.H.; Hazelton, R.A.; McNeil,
     C.J.; Smith, W.E.; Sturrock, R.D.; Rheumatology
     International 1982; in press.
43. Banford, J.C.; Brown, D.H.; McNeil, C.J.; Smith,
     W.E.; Inorg.Chim.Acta. 1982; 66, L21.
44. Ugai, K.; Ziff, M.; Lipsky, P.E.; Arthr. Rheum.
     1979, 22, 1352.

RECEIVED October 4, 1982

POSSIBLE OSMIUM ANTIARTHRITIC DRUGS

Osmium Carbohydrate Polymers as Potential Antiarthritic Drugs

C. C. HINCKLEY and J. N. BEMILLER—Southern Illinois University at
Carbondale, Department of Chemistry and Biochemistry, Carbondale, IL 62901

L. E. STRACK—Southern Illinois University at Carbondale, Department of
Animal Industries, Carbondale, IL 62901

L. D. RUSSELL—Southern Illinois University at Carbondale, Department of
Physiology, Carbondale, IL 62901

Osmium carbohydrate polymers, termed osmarins,
have been investigated as potential antiarthritic
agents. They are prepared in three steps from
OsO_4, and have been characterized by elemental
analysis, gel filtration, gel electrophoresis,
solution density and viscosity measurements, and
ultracentrifugation. The polymers are of variable
composition dependent upon the details of preparation. They are polydisperse anionic polyelectro-
lytes, and preparations containing 30%-40% osmium
have average molecular weights in the range,
50-100K daltons. The polymers react in strong
base with the oxygen species O_2, O_2^-, and H_2O_2.
They form complexes in solution with proteins.
In antiarthritic application, dilute solutions of
the compounds are injected directly into the
synovial spaces of effected joints. Though some
evidence of microscopic toxicity has been found,
the materials have very low toxicity. In mice,
IP injection at dose levels of 1g/Kg body weight
produce no mortality. In pigs and rabbits,
osmarins of high molecular weight stain the joint
capsules and articular surfaces of injected
joints irreversibly. In limited experimental
treatments of arthritic dogs, improvements have
been noted in five of six cases. It is proposed
that, in vivo, osmarins may react with superoxide
ion and remove this damaging species.

New osmium compounds may prove to be antiinflammatory
agents useful in the treatment of some forms of arthritis. The
materials are osmium-carbohydrate polymers (1), termed osmarins.
These compounds bind irreversibly with living tissue and exhibit
other properties which suggest their use.

There is a long standing connection between arthritis
treatment and osmium (2). Osmium tetroxide has been used on a
limited basis for the treatment of arthritis in humans, principally in Europe, for about 30 years. Osmium tetroxide treatment
is not used in the United States and is controversial everywhere.
In theory, the treatment makes use of the toxicity of osmium
tetroxide to achieve a "chemical synovectomy". Detractors
believe that the damage to joint tissues inherent in the procedure exacts a price too high for the method to be generally
acceptable. Still, the small but persistent literature which
has developed over the years provides a growing list of apparent
successes.

In 1976 a group of researchers in Switzerland reported a
study of over seventy people who had been helped by the treatment (3). They found that there were osmium containing deposits
in the joints of these people long after the osmium tetroxide
treatment. They included in their paper a suggestion, upon
which our work is partly based, that the osmium containing
deposits may contribute to the long term efficacy of the procedure.

Recent work provides support for their suggestion (4).
Involvement of superoxide ion, O_2^-, in inflammation is well
established (5,6). In arthritis, superoxide may be present in
an effected joint as part of a response to the disease (4).
There it may attack the synovial fluid, destroying its capacity
to lubricate the joint surfaces (7,8). Metal complexes have
been shown to catalytically remove superoxide (9), and osmium
containing deposits could perform a similar function. Osmium
exhibits many of the characteristics believed necessary for
these catalytic properties. The fact that the enzyme superoxide
dismutase has been successfully used to treat arthritis in both
animals (10) and humans (11,12) is further support for the
suggestion.

In our proposed application, solutions of osmarins are to
be injected directly into the synovial spaces of arthritic
joints. The aim is to provide osmium deposits similar to those
which Bousinna, et. al., (3) have suggested may be beneficial,
while at the same time, avoiding the damage that accompanies
OsO_4 injections.

In this paper, we first present the preparation and
characterization of osmium-carbohydrate polymers. This discussion is followed by a review of our studies involving animals.
Mice have been used for toxicity screening, and we have examined
the effect of osmarins upon the tissues of the synovial space
in both pigs and rabbits. Finally, we report the results of a
small number of experimental treatments of arthritic dogs.

Our findings are that osmarins of high average molecular
weight appear to have the properties we seek, that is, they
have minimal toxicity, no evident persistent side effects, are
retained for long periods within the joint, and are effective

in some cases in restoring freedom of movement of arthritic
joints and allowing recovery of the joint surfaces. Comments
concerning apparent efficacy are not presented as assertions of
proven fact, but rather as indications which prompt our continuing study.

Osmarins

Preparation and characterization. Osmarins are prepared
in three steps, the first of which begins with osmium tetroxide.
OsO_4 (0.5 g), dissolved in a small amount (15 mL) of methanol
containing 0.1M KOH, reacts with the alcohol to produce di-
potassium tetramethylosmate(VI), $K_2[Os(OCH_3)_4O_2]$, which

Table I. Elemental compositions for several osmarin pre-
          parations.

Preparation	% Os	% C	% H	% K
1	9.7	26.7	4.5	11.7
2	13.6	26.0	4.3	10.0
3	15.0	14.5	3.6	0.7
4	23.0	32.4	5.6	6.9
5	35.0	14.6	5.8	4.9

precipitates as a green solid (13). When this product is
dissolved in acetic acid (100 mL), blue potassium triacetatodi-
oxoosmate(VI) is formed. Glucose (1.0 g), dissolved first in a
small amount of water (20 mL) and then mixed with a larger
quantity of acetic acid (100 mL) is added to the blue solution
and allowed to react overnight at room temperature to form the
osmarin. Purification is effected by gel filtration of an
aqueous solution through Sephadex G-25 after the acetic acid
has been removed by evaporation under reduced pressure.
     Osmarins of widely differing composition (Table I) have
been prepared by varying the reaction temperature, the concentrations of osmium and carbohydrate in the preparative mixture,
the nature of the carbohydrate, and the time of reaction. For
instance, when the quantities of reactants indicated above are
allowed to react at room temperature for twenty-four hours, the
final preparation will contain 30 to 40% osmium. Longer reaction
times (1 week) with mild heating on a steam bath yield preparations having 20 to 30% osmiums. Increasing the quantity of
glucose (2-3 g) and heating yields preparations having less
than 20% osmium. The preparations are brown or black depending
upon their composition. Preparations containing less than 20%
osmium are brown, those containing more than 20% are black.
The very intense colors are the consequence of broad absorption

throughout the visible region. Extinction coefficients are on
the order of 2000 L/cm. mole of Os. These values compare
favorably to those found for some charge transfer complexes
(14).

The relatively high percentages of carbon in the polymers
and their high aqueous solubility suggest the presence of bound
carbohydrate. Infrared spectra of the polymers exhibit broad
bands in the regions 1610-1550 cm^{-1}, 1400-1300 cm^{-1}, and
1200-950 cm^{-1}, consistent with the presence of gluconate and
glucose. Permanganate titrations of the polymers in acid
solution indicate an oxidation state for osmium of +4, but do
not eliminate the possibility of mixed oxidation states. These
factors are consistent with the empirical formula:
$K_u OsO_v (glucose)_x (gluconate)_y (H_2O)_z$. This formula embodies an
interpretation of the materials as glucose and/or gluconate
solubilized osmium dioxide. In this interpretation, direct
Os-Os bonds are not assumed. Bridging between osmium ions
through oxo and/or carbohydrate groups is thought to be most
likely. Recently, a new class of osmium(IV) complexes containing both oxide and carboxylate bridges has been reported
(15). The compounds, $Os_2(\mu\text{-}O)(\mu\text{-}O_2CCH_3)_2X_4(PR_3)_2$ where X=Cl,Br,
exhibit bridging between the osmium atoms of the kind suggested
for osmarins.

Gel filtration has indicated that the components have
relatively large molecular volumes. They elute as broad bands
at or near the void volume of a Sepharose 6-B column. This gel
excludes globular proteins which exceed 10^6 daltons in molecular
weight. Since the gel is not calibrated for osmarins, gel
filtration does not provide estimates of molecular weight.

In gel electrophoresis, the preparations migrate as single
broad bands toward the positive electrode. Plots of migration
distance versus gel concentration (Ferguson plots), measured
for the same conditions of temperature and electric field, show
that molecules in the trailing edge of the bands are larger
than those in the leading edge. This demonstrates that the
preparations are polydisperse, an indication which is confirmed
in sedimentation velocity experiments.

Osmarins are extremely soluble; aqueous solutions containing up to 10% osmarin were used for solution density,
partial specific volume, and viscosity measurements. The
effect of the dissolved polymer upon the viscosity of the
liquid is slight, even at the extreme concentration studied,
indicating that, in aqueous solution, the polymers are generally
spherical in shape.

Sedimentation velocity experiments, supplemented by partial
specific volume and viscosity measurements, provide estimates
of molecular weights (Figure 1). Molecular weights may vary
from 10,000 to 100,000 daltons or more in a single preparation.
There is a general relationship between the composition of the
osmarin preparation and the range of molecular weights of the
components of the mixture. The molecular weights of osmarin

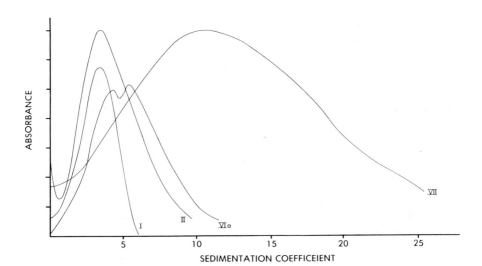

Figure 1. Sedimentation profiles for several osmarins plotted as absorbance vs. sedimentation coefficient.

preparations containing as little as 15% osmium average 10K daltons, while the average molecular weight of those containing 35% is 80K daltons or more.

The combined results allow us to draw the outlines of structure of black osmarins. The preparations are polydiperse mixtures of osmium-carbohydrate polymers. The number of osmarin atoms varies from 10 to 50 per molecule most çommonly, with some having as many as 100 or more. Within the molecules, osmium atoms are linked together with oxygen or carbohydrate bridges (gluconate or glucose). Osmium exhibits an average +4 oxidation state, and the polymers are anionic. In solution, the molecules are distorted spheres. A suggested organizational geometry is that of coiled chains of varying length. The chains may be branched and/or crosslinked, but not linearly extended.

Chemical Properties. Chemical properties of the polymers are consistent with those expected for the constituents of the materials, and with those expected of anionic polymers. Osmarins are oxidized by a wide variety of common oxidizing agents including potassium permanganate and ceric ammonium nitrate. In these reactions, both the osmium and the bound carbohydrate are oxidized.

Studies of osmarin-oxygen species chemistry are in progress and will be reported later. Preliminary experiments indicate an extensive oxygen chemistry. The polymers react in vitro with the oxygen species H_2O_2, O_2^-, and O_2, in the presence of strong base. The reaction with hydrogen peroxide is accompanied by vigorous gas evolution indicating that the peroxide has decomposed. Osmium is oxidized to OsO_4 which may be removed by extraction into chloroform. In the reaction of osmarins with KO_2 in DMSO, no gas is evolved in spite of the presence of water in the solution. Gas is evolved when osmarins are not present.

Figure 2 is a plot of absorbance at 480 mμ as a function of time, for the reaction of an osmarin with the oxygen in air. The reaction with oxygen is complicated by the fact that both the osmium in the compound and the attached carbohydrate react with the oxygen. Product mixtures are complex, and contain several osmium containing components as well as a carbohydrate mix that includes hexoses and evidence for pentoses.

Osmarins react with proteins. Evidence for reaction is the formation of precipitates and the presence of protein dependent bands in electrophoresis. Proteins studied are albumin, cytochrome C, myglobin, and lysozyme. In these experiments, solutions containing an osmarin preparation and the protein are mixed and allowed to stand for some time. Reaction is not immediate, and reaction time is dependent upon the osmium content of the osmarin preparation. When the osmium percentage is high (25%), precipitates form in two or three

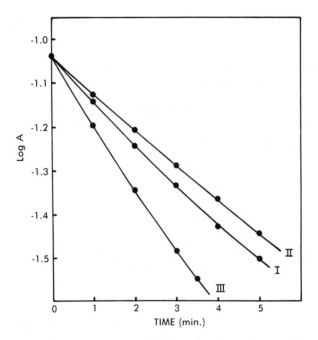

Figure 2. Logarithms of absorbance (480 nm) are plotted vs. time for basic solution of an osmarin reacting with air. Key: I, no pretreatment; II, helium bubbled through prior to beginning reaction by adding strong base; and III, O₂ gas pretreatment.

hours, if the osmium percentage is low (15%) precipitates may
not form at all. In every case, however, electrophoresis
demonstrates the formation of complexes which appear as distinct
and narrow bands, present only when protein is present.

Protein binding is a reasonable expectation for osmarins.
It is consistent with the known structure of the polymers and
the properties of osmium (IV). Osmarins are polyanionic, a
structural feature which provides the means to form multiple
ionic linkages with proteins, and additionally, Os(IV) is known
to form complexes with protein sidegroups (16).

Animal studies

Toxicity in mice. Osmarin preparations to be used in
animal experiments are screened for acute toxicity. IP injections in mice at dose levels of 1g osmarin/kg body weight
produce no mortality. As yet, no lethal dose has been determined. At the 1 g/kg.b.w. dose level the skin and eye color of
the mice are darkened. No other effects are observed. After
about an hour, the urine of injected mice is darkened by osmarin,
but significant amounts are retained in the animal. Gross
examination of both liver and kidney shows that they are slightly
darkened. In microscopic examination of these tissues, dense
deposits not seen in uninjected mice are found in the Kuppfer
cells of the liver and in the kidney proximal convoluted tubule
cells. These deposits are presumed to be osmarin walled off
within lysosomes. After about a month, mice which are not
sacrificed regain their normal color.

Staining and Retention in procine synovia. If the Boussina,
et al., (3) suggestion that osmium containing deposits have a
long term beneficial effect is correct, then to be useful,
osmarins should stain tissue within synovial spaces and be
retained there for long periods. Initial experiments with pigs
and rabbits have been directed toward examining this and related
issues. In these experiments, osmarin solutions are injected
into the synovial spaces of the living animal, and some time
later, the tissues of the joint are examined after sacrifice of
the animal. Our gross and microscopic findings are that osmarins
will stain tissue in joints and be retained there. The
effectiveness of both staining and retention, however, is dependent upon the composition of the osmarin.

Pigs used in this study have been, for the most part,
arthritic. Mycoplasmal arthritis is common in large herds, and
is enzootic in the SIU herd.

Initial experiments with pigs were short term and involved
four arthritic pigs which received different osmarin preparations. Joint tissues were examined for retained osmarin and
photographed one to three days after injection. A second group
of pigs including nonarthritic controls, were injected and

examined one month after the injection. Tissue samples for
microscopic study were obtained from these animals.

Osmarin staining was observed through the color imparted
to the tissue. In most cases, the staining was obvious as a
grey or black color when the staining was due to an osmarin
preparation containing more than 30% osmium, or a brown color
for less osmium rich osmarins. The color of the stained tissue
was clearly related to that of the injected osmarin, which
suggests that the binding is associative, and not accompanied
by changes in osmium oxidation state or the connectivity of the
osmium ions.

Figure 3 is a photograph of a stained joint. The osmarin
used in this case contained 35% osmium as a dry solid. All
surfaces within the synovial space were stained, articular
cartilage on the joint surfaces and the joint capsule which
encloses the space. The most proximal lymph node was stained
(not shown).

Except for the color, the stained tissue appears normal.
There was no gross evidence of toxicity. In the month-long
study from which Figure 3 is drawn, only one tarsal and carpal
joint of the pigs were injected with osmarin solution. The
other joints were untreated and served as controls on the same
animal. In the arthritic animals, the untreated tarsal joints
exhibited lesions, confirming the original diagnosis. The
treated joints either exhibited no lesion (one case) or structures which are interpreted as healing lesions (two cases).
This last assessment is tentative and is based upon microscopic
evidence of cartilage growth into the lesion areas (following
section).

In a following experiment, two arthritic pigs and one
normal control were injected in right tarsal and carpal joints
and sacrificed one month later. The osmarin preparation used
in this case contained only 17% osmium as a dry solid. On
examination, the treated joints were found to be unstained.
There was no difference between injected and uninjected joints.
The earlier short term experiments (discussed above) indicated
that staining from low osmium percentage polymers was light.
These findings indicate a rapid clearing time as well, and in
these cases, no evidence of beneficial effect could be found.
In subsequent experiments involving rabbits and dogs, only
osmarin preparations containing more than 30% osmium in the dry
solid were used.

An interesting secondary finding was made in the experiment
in which one month separated injection and sacrifice of the
animal. In these cases, the stained articular surface was
marked with a lacework pattern of unstained cartilage (Figure
3). The pattern is attributed to growth since pigs used in
these studies are young (3 mo) animals and double their weight
in the one month interval prior to sacrifice.

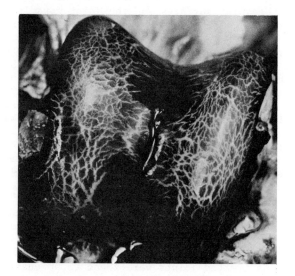

Figure 3.   The osmarin-stained surface of a pig tarsal joint. The pattern of white lines (unstained cartilage) is attributed to growth.

The white lined pattern observed appears to be due to the new cartilage formed as the pigs grew. Osmarin bound to the cartilage surface did not stain the new cartilage. The pattern is an indication of the strength and stability of the binding. It serves to demonstrate that once the osmium polymers have bound to the cartilage surface they do not move. The pattern is not a reflection of normal growth and is an effect of the osmarin.

Histology of stained tissue in pigs. Histological studies have had several objectives. First is the determination of what the osmarin stains. Secondly, these studies reveal the extent of microscopic toxicity. Stained tissue appears healthy and entirely undamaged. Microscopically, some dose related cell death is observed. Finally, microscopic examination of the pig cartilage confirmed that the unusual lined pattern is due to growth of cartilage. Evidence of cartilage growth has been found, associated with lesions in osmarin treated joints, which suggests regeneration.

Tissue samples for microscopic study were obtained from pigs sacrificed one month after injection. Samples were obtained from the joint capsules and articular surfaces. When arthritic lesions were found, samples from these areas were obtained. The experiment includes two levels of control. First, all of the pigs received injections of osmarin solution only in the right tarsal and carpal joints. Thus, stained and unstained tissue was obtained from the same animal by examining both tarsal and carpal joints. Secondly, three of the pigs were arthritic and one was healthy. Assessments of the affects accompanying osmarin staining are made on the basis of comparisons of stained and unstained tissue from both arthritic and non-arthritic animals.

The distribution of osmarin in a stained synovial space is, for the most part, independent of arthritic conditions. Joint capsule and cartilage of arthritic and healthy animals are similarly stained. The growth related lined pattern is observed in both arthritic and healthy animals. Disease related differences are found only in tissues relating to arthritic lesions.

Histological examination of the synovial membrane revealed osmarin to be taken up by subsynovial macrophages (Figure 4). Accumulations of this type are not seen in control tissues. In both osmarin treated and uninjected joints the synovial membrane appeared intact.

Stained articular cartilage appears healthy and undamaged. Microscopically, staining of the surface layer of the pig cartilage was confirmed by a strong affinity of toluidine blue for this region which was not seen in control tissues (Figure 5). Most surface cells of the articular cartilage appeared healthy and were present as single cells. In white line regions,

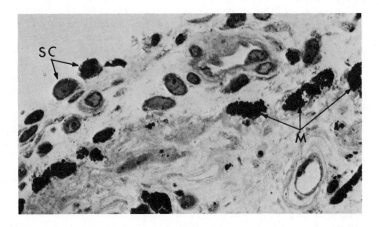

Figure 4. A tissue section taken through the synovial membrane and underlying connective tissue from a pig that received a single osmarin injection 30 d previously. Synovial cells (SC) appear healthy and line the joint cavity. Numerous sybsynovial macrophages (M) show dense osmarin deposits.

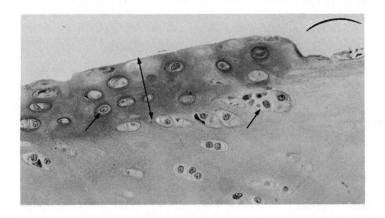

Figure 5. A section of the articular cartilage from a pig injected 30 d previously with osmarin. The surface zone (length of double-headed arrow) shows dense staining with toluidine blue to a depth of about 0.1 mm. Chrondrocyte nests (arrows) usually display one or two cells on the surface and one to ten cells in the deeper zones. At the right is a region that corresponds to a white line (arc) seen in Figure 3. Surface staining is not apparent at the white line region.

all cells appeared healthy and numerous multicellular lacunae
were present. Cartilage in this region appears pink with the
metachromatic toluidine blue stain. The matrix was less dense
with the electron microscope.

Ultrastructurally the osmarin-treated cartilage appeared
normal except for evidence for an occasional dead chondrocyte.
These chondrocytes inevitably displayed electron dense inclusions which were most likely osmarin. For the most part the
cellular reaction to osmarin appears to be phagocytosis. The
compound is absorbed and walled off in specific inclusions.

In regions of arthritic lesions the cartilage was less
darkened by the osmarin. This indicated active growth of
cartilage. This was confirmed by light microscope observations
(Figure 6). Cartilage nests contained numerous cells, and the
matrix stained pink with toluidine blue.

Rabbit studies. An on going companion study involving
thirty-five rabbits yielded prelimary results somewhat similar
to those of the pig studies. Osmarin solutions injected into
the knee joints of the rabbits stain articular cartilage and
the joint capsule, as in the pig. In this study, a measure of
osmarin retention has been developed based upon the standard
grey scale. Sections of stained articular cartilage were
removed and compared visually with standard grey scales. In
this study groups of ten rabbits were injected at the same
time, and then animals were sacrificed and the joints examined
at intervals from one day to seven weeks post injection. There
appears to be very little change in cartilage discoloration
with time, indicating strong binding of osmarin. Grossly, the
cartilage and synovium of the joints, through stained, appeared
otherwise normal at all time periods. The interlacing white
lines seen in long term injected pigs were not present, even
when young growing rabbits were examined. The darkening of the
synovial membrane appeared upon microscopic examinations to be
due to accumulation of osmarin in subsynovial macrophages,
similar to those found in pigs. The articular cartilage was
minimally disrupted with osmarin. Little evidence of cell
death in the cartilage was noted. Synovial tissue examined one
day after osmarin injection was disrupted and contained numerous
dead cells. Synovial tissue examined three weeks or later
after injection was normal. This is a potentially important
observation. An effect upon the synovium suggests possible
short term benefits.

In order to provide comparisons with osmarin treated joint
tissues, a number of rabbits were injected with equivalent
amounts (based upon osmium content) of osmium tetroxide solutions.
The rabbits were sacrificed and the joints examined according
to the same time intervals that were employed in the osmarin
studies. The results of these studies were similar to those
reported by others (17). Histologically, the osmium tetroxide

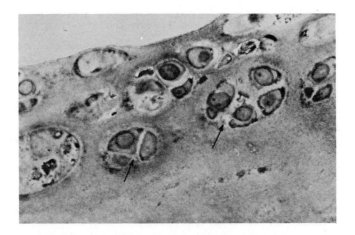

Figure 6. Articular cartilage taken from a region less than 2 mm from an arthritic lesion. The surface is not differentially stained as shown in Figure 5. Chrondrocyte nests (arrows) contain from one to eight cells and suggest active growth in this region.

treatments, were harsher on joint tissues than were osmarin treatments and their deleterious effects were longer lasting. After one day the synovial membranes of both groups appeared necrotic. However, the osmarin treated joints regenerated a healthy appearing synovial membrane by three weeks. The synovial membrane of the osmium tetroxide group regenerated after seven weeks, although there remained much subsynovial fibrosis and many foreign body giant cells. For the OsO_4 treated rabbits, the entire cartilage surface (about 2mm deep) showed necrotic cells. In addition, in the osmium tetroxide injected rabbits, there was a surface exudate upon the cartilage and a highly granulated cartilage matrix.

Clinical data in dogs. Osmarins have been used in a limited number of clinical situations in dogs. Six dogs have been treated so far. With special permission from the owners of the dogs, intraarticular injections of osmarin solutions were made into joints afflicted with arthritis. The etiology ranged from trauma to probable genetic to old age. The treatments and clinical evaluations of the effects of treatments were made by licensed veterinarians in private practice. In some cases, pre- and post-treatment roentgenograms were used in the clinical evaluations. There was no opportunity for necropsy and histological evolution of the treated joints. No clinically normal joints were injected. Criteria for improvement included increased locomotor activity, increased freedom of movement of the affected joint, decreased limping, and diminished evidence of pain upon palpation of the joint. Where roentgenograms were made, a smoother, more clearly defined articular surface and decreased radioopacity in the soft tissues immediately surrounding the joint were interpreted as post-treatment signs of improvement.

For a period of 1 to 3 days following osmarin injection the dogs exhibited evidence of increased discomfort in the treated joint. A similar period of increased discomfort was noted when normal rabbit joints were treated with osmarin, but was not seen in either normal or arthritic osmarin treated joints of pigs. The authors do not attirbute this short period of discomfort to the physical trauma of the injection. More likely explanations could be that osmarins cause a temporary decrease in synovial fluid viscosity, or that the discomfort is due to a type of chemical synovectomy which was previously noted in the rabbits.

In five of the six dogs, the temporary increase in discomfort was followed by a period of gradual improvement over the original arthritic conditions. Two of the dogs have recovered normal function in the effected joints. Three of the dogs have improved, but still retain some loss of function in the arthritic joints at this time. In the dog which failed to show any improvement, the knee joint was markedly deformed by exostosis due to the long standing arthritis.

Conclusions

The study of osmarins as potential arthritic agents follows directly, in this case, from the Boussina, et al., suggestion that osmium containing deposits may have long term beneficial effects in arthritis treatment. Osmarins exhibit properties, e.g. low toxicity and tissue staining and retention, which are thought necessary for such an application. In preliminary experiments involving dogs and pigs, favorable responses to treatment have been observed. We propose that osmarins in a joint, may react with superoxide ion and thereby protect the synovial fluid from damage by this species.

A secondary finding in the study is that osmarins have a short term effect upon the synovial membrane. This effect may also contribute to the utility of these substances.

It is important to emphasize the preliminary character of the research discussed in this paper. No claims of cures are implied. At the same time, it is also important to recognize the potentialities that the research findings suggest. If the several uncertainties in the proposed application of osmarins can be successfully resolved, then new alternatives in arthritis treatment will be available.

Acknowledgments

This research has been supported by the departments listed and by the office of Research Development and Administration of Southern Illinois University. Drs. T. O. Miller and D. M. Lane of Murphysboro, Illinois and L. F. Striegel of Carbondale, Illinois are veterinarians in private practice and have treated the dogs included in the study. Dr. G. H. Gass guided early studies of toxicity. Dr. W. J. Roth characterized osmarins. P. S. Ostenburg prepared many of the materials used in the study. A. M. Islam and P. A. Kibala are currently studying osmarin reactivities. Several undergraduate research assistants have contributed to the project.

Literature Cited

1. Hinckley, C. C.; Ostenburg, P. S.; Roth, W. J. Polyhedron 1982, in press.
2. Nissila, M. Scand. J. Rheumatology 1979, Suppl. 29, 1.
3. Bonssina, I; Lagier, R.; Ott, H.; Fallet, G. H. Scand. J. Rheumatology 1976, 5, 53.
4. Fridovitch, Irwin. Science 1978, 201, 875.
5. Bannister, W. H.; Bannister, J. V., Eds,; "Biological and Clinical Aspects of Superoxide and Superoxide Dismutase", Elsevier/North Holland, New York, 1980, pp. 147-153.
6. Bannister, W. H.; Bannister, J. V., Eds.; "Biological and Clinical Aspects of Superoxide and Superoxide Dismutase", Elsevier/North Holland, New York, 1980, pp. 154-159.

7.   McCord, J. M. Science 1974, 185, 530.
8.   Greenwald, R. A.; Moy, W. W. Arthritis Rheum. 1980, 23, 455-463.
9.   Spiro, T. G., Ed.; "Metals Ion Activation of Dioxygen", John Wiley and Sons, New York, 1980, pp. 209-237.
10. Michelson, A. M.; McCord, J. M.; Fridovitch, I., Eds.; "Superoxide and Superoxide Dismutases", Academic Press, New York, 1977, pp. 517-536.
11. Michelson, A. M.; McCord, J. M.; Fridovitch, I., Eds.; "Superoxide and Superoxide Dismutases", Academic Press, New York, 1977, pp. 537-550.
12. Bannister, W. H.; Bannister, J. V., Eds.; "Biological and Clinical Aspects of Superoxide and Superoxide Dismutase", Elsevier/North Holland, New York, 1980, pp. 424-430.
13. Criegee, R.; Marchand, B.; Wannowius, H.; Ann. der Chem. 1942, 550, 99-133.
14. Cotton, F. A.; Wilkinson, G.; "Advanced Inorganic Chemistry", 4th Ed., "John Wiley and Sons, New York, 1980.
15. Armstrong, J. E.; Robinson, W. R.; Walton, R.A. J. C. S. Chem. Comm. 1981, 1120-1121.
16. Nielson, A. J.; Griffith, W. P.; J. Chem. Soc. Dalton 1979, 1084.
17. Mitchell, N; Laurin, C.; Shepart, N.; J. Bone Joint Surgery (British) 1973, 55B, 814-821.

RECEIVED October 13, 1982

INDEX

Jacket design by Martha Sewall
Editing and production by Florence H. Edwards and Paula Bérard

Elements typeset by Service Composition Co., Baltimore, MD
Printed and bound by Maple Press Co., York, PA